1968

A BRIEF
SURVEY
OF
Modern
Algebra

SECOND EDITION

Garrett Birkhoff
Harvard University

Saunders Mac Lane
The University of Chicago

THE MACMILLAN COMPANY, NEW YORK
COLLIER - MACMILLAN LIMITED, LONDON

Preface to the
Second Edition

During the twenty-five years since the first version of this book appeared, courses in "modern algebra" have become standard all over the world, and many books have been written for such courses. Nevertheless, it seems desirable to recall our basic philosophy, which remains that of the present edition.

"We have tried throughout to express the conceptual background of the various definitions used. We have done this by illustrating each new term by as many familiar examples as possible. This seems especially important in an elementary text, because it serves to emphasize the fact that the abstract concepts all arise from the analysis of concrete situations.

"To develop the student's power to think for himself in terms of the new concepts, we have included a wide variety of exercises on each topic. Some of these exercises are computational, some explore further examples of the new concepts, and others give additional theoretical developments. Exercises of the latter type serve the important function of familiarizing the student with the construction of a formal proof. The selection of exercises is sufficient to allow an instructor to adapt the text to students of quite varied degrees of maturity, of undergraduate or first year graduate level.

"Modern algebra also enables one to reinterpret the results of classical algebra, giving them far greater unity and generality. Therefore, instead of omitting these results, we have attempted to incorporate them systematically within the framework of the ideas of modern algebra.

"We have also tried not to lose sight of the fact that, for many students, the value of algebra lies in its applications to other fields; higher analysis, geometry, physics, and philosophy. This has influenced us in our emphasis on the real and complex fields, on groups of transformations as contrasted with abstract groups, on symmetric matrices and reduction to diagonal form, on the classification of quadratic forms under the orthogonal and Euclidean groups, and, finally, in the inclusion of Boolean algebra, lattice theory, and transfinite numbers, all of which are important in mathematical logic and in the modern theory of real functions."

In this brief survey we have tried to provide the student with a minimum working knowledge of algebra. We feel that any substantial further abbreviation would either be too condensed for easy assimilation, or eliminate so much as to give a very superficial acquaintance with algebraic ideas and techniques.

This new edition differs from the first abbreviated edition mainly in including an entirely new chapter on Boolean algebras and lattices, though also in that it defines "ideals" early, and has been carefully revised in detail in many places.

The brief edition can be adapted to various types of courses. A full year course could cover most of it. A term course on the theory of equations, enriched by some number theory and an introduction to the technique of formal proof, may be based on Chapters I–V. A semester course on linear algebra may cover Chapters VI through X, the word "field" being understood to mean the real or complex field. A semester course on abstract algebra may be based on selections from Chapters I–III, VI–VIII, and XI.

In order that students may use the brief edition and the complete edition in the same course without confusion in the course assignments, both editions have the same chapter and section numbering, while the corresponding page numbers in the complete edition are given on the margin of the brief edition.

GARRETT BIRKHOFF
SAUNDERS MAC LANE

Cambridge, Mass.
Chicago, Illinois

Contents

X. Determinants and Canonical Forms   233

XI. Boolean Algebras and Lattices   254

List of Special Symbols   271
Index   273

Contents vi

I. The Integers

1. Commutative Rings; Integral Domains

Modern algebra has exposed for the first time the full variety and richness of possible mathematical systems. We shall construct and examine many such systems, but the most fundamental of them all is the oldest mathematical system—that consisting of all the positive integers (whole numbers). A related but somewhat larger system is the collection **Z** of *all* integers 0, ± 1, ± 2, ± 3, $\cdots$. We begin our discussion with this system because it more closely resembles the other systems which arise in modern algebra.

The integers have many interesting algebraic properties. In this chapter, we will assume some especially obvious such properties as *postulates*, and deduce from them many other properties as logical consequences.

We first assume eight postulates for addition and multiplication. These postulates hold not only for the integers, but for many other systems of numbers, such as that of all rational numbers (fractions), all real numbers (unlimited decimals), and all complex numbers. They are also satisfied by polynomials, and by continuous real functions on any given interval. When these eight postulates hold for a system R, we shall say that R is a *commutative ring*.

Definition. *Let R be a set of elements a, b, c, $\cdots$ for which the sum $a + b$ and the product ab of any two elements a and b (distinct or not) of R are defined. Then R is called a* commutative ring *if the following postulates (i)–(ix) hold:*

(i) *Closure.* If a and b are in R, then the sum $a + b$ and the product ab are in R;

(ii) *Uniqueness.* If $a = a'$ and $b = b'$ in R, then

$$a + b = a' + b' \qquad and \qquad ab = a'b';$$

(iii) *Commutative laws.* For all a and b in R,

$$a + b = b + a, \qquad ab = ba;$$

(iv) *Associative laws.* For all a, b, and c in R,

$$a + (b + c) = (a + b) + c, \qquad a(bc) = (ab)c;$$

1

(v) *Distributive law.   For all a, b, and c in R,*

$$a(b + c) = ab + ac;$$

(vi) *Zero.   R contains an element 0 such that*

$$a + 0 = a, \quad \text{for all a in R;}$$

(vii) *Unity.   R contains an element $1 \neq 0$ such that*

$$a1 = a, \quad \text{for all a in R;}$$

(viii) *Additive inverse.   For each a in R, the equation $a + x = 0$ has a solution x in R.*

It is a familiar fact that the set **Z** of all integers satisfies these postulates. For example, the commutative and associative laws are so familiar that they are ordinarily used without explicit mention: thus $a + b + c$ customarily denotes the equal numbers $a + (b + c)$ and $(a + b) + c$. The property of zero stated in (vi) is the characteristic property of the number zero; and similarly, the property of 1 stated in (vii) is the characteristic property of the number one. Since these laws are formally analogous, we may say that 0 and 1 are the "identity elements" for addition and multiplication, respectively. The assumption $1 \neq 0$ in (vii) is included to eliminate trivial cases (otherwise the set consisting of the integer 0 alone would be a commutative ring).

The system **Z** of all integers has another property which cannot be deduced from the preceding postulates. Namely, if $c \neq 0$ and $ca = cb$ in **Z**, then necessarily $a = b$ (partial converse of (ii)). This property is not satisfied by real functions on a given interval, for example, though these form a commutative ring. The integers therefore constitute not only a commutative ring but an *integral domain* in the sense of the following definition.

Definition.   *An* integral domain *is a commutative ring in which the following additional postulate holds:*

(ix) *Cancellation law.   If $c \neq 0$ and $ca = cb$, then $a = b$.*

The domain **Z**[$\sqrt{2}$]. An integral domain of interest for number theory consists of all numbers of the form $a + b\sqrt{2}$, where a and b are ordinary integers (in **Z**). In **Z**[$\sqrt{2}$], $a + b\sqrt{2} = c + d\sqrt{2}$ if and only if $a = c$, $b = d$. Addition and multiplication are defined by

$$(a + b\sqrt{2}) + (c + d\sqrt{2}) = (a + c) + (b + d)\sqrt{2}$$
$$(a + b\sqrt{2})(c + d\sqrt{2}) = (ac + 2bd) + (ad + bc)\sqrt{2}.$$

Uniqueness and commutativity are easily verified for these operations, while $0 + 0\sqrt{2}$ acts as a zero and $1 + 0\sqrt{2}$ as a unity. The additive inverse of $a + b\sqrt{2}$ is $(-a) + (-b)\sqrt{2}$. The verification of the associative and distributive laws is a little more tedious, while that of the cancellation law will be deferred to the end of §2.

2. Elementary Properties of Domains

In elementary algebra, one often takes the preceding postulates and their elementary consequences for granted. This seldom leads to serious errors, provided algebraic manipulations are checked against specific examples. However, much more care must be taken when one wishes to reach reliable conclusions about whole families of algebraic systems (e.g., valid for *all* integral domains generally). One must be sure that all proofs use only postulates listed explicitly and standard rules of logic.

Among the most fundamental rules of logic are the three basic laws for equality:

Reflexive law: $a = a$,
Symmetric law: If $a = b$,   then $b = a$,
Transitive law: If $a = b$ and $b = c$,   then $a = c$, valid for all a, b, and c.

We now illustrate the idea of a formal proof for several rules valid in any commutative ring R.

RULE 1. $(a + b)c = ac + bc$, for all a, b, c in R.

This rule may be called the right *distributive law*, in contrast to postulate (v), which is the left distributive law.

Proof.   For all a, b, and c in R:

1. $(a + b)c = c(a + b)$ (commutative law, mult.),
2. $c(a + b) = ca + cb$ (distributive law),
3. $(a + b)c = ca + cb$ (*1, 2*, transitive law),
4. $ca = ac$, $cb = bc$ (commutative law, mult.),
5. $ca + cb = ac + bc$ (*4*, uniqueness of addn.),
6. $(a + b)c = ac + bc$ (*3, 5*, transitive law).

RULE 2.   For all a in R, $0 + a = a$ and $1 \cdot a = a$.

Proof.   For all a in R:

1. $0 + a = a + 0$ (commutative law, addn.),
2. $a + 0 = a$ (zero),
3. $0 + a = a$ (*1, 2*, transitive law).

The proof for $1 \cdot a = a$ is similar.

RULE 3.   If z in R has the property that $a + z = a$ for all a in R, then $z = 0$.

This rule states that R contains only one element 0 which can act as the identity element for addition.

Proof. Since $a + z = a$ holds for all a, it holds if a is 0.

1. $0 + z = 0$
2. $\quad 0 = 0 + z$ (*1*, symmetric law),
3. $0 + z = z$ (Rule 2, when a is z),
4. $\quad 0 = z$ (*2, 3*, transitive law).

In subsequent proofs such as this, we shall condense the repeated use of the symmetric and transitive laws for equality.

RULE 4.   For all a, b, c in R:

$$a + b = a + c \quad \text{implies } b = c.$$

This rule is called the cancellation law for addition.

Proof. By postulate (viii) there is for the element a an element x with $a + x = 0$. Then

1. $x + a = a + x = 0$ (comm. addn.; trans. law),
2. $x = x,\ a + b = a + c$ (reflexive law; hypothesis),
3. $x + (a + b) = x + (a + c)$ (*2*, uniqueness of addn.),
4. $b = 0 + b = (x + a) + b = x + (a + b)$
   $\quad = x + (a + c) = (x + a) + c = 0 + c = c.$

(Supply the reason for each step of 4!)

RULE 5.   For each a, R contains one and only one solution x of the equation $a + x = 0$.

This solution is denoted by $x = -a$, as usual. The rule may then be quoted as $a + (-a) = 0$. As customary, the symbol $a - b$ denotes $a + (-b)$.

Proof. By postulate (viii), there is a solution x. If y is a second solution, then $a + x = 0 = a + y$ by the transitive and symmetric laws. Hence by Rule 4, $x = y$, Q.E.D.

RULE 6.   For given a and b in R, there is one and only one x in R with $a + x = b$.

This rule asserts that subtraction is possible and unique.

Proof. Take $x = (-a) + b$. Then (give reasons!)

$$a + x = a + ((-a) + b) = (a + (-a)) + b = 0 + b = b.$$

If y is a second solution, then $a + x = b = a + y$ by the transitive law, hence $x = y$ by Rule 4, Q.E.D.

RULE 7.   For all a in R, $a \cdot 0 = 0 = 0 \cdot a$.

Proof.

1. $a = a, \; a + 0 = a$ (reflexive law; postulate (vi)),
2. $a(a + 0) = aa$ (*1*, uniqueness of multiplication),
3. $aa + a \cdot 0 = a(a + 0) = aa$ (distributive law, etc.),
   $$= aa + 0$$
4. $a \cdot 0 = 0$ (*3*, Rule *4*),
5. $0 \cdot a = a \cdot 0 = 0$ (*4*; commutative law, mult.).

RULE 8. If u in R has the property that $au = a$ for all a in R, then $u = 1$.

This rule asserts the uniqueness of the identity element 1 for multiplication. The proof, which resembles that of Rule 3, is left as an exercise.

RULE 9. For all a and b in R, $(-a)(-b) = ab$.

A special case of this rule is the "mysterious" law $(-1)(-1) = 1$.
Proof. Consider the triple sum (associative law!)

1. $[ab + a(-b)] + (-a)(-b) = ab + [a(-b) + (-a)(-b)]$.

By the distributive law, the definition of $-a$, Rule 7, and (vi)

2. $ab + [a(-b) + (-a)(-b)] = ab + [a + (-a)](-b)$
   $$= ab + 0(-b) = ab.$$

For similar reasons,

3. $[ab + a(-b)] + (-a)(-b) = a[b + (-b)] + (-a)(-b)$
   $$= a \cdot 0 + (-a)(-b) = (-a)(-b).$$

The result then follows from 1, 2, and 3 by the transitive and symmetric laws for equality, Q.E.D.

Various other simple and familiar rules are consequences of our postulates; some are stated in the exercises below.

Another basic algebraic law is the one used in the solution of quadratic equations, when it is argued that $(x + 2)(x = 3) = 0$ means either that $x + 2 = 0$ or that $x - 3 = 0$. The general law involved is the assertion

(1)   if $ab = 0$,   then either $a = 0$ or $b = 0$.

This assertion is not true in all commutative rings. But the proof is immediate in any integral domain D, by the cancellation law. For suppose that the first factor a is not zero. Then $ab = 0 = a \cdot 0$, and a may be cancelled; whence $b = 0$. Conversely, the cancellation law follows from this assertion (1) in any commutative ring R, for if $a \neq 0$, $ab = ac$ means that $ab - ac = a(b - c) = 0$, which by (1) makes $b - c = 0$. We therefore have

Theorem 1. *The cancellation law of multiplication is equivalent in a commutative ring to the assertion that a product of non-zero factors is not zero.*

Non-zero elements a and b with a product $ab = 0$ are sometimes called "divisors of zero," so that the cancellation law in a commutative ring R is equivalent to the assumption that R contains no divisors of zero.

Using Theorem 1, the cancellation law can be proved for the domain $\mathbf{Z}[\sqrt{2}]$ defined at the end of §1, as follows. Suppose that $\mathbf{Z}[\sqrt{2}]$ included divisors of zero, with

$$(a + b\sqrt{2})(c + d\sqrt{2}) = (ac + 2bd) + (ad + bc)\sqrt{2} = 0.$$

By definition, this gives $ac + 2bd = 0$, $ad + bc = 0$. Multiply the first by d, the second by c, and subtract; this gives $b(2d^2 - c^2) = 0$, whence either $b = 0$ or $c^2 = 2d^2$. If $b = 0$, then the two preceding equations give $ac = ad = 0$, so either $a = 0$ or $c = d = 0$ by Theorem 1. But the first alternative would imply $a + b\sqrt{2} = 0$ (since $b = 0$); the second that $c + d\sqrt{2} = 0$—in neither case do we have divisors of zero.

There remains the possibility $c^2 = 2d^2$; this would imply $\sqrt{2} = d/c$ rational, whose impossibility will be proved in Chap. III.

If one admits that $\sqrt{2}$ is a real number, and that the set of all real numbers forms an integral domain $\mathbf{R}$, then one can very easily prove that $\mathbf{Z}[\sqrt{2}]$ is an integral domain, by appealing to the following concept of a subdomain.

Definition. *A subdomain of an integral domain D is a subset of D which is also an integral domain, for the same operations of addition and multiplication.*

It is obvious that such a subset S is a subdomain if and only if it contains 0 and 1, with any element a its additive inverse, and with any two elements a and b their sum $a + b$ and product ab.

EXERCISES

In each of Exercises 1–5 give a complete proof, supporting each step by a postulate, a previous step, one of the rules established in the text, or by an already established exercise.

1. Prove that the following rules hold in any integral domain:
   (a) $(a + b)(c + d) = (ac + bc) + (ad + bd)$,
   (b) $a + [b + (c + d)] = (a + b) + (c + d) = [(a + b) + c] + d$,
   (c) $a + (b + c) = (c + a) + b$,   (e) $a(b + (c + d)) = (ab + ac) + ad$,
   (d) $a(bc) = c(ab)$,   (f) $a(b + c)d = (ab)d + a(cd)$.
2. (a) Prove Rule 8;   (b) Prove $1 \cdot 1 = 1$;
   (c) Prove that the only "idempotents" (that is, elements x satisfying $xx = x$) in an integral domain are 0 and 1.
3. Prove that the following rules hold for $-a$ in any integral domain:
   (a) $-(-a) = a$,   (d) $-a = (-1)a$,
   (b) $-0 = 0$,   (e) $(-a)b = a(-b) = -(ab)$.
   (c) $-(a + b) = (-a) + (-b)$,

4. Prove Rule 9 from Ex. 3(d) and the special case $(-1)(-1) = 1$.

5. Prove that the following rules hold for the operation $a - b = a + (-b)$ in any integral domain:

(a) $(a - b) + (c - d) = (a + c) - (b + d)$,
(b) $(a - b) - (c - d) = (a + d) - (b + c)$,
(c) $(a - b)(c - d) = (ac + bd) - (ad + bc)$,
(d) $a - b = c - d$ if and only if $a + d = b + c$,
(e) $(a - b)c = ac - bc$.

6. Are the following sets of real numbers integral domains? Why?

(a) all even integers,   (b) all odd integers,
(c) all positive integers,
(d) all real numbers $a + b5^{1/4}$, where a and b are integers,
(e) all real numbers $a + b9^{1/4}$, where a and b are integers,
(f) all rational numbers whose denominators are 1 or a power of 2.

7. (a) Show that the system consisting of 0 and 1 alone, with addition and multiplication defined as usual, except that $1 + 1 = 0$ (instead of 2) is an integral domain.

(b) Show that the system which consists of 0 alone, with $0 + 0 = 0 \cdot 0 = 0$, satisfies all postulates for an integral domain except for the requirement $0 \neq 1$ in (vii).

8. (a) Show that if an algebraic system S satisfies all the postulates for an integral domain except possibly for the requirement $0 \neq 1$ in (vii), then S is either an integral domain or the system consisting of 0 alone, as described in Ex. 7 (b).

(b) Is $0 \neq 1$ used in proving Rules 1–9?

9. Suppose that the sum of any two integers is defined as usual, but that the product of any two integers is defined to be 0. With this interpretation, which ones among the postulates for an integral domain are still satisfied?

10. Find two functions $f \neq 0$ and $g \neq 0$ such that $fg \equiv 0$.

3. Properties of Order

Another aspect of the ordinary integers is the possibility of listing them in the usual order

$$\cdots -4, -3, -2, -1, 0, 1, 2, 3, 4, \cdots .$$

This order is customarily expressed in terms of the *relation* $a < b$, where the assertion $a < b$ (a is less than b) is taken to mean that the integer a stands to the left of the integer b in the list above. But the relation $a < b$ holds if and only if the difference $b - a$ is a positive integer. Consequently, every property of the relation $a < b$ can be derived from properties of the set of *positive* integers. We assume then as postulates the following three properties of the set of positive integers $1, 2, 3, \cdots$.

Addition: The sum of two positive integers is positive.
Multiplication: The product of two positive integers is positive.

Law of trichotomy: For a given integer a, one and only one of the follow-ing alternatives holds: either a is positive, or $a = 0$, or $-a$ is positive.

Incidentally, these properties are shared by the positive rational numbers and the positive real numbers; hence all the consequences of these properties are also shared. It is convenient to call an integral domain containing positive elements with these properties an *ordered domain*.

Definition. *An integral domain D is said to be ordered if there are certain elements of D, called the positive elements, which satisfy the addi-tion, multiplication, and trichotomy laws stated above for integers.*

Theorem 2. *In any ordered domain all squares of non-zero elements are positive.*

Proof. Let a^2 be given, with $a \neq 0$. By the law of trichotomy, either a or $-a$ is positive. In the first case, a^2 is positive by the multiplication law for positive elements; in the second case, $(-a)^2 = a^2$ by Rule 9 of §2, so a^2 is still positive, Q.E.D.

It is a corollary that $1 = 1^2$ is always positive.

Definition. *In an ordered domain, the two equivalent statements $a < b$ (read "a is less than b"), $b > a$ ("b is greater than a") both mean that $b - a$ is positive. Also $a \leq b$ means that either $a < b$ or $a = b$.*

According to this definition, the positive elements a can now be described as the elements a greater than 0. Elements $b < 0$ are called *negative.* One can deduce a number of familiar properties of the relation "less than" from its definition above.

Transitive law: If $a < b$ and $b < c$, then $a < c$.

Proof. By definition, the hypotheses $a < b$ and $b < c$ mean that $b - a$ and $c - b$ are positive. Hence by the addition principle, the sum $(b - a) + (c - b) = c - a$ is positive, which means that $a < c$.

The three basic postulates for positive elements are reflected by three corresponding properties of inequalities:

Addition to an inequality: If $a < b$, then $a + c < b + c$.

Multiplication of an inequality: If $a < b$ and $0 < c$, then $ac < bc$.

Law of trichotomy: For any a and b, one and only one of the relations $a < b$, $a = b$, or $a > b$ holds.

As an example, we prove the principle that an inequality may be multi-plied by a positive number c. The conclusion requires us to prove that $bc - ac = (b - a)c$ is positive (cf. Ex. 5(e) of §2). But this is an immediate consequence of the multiplication postulate, for the factors $b - a$ and c are both positive by hypothesis. By a similar argument one may demonstrate that the multiplication of an inequality by a negative number inverts the sense of the inequality (see Ex. 1(c) below).

Definition. *In an ordered domain, the* absolute value $|a|$ *of a number is 0 if a is 0, and otherwise is the positive member of the couple a, $-a$.*

This definition might be restated as an alternative:

(2) $|a| = +a$ if $a \geq 0$; $|a| = -a$ if $a < 0$.

By appropriate separate consideration of these two cases one may prove the laws for absolute values of sums and products,

(3) $|ab| = |a| \cdot |b|,$ $|a + b| \leq |a| + |b|.$

The sum law may also be obtained thus: by the definition, we have $-|a| \leq a \leq |a|$ and $-|b| \leq b \leq |b|$; hence adding inequalities,

$$-(|a| + |b|) \leq a + b \leq |a| + |b|.$$

This indicates at once that, whether $a + b$ is positive or negative, its absolute value cannot exceed $|a| + |b|$.

EXERCISES

1. Deduce from the postulates for an ordered domain the following rules:
    (a) if $a < b$, then $a + c < b + c$, and conversely,
    (b) $a - x < a - y$ if and only if $x > y$,
    (c) if $a < 0$, then $ax > ay$ if and only if $x < y$,
    (d) $0 < c$ and $ac < bc$ imply $a < b$,
    (e) $x + x + x + x = 0$ implies $x = 0$,
    (f) $a < b$ implies $a^3 < b^3$.
    (g) if $c \geq 0$, then $a \geq b$ implies $ac \geq bc$.
2. Prove that the equation $x^2 + 1 = 0$ has no solution in an ordered domain.
3. Prove as many laws on the relation $a \leq b$ as you can.
4. Prove that $||a| - |b|| \leq |a - b|$ in any ordered domain.
★5. Prove that $a^7 = b^7$ implies $a = b$ in any ordered domain.
★6. Show that, in an ordered domain, the cancellation law of multiplication can be proved from the other assumptions. (*Hint:* Apply the law of trichotomy.)
★7. In any ordered domain, show that $a^2 - ab + b^2 \geq 0$ for all a, b.
★8. Define "positive" element in the domain $\mathbf{Z}[\sqrt{2}]$, and show that the addition, multiplication, and trichotomy laws hold.
★9. Let D be an integral domain in which there is defined a relation $a < b$ which satisfies the transitive law, the principles for addition and multiplication of inequalities, and the law of trichotomy stated in the text. Prove that if a set of "positive" elements is suitably chosen, D is an ordered domain.
★10. Prove in detail that any subdomain of an ordered domain is an ordered domain.

★ Here and subsequently exercises of greater difficulty are starred.

4. Well-ordering Principle

A subset S of an ordered domain (such as the real number system) is called *well-ordered* if each nonempty subset of S contains a smallest member. In terms of this concept, one can formulate an important property of the integers, not characteristically algebraic and not shared by other number systems. This is the

Well-ordering Principle.   The positive integers are well-ordered.

In other words, any nonempty collection C of positive integers must contain some smallest member m, such that whenever c is in C, $m \leqq c$. For instance, the least positive even integer is 2.

To illustrate the force of this principle, we prove

Theorem 3.   *There is no integer between 0 and 1.*

This is immediately clear, by a glance at the natural order of the integers, but we wish to show that this fact can also be *proved* from our assumptions without "looking" at the integers. We give an indirect proof. If there is any integer c with $0 < c < 1$, then the set of all such integers is nonempty. By the well-ordering principle, there is a least integer m in this set, and $0 < m < 1$. If we multiply both sides of these inequalities by the positive number m, we have $0 < m^2 < m$. Thus m^2 is another integer in the set C, smaller than the supposedly minimum element m of C. This contradiction establishes Theorem 3.

Theorem 4.   *A set S of positive integers which includes 1, and which includes $n + 1$ whenever it includes n, includes every positive integer.*

Proof.   It is enough to show that the set S', consisting of those positive integers *not* included in S, is empty. Suppose S' were not empty; it would have to contain a least element m. But $m \neq 1$ by hypothesis; hence by Theorem 3, $m > 1$, and so $m - 1$ would be positive. But since $1 > 0$, $m - 1 < m$; hence by the choice of m, $m - 1$ would be in S. It follows by hypothesis that $(m - 1) + 1 = m$ would be in S. This contradiction establishes the theorem.

EXERCISES

1. Show that for any integer a, $a - 1$ is the greatest integer less than a.
2. Which of the following sets are well-ordered: (a) all odd positive integers,   (b) all even negative integers,   (c) all integers greater than -7,   (d) all odd integers greater than 249?
3. Prove that any subset of a well-ordered set is well-ordered.
4. Prove that a set of integers which contains -1000, and contains $x + 1$ when it contains x, contains all the positive integers.

5. (a) A set S of integers is said to have the integer b as "lower bound" if $b \leqq x$ for all x in S; b itself need not be in S. Show that any nonempty set S having a lower bound has a least element.

   (b) Show that any nonempty set of integers having an "upper bound" has a greatest element.

5. Finite Induction; Laws of Exponents

We have now formulated a complete list of basic properties for the integers in terms of addition, multiplication, and order. Henceforth we assume that *the integers form an ordered integral domain* **Z** *in which the positive elements are well-ordered.* Every other mathematical property of the integers can be proved, by strictly logical processes, from those assumed. In particular, we can deduce the extremely important.

Principle of Finite Induction. Let there be associated with each positive integer n a proposition $P(n)$ which is either true or false. If, firstly, $P(1)$ is true, and secondly, for all k, $P(k)$ implies $P(k + 1)$, then $P(n)$ is true for all positive integers n.

For, the set of those integers k for which $P(k)$ is true satisfies the hypotheses and hence the conclusion of Theorem 4.

The method of proof by induction will now be used to prove various laws valid in any integral domain D. We first use it to establish formally the general distributive law for any number n of summands,

$$(4) \qquad a(b_1 + b_2 + \cdots + b_n) = ab_1 + ab_2 + \cdots + ab_n.$$

To be explicit, we define the repeated sum $b_1 + \cdots + b_n$ as follows:

$$b_1 + b_2 + b_3 = (b_1 + b_2) + b_3,$$
$$b_1 + b_2 + b_3 + b_4 = [(b_1 + b_2) + b_3] + b_4.$$

This convention can be stated in general as a recursive formula (for $k \geqq 1$)

$$(5) \qquad b_1 + \cdots + b_k + b_{k+1} = (b_1 + \cdots + b_k) + b_{k+1},$$

which determines the arrangement of parentheses in $k + 1$ terms, given that for k terms.

The inductive proof of (4) requires first the proof for $n = 1$, which is immediate. Secondly, we assume the law (4) for $n = k$ and try to prove it for $n = k + 1$. By the definition (5) and the simple distributive law (v),

$$a(b_1 + \cdots + b_{k+1}) = a[(b_1 + \cdots + b_k) + b_{k+1}]$$
$$= a(b_1 + \cdots + b_k) + ab_{k+1}.$$

On the right, the first term can now be reduced by the assumed case of (4) for k summands, as

$$a(b_1 + \cdots + b_{k+1}) = (ab_1 + \cdots + ab_k) + ab_{k+1}.$$

Since the right-hand side is $ab_1 + \cdots + ab_{k+1}$, by the definition (5), we have completed the inductive proof of (4).

Similar but more complicated inductive arguments will yield the *general associative law*, which asserts· that a sum $b_1 + \cdots + b_k$ or a product $b_1 \cdots b_k$ has the same value for any arrangement of parentheses (a special case appears in Ex. 9 below). Using this result and (4), one can then also establish the two-sided general distributive law

$$(a_1 + \cdots + a_m)(b_1 + \cdots + b_n)$$
$$= a_1b_1 + \cdots + a_1b_n + \cdots + a_mb_1 + \cdots + a_mb_n.$$

Note also the general associative and commutative law, according to which the sum of k given terms always has the same value, whatever the order or the grouping of the terms.

Positive integral exponents in any integral domain D may also be treated by induction. If n is a positive integer, the power a^n stands for the product $a \cdot a \cdots a$, to n factors. This can also be stated as a "recursive" definition

$$(6) \qquad\qquad a^1 = a, \qquad a^{n+1} = a^n \cdot a, \qquad \text{(any } a \text{ in } D),$$

which makes it possible to compute any power a^{n+1} in terms of an already computed lower power a^n. From these definitions one may prove the usual laws, for any positive integral exponents m and n, as follows:

$$(7) \qquad\qquad\qquad\qquad a^m a^n = a^{m+n},$$
$$(8) \qquad\qquad\qquad (a^m)^n = a^{mn}, \qquad (ab)^m = a^m b^m.$$

For instance, the first law may be proved by induction on n. If $n = 1$, the law becomes $a^m \cdot a = a^{m+1}$, which is exactly the definition of a^{m+1}. Next assume that the law (7) is true for every m and for a given positive integer $n = k$, and consider the analogous expression $a^m a^{k+1}$ for the next larger exponent $k + 1$. One finds

$$a^m a^{k+1} = a^m(a^k a) = (a^m a^k)a = a^{m+k}a = a^{(m+k)+1},$$

by successive applications of the definition, the associative law, the induction assumption, and the definition again. This gives the law (7) for the case $n = k + 1$, and so completes the induction.

The Principle of Finite Induction permits one to assume the truth of $P(n)$ *gratis* in proving $P(n + 1)$. We shall now show that one can even assume the truth of $P(k)$ for all $k \leqq n$. This is called the

Second Principle of Finite Induction. Let there be associated with each positive integer n a proposition $P(n)$. If, for each m, the assumption that $P(k)$ is true for all $k < m$ implies the conclusion that $P(m)$ is itself true, then $P(n)$ is true for all n.

Proof. Let S be the set of integers for which $P(n)$ is false. Unless S is empty, it will have a first member m. By choice of m, $P(k)$ will be true for all $k < m$; hence by hypothesis, $P(m)$ must itself be true, giving a contradiction. The only way out is to admit that S is empty. Q.E.D.

Caution: In case $m = 1$, the set of all $k < 1$ is void, so that one must implicitly include a proof of $P(1)$.

EXERCISES

1. Prove by induction that the following laws for positive exponents are valid in any integral domain:
   (a) $(a^m)^n = a^{mn}$,   (b) $(ab)^n = a^n b^n$,   (c) $1^n = 1$.
2. Prove by induction that $1 + 2 + \cdots + n = n(n + 1)/2$.
★3. Define the factorial function $n!$ by $0! = 1$ and $(n + 1)! = (n!)(n + 1)$,

   and the binomial coefficients $\dbinom{n}{k}$ by $\dbinom{n}{0} = \dbinom{n}{n} = 1$ and

   $$\dbinom{n + 1}{k} = \dbinom{n}{k - 1} + \dbinom{n}{k}.$$

   (a) Prove that $\dbinom{n}{k} = n!/k!(n - k)!$

   (b) Prove by induction the binomial formula $(x + y)^n = \sum_{k=0}^{n} \dbinom{n}{k} x^{n-k} y^k$.

4. Prove by induction that $x_1^2 + \cdots + x_n^2 > 0$ unless $x_1 = \cdots = x_n = 0$.
5. Prove by induction the following summation formulas:
   (a) $1 + 4 + 9 + \cdots + n^2 = n(n + 1)(2n + 1)/6$;
   (b) $1 + 8 + 27 + \cdots + n^3 = [n(n + 1)/2]^2$.
6. In any ordered domain, show that every odd power of a negative element is negative.
7. Using induction, but not the well-ordering principle, prove Theorem 3. (*Hint:* Let $P(n)$ mean $n \geq 1$.)
★8. Using Ex. 7, prove the well-ordering principle from the principle of finite induction. (*Hint:* Let $P(n)$ be the proposition that any class of positive integers containing a number $\leq n$ has a least member.)
9. Using the definition (5), prove the following associative law:

$$(a_1 + \cdots + a_m) + (b_1 + \cdots + b_n) = a_1 + \cdots + a_m + b_1 + \cdots + b_n.$$

10. Obtain a formula for the nth derivative of the product of two functions and prove the formula by induction on n.
★11. Prove that to any base $a > 1$, each positive integer m has a unique expression of the form

$$a^n r_n + a^{n-1} r_{n-1} + \cdots + a^2 r_2 + a r_1 + r_0,$$

where the integers r_k satisfy $0 \leq r_k < a$, $r_n \neq 0$.

*12. Illustrate Ex. 11 by converting the equation $63 \cdot 111 = 6993$ to the base 7, checking by multiplying out.

13. A druggist has only the five weights of 1, 3, 9, 27, 81 ounces, respectively, and a two-pan balance (weights may be placed in either pan). Show that he can weigh any amount up to 121 ounces.

14. Prove that the sum of the digits of any multiple of 9 is itself divisible by 9.

6. Divisibility

An equation $ax = b$ with integral coefficients does not always have an integral solution x. If there is an integral solution, b is said to be *divisible by a*; the investigation of this situation is the first problem of number theory.

An analogous concept of divisibility arises in every integral domain; it is defined as follows:

Definition.   *In an integral domain D, an element a is divisible by an element b when $b = aq$ for some q in D. When b is divisible by a, we write $a \mid b$; we also call a a* factor *or* divisor *of b, and b a* multiple *of a. The divisors of 1 in D are called* units *of D.*

Like the equality relation $a = b$, the relation $a \mid b$ is reflexive and transitive:

(9) $a \mid a;$ $a \mid b$ and $b \mid c$ imply $a \mid c.$

The first law of (9) is trivial, since $a = a \cdot 1$ means that $a \mid a$. To prove the second, recall that the hypotheses $a \mid b$ and $b \mid c$ are defined to mean $b = ad_1$ and $c = bd_2$, for some integers d_1 and d_2. Substitution of the first equation in the second gives $c = a(d_1d_2)$. Since d_1d_2 is an integer, this states according to the definition that $a \mid c$, as asserted in the conclusion of (9).

Theorem 5.   *The only units of $\mathbf{Z}$ are ± 1.*

This theorem asserts in effect that, for integers a and b, $ab = 1$ implies $a = \pm 1$ and $b = \pm 1$. But according to the rules for the absolute value of a product, $ab = 1$ gives $\mid ab \mid = \mid a \mid \cdot \mid b \mid = 1$. Since neither a nor b is zero, $\mid a \mid$ and $\mid b \mid$ are positive numbers. There are no positive integers between 0 and 1 (Theorem 3), so by the law of trichotomy $\mid a \mid \geq 1$ and $\mid b \mid \geq 1$. If either inequality held, the product $\mid a \mid \cdot \mid b \mid$ could not be 1. Therefore $\mid a \mid = \mid b \mid = 1$, so that $a = \pm 1$, $b = \pm 1$, as asserted.

Corollary.   *If the integers a and b divide each other ($a \mid b$ and $b \mid a$), then $a = \pm b$.*

Proof.   By hypothesis $a = bd_1$ and $b = ad_2$, hence $a = ad_2d_1$. If $a = 0$, then $b = 0$; if $a \neq 0$, cancellation yields $1 = d_2 d_1$. Then $d_1 = \pm 1$ by the theorem, and hence $a = \pm b$, Q.E.D.

Since $a = a \cdot 1 = (-a)(-1)$, any integer a is divisible by a, $-a$, $+1$, and -1.

Definition. *An integer p is a* prime *if p is not 0 or ± 1 and if p is divisible only by ± 1 and $\pm p$.*

The first few positive primes are

$$2, 3, 5, 7, 11, 13, 17, 19, 23, 29, 31, \cdots .$$

Any positive integer which is not one or a prime can be factored into prime factors; thus

$$128 = 2^7; \qquad 90 = 9 \cdot 10 = 3^2 \cdot 2 \cdot 5;$$
$$672 = 7 \cdot 96 = 7 \cdot 12 \cdot 8 = 7 \cdot 3 \cdot 2^5.$$

It is a matter of experience that we always get the same prime factors no matter how we proceed to obtain them. This uniqueness of the prime factorization can be proved by studying greatest common divisors, which we now do.

EXERCISES

1. Prove the following properties of units in any domain:
   (a) the product of two units is a unit,
   (b) a unit u of D divides every element of D,
   (c) if c divides every x in D, c is a unit.
2. Prove that if $a \mid b$ and $a \mid c$, then $a \mid (b + c)$.
3. Prove: if b is positive and not prime, it has a positive prime divisor $d \leq \sqrt{b}$.
4. List all positive primes less than 100. (*Hint:* Throw away multiples of 2, 3, 5, 7, and use Ex. 3.)
5. If $a \mid b$, prove that $\mid a \mid \leq \mid b \mid$ when $b \neq 0$.

7. The Euclidean Algorithm

The ordinary process of dividing an integer a by b yields a quotient q and a remainder r. Formally, this amounts to the following assertion.

Division Algorithm. *For given integers a and b, with $b > 0$, there exist integers q and r such that*

$$(10) \qquad\qquad a = bq + r, \qquad 0 \leq r < b.$$

Geometric picture. If we imagine the whole numbers displayed on the real axis, the possible multiples bq of b form a set of equally spaced division points on the line

-3b   -2b   -b   0   b   2b   3b

The point representing a must fall in one of the intervals determined by these points, say in the interval between bq and $b(q + 1)$, exclusive of the right-hand end point. This means that $a - bq = r$, where r represents a length shorter than the whole length b of an interval. Hence $0 \leqq r < b$, as asserted. This picture suggests the following proof based on our postulates.

Proof.   There certainly is some integral multiple of b not exceeding a; for instance, since $b > 0$, $b \geqq 1$ by Theorem 3, so $(-|a|)b \leqq -|a| \leqq a$. Therefore the set of differences $a - bx$ contains at least one nonnegative integer, namely, $a - (-|a|)b$. Hence, by the well-ordering postulate, there is a *least* nonnegative $a - bx$, say $a - bq = r$. By construction, $r \geqq 0$; while if $r \geqq b$, then $a - b(q + 1) = r - b \geqq 0$ would be less than $a - bq$, contrary to our choice of q. We conclude that $0 \leqq r < b$, while $a = bq + (a - bq) = bq + r$.

Corollary 1.   *For given integers a and b, the quotient q and the remainder r which satisfy (10) are uniquely determined.*

Proof.   Suppose that $a = bq + r = bq' + r'$, where $0 \leq r < b$, $0 \leq r' < b$. Then $r - r' = b(q' - q)$ is numerically smaller than b, but is a multiple of b. It follows that $r - r'$ must be zero. Hence $r = r'$, $bq = bq'$, $q = q'$, which gives the uniqueness of q and r, Q.E.D.

Frequently we have occasion to deal not with individual integers but with certain sets of integers, such as the set $\cdots -6, -3, 0, 3, 6, 9, \cdots$ which consists of all multiples of 3. This set has the important property that the sum or the difference of any two integers in the set is again an integer in the set. In general, a set S of integers is said to be *closed* under addition and subtraction if S contains the sum $a + b$ and the difference $a - b$ of any two integers a and b in S. All the even integers (positive, negative, and zero) form such a set. More generally, the set of all multiples xm of any fixed integer m is closed under addition and subtraction, for $xm \pm ym = (x \pm y)m$ is a multiple of m. We now prove that such sets of multiples are the only sets of integers with these properties.

Theorem 6.   *Any nonvoid set of integers closed under addition and subtraction either consists of zero alone or else contains a least positive element and consists of all the multiples of this integer.*

Proof.   Let such a set S contain an element $a \neq 0$. Then S contains the difference $a - a = 0$, and hence the difference $0 - a = -a$. Consequently, there is at least one positive element $|a| = \pm a$ in S. The well-ordering principle will provide a least positive element b in S.

The set S must contain all integral multiples of b. For one may first show by induction on n that any positive multiple nb is in S: if $n = 1$, b is in S; if kb is already known to lie in S, then $(k + 1)b = kb + b$ is a sum of two elements of S, hence is in S. Therefore, any negative multiple $(-n)b = 0 - (nb)$ is a difference of two elements of S, hence is in S.

The set S can contain nothing but the integral multiples of b. For if a is any element of S, the Division Algorithm may be applied to give a difference $a - bq = r$ which is also in S. The remainder r is non-negative and less than b, while b is the smallest positive element in S. Therefore $r = 0$, and $a = bq$ is a multiple of b, as asserted. Q.E.D.

Definition. *An integer d is a* greatest common divisor *(g.c.d.) of the integers a and b if d is a common divisor of a and b which is a multiple of every other common divisor. In symbols, d must have the properties*

$$d \mid a; \qquad d \mid b; \qquad c \mid a \text{ and } c \mid b \qquad imply \qquad c \mid d.$$

For example, both 3 and -3 are greatest common divisors of 6 and 9. According to the definition two different g.c.d.'s must divide each other, hence differ only in sign. Of the two possible g.c.d.'s $\pm d$ for a and b, the positive one is often denoted by the symbol (a, b). Note that the adjective "greatest" in the definition of a g.c.d. means not primarily that d has a greater *magnitude* than any other common divisor c, but that d is a *multiple* of any such c.

Theorem 7. *Any two integers $a \neq 0$ and $b \neq 0$ have a positive greatest common divisor (a, b). It can be expressed as a "linear combination" of a and b, with integral coefficients s and t, in the form*

$$(11) \qquad\qquad\qquad (a, b) = sa + tb.$$

Proof. Consider the numbers of the form $sa + tb$. For any two such

$$(s_1 a + t_1 b) \pm (s_2 a + t_2 b) = (s_1 \pm s_2)a + (t_1 \pm t_2)b.$$

Therefore the set S of all integers $sa + tb$ is closed under addition and subtraction, so by Theorem 6 consists of all multiples of some minimum positive number $d = sa + tb$. From this formula it is clear that any common factor c of a and b must be a factor of d. On the other hand, the original integers $a = 1 \cdot a + 0 \cdot b$ and $b = 0 \cdot a + 1 \cdot b$ both lie in the set S under consideration, and hence must be multiples of the minimum number d in this set. In other words, d is a common divisor. Hence it is the desired greatest common divisor, Q.E.D.

Similarly, the set M of common *multiples* of a and b is closed under addition and subtraction. Its least positive member m will be a common multiple of a and b dividing every common multiple. Thus m is a "least common multiple" (or l.c.m.).

Theorem 8. *Any two integers a and b have a least common multiple $m = [a, b]$, which is a divisor of every common multiple and which itself is a common multiple.*

To explicitly find the g.c.d. of two integers a and b, one may use the so-called *Euclidean Algorithm*. We may suppose that a and b are both positive, since a negative integer b could be replaced by $-b$ without altering the g.c.d. $(a, b) = (a, -b)$. The Division Algorithm gives

$$(12) \qquad a = bq_1 + r_1, \qquad 0 \leqq r_1 < b.$$

Every integer which divides the terms a and b must divide the remainder r_1; conversely, every common divisor of b and r_1 is a divisor of a in (12). Therefore the common divisors of a and b are the same as the common divisors of b and r_1, so the g.c.d.'s (a, b) and (b, r_1) are identical. This reduction can be repeated on b and r_1:

$$
\begin{aligned}
b &= r_1 q_2 + r_2, & 0 &< r_2 < r_1; \\
r_1 &= r_2 q_3 + r_3, & 0 &< r_3 < r_2; \\
&\qquad \cdot & &\qquad \cdot \\
&\qquad \cdot & &\qquad \cdot \\
&\qquad \cdot & &\qquad \cdot \\
r_{n-2} &= r_{n-1} q_n + r_n, & 0 &< r_n < r_{n-1}; \\
r_{n-1} &= r_n q_{n+1}.
\end{aligned}
$$

(13)

Since the remainders continually decrease, there must ultimately† be a remainder r_{n+1} which is zero, as we have indicated in the last equation. The argument above shows that the desired greatest common divisor is

$$(a, b) = (b, r_1) = (r_1, r_2) = \cdots = (r_{n-1}, r_n).$$

But the last equation of (13) shows that r_n is itself a divisor of r_{n-1}, so that the last g.c.d. is just r_n itself. The g.c.d of the given integers a and b is thus the last non-zero remainder r_n in the Euclidean Algorithm (12) and (13).

The algorithm can also be used to represent the g.c.d. explicitly as a linear combination $sa + tb$. This can be done by expressing the successive remainders r_i in terms of a and b, as

$$
\begin{aligned}
r_1 &= a - bq_1 = a + (-q_1)b, \\
r_2 &= b - q_2 r_1 = (-q_2)a + (1 + q_1 q_2)b.
\end{aligned}
$$

The form of these equations indicates that one would eventually obtain

† Why? Does a proof of this involve the well-ordering principle?

r_n as a linear combination of a and b with integral coefficients s and t which involve the quotients q_i.

The expression $(a, b) = sa + tb$ for the g.c.d. is of the greatest utility. One important consequence is the fact that a prime which divides a product of two numbers must always divide at least one of the factors:

Theorem 9.   *If p is a prime, then $p \mid ab$ implies $p \mid a$ or $p \mid b$.*

Proof.   By the definition of a prime, the only factors of p are ± 1 and $\pm p$. If the conclusion $p \mid a$ is false, the only common divisors of p and a are ± 1, so that 1 is a g.c.d. of a and p and can thus be expressed in the form $1 = sa + tp$. On multiplying through by b, we have

$$b = sab + tbp.$$

Both terms on the right are divisible by p, hence the left side b is divisible by p, as in the second alternative in the theorem, Q.E.D.

If $(a, b) = 1$, we call a and b *relatively prime*. In other words, two integers a and b are relatively prime if they have no common divisors except ± 1. The argument used to prove Theorem 9 will also prove the following generalization:

Theorem 10.   *If $(c, a) = 1$ and $c \mid ab$, then $c \mid b$.*

One consequence may be drawn for an integer m which is a multiple of each of two relatively prime integers a and c. Such an m has the form $m = ad$, and is divisible by c, so by this theorem $c \mid d$, and $m = ad = a(cd')$. Therefore the product ac divides m. This argument proves

Theorem 11.   *If $(a, c) = 1$, $a \mid m$, and $c \mid m$, then $ac \mid m$.*

EXERCISES

1. Use the Euclidean Algorithm to find the g.c.d. of
   (a) $(14, 35)$,   (b) $(11, 15)$,   (c) $(180, 252)$,
   (d) $(2873, 6643)$,   (e) $(4148, 7684)$,   (f) $(1001, 7655)$.
2. Write (x, y) in the form $sx + ty$ (s, t integers) in the first three cases of Ex. 1.
3. Prove that $(0, a) = \mid a \mid$ for any integer a.
4. If $a > 0$, prove that $(ab, ac) = a(b, c)$.
5. Show that $b \mid c$ and $\mid c \mid < b$ imply $c = 0$. (This fact is used in Corollary 1.)
6. (a) Prove that any three integers a, b, c have a g.c.d. which can be expressed in the form $sa + tb + uc$.
   (b) Prove that $((a, b), c) = (a, (b, c)) = ((a, c), b)$.
7. Discuss Exs. 3–5 and 6(b) for the case of l.c.m.
8. Show that a set of integers closed under subtraction is necessarily also closed under addition.

9. Show that a set of integers closed under addition alone need not consist of all multiples of one fixed element.

10. In the Euclidean Algorithm, show by induction on k that each remainder can be expressed in the form $r_k = s_k a + t_k b$, where s_k and t_k are integers.

11. Give a detailed proof of Theorem 10..

★12. Show that, for any positive integers a, b the set of all $ma + nb$ (m, n positive integers) includes all multiples of (a, b) larger than ab.

13. If q is an integer such that for all integers a and b, $q \mid ab$ implies $q \mid a$ or $q \mid b$, prove that q is 0, ± 1, or a prime (cf. Theorem 9).

14. (a) Prove that if $(a, m) = (b, m) = 1$, then $(ab, m) = 1$.
    (b) Prove that if $(a, c) = d$, $a \mid b$, and $c \mid b$, then $ac \mid bd$.
    (c) Prove that $[a, c] = ac/d$.

8. Fundamental Theorem of Arithmetic

It is now easy to prove the unique factorization theorem for integers, also called the fundamental theorem of arithmetic.

Theorem 12. *Any integer not zero can be expressed as a unit* (± 1) *times a product of positive primes. This expression is unique except for the order in which the prime factors occur.*

Proof. That any integer a can be written as such a product may be proved by successively breaking a up into smaller factors. This process involves the second principle of finite induction and can be described as follows. (It suffices to consider only positive integers a.)

Let $P(a)$ be the proposition that a can be factored as in Theorem 12. If $a = 1$ or if a is a prime, then $P(a)$ is trivially true. On the other hand, if a is composite, then it has a positive divisor b which is neither 1 nor a, so that $a = bc$, with $b < a$, $c < a$. But by the second induction principle, we can assume $P(b)$ and $P(c)$ to be true, so that b and c can be expressed as products of primes:

$$b = p_1 p_2 \cdots p_r, \qquad c = q_1 q_2 \cdots q_s,$$

yielding for a the composite expression

$$a = bc = p_1 p_2 \cdots p_r q_1 q_2 \cdots q_s,$$

which is of the desired form.

To prove the uniqueness, we have to consider two possible prime factorizations of an integer a,

$$a = (\pm 1) p_1 p_2 \cdots p_m = (\pm 1) q_1 q_2 \cdots q_n.$$

Since the primes p_i and q_j are all positive, the terms ± 1 in the two decompositions must agree. The prime p_1 in the first factorization is a divisor of the product $a = \pm q_1 \cdots q_n$, so that repeated application of Theorem 9 insures that p_1 must divide at least one factor q_j of this product. Since

$p_1 \mid q_j$ and both are positive primes, $p_1 = q_j$. Rearrange the factorization $q_1 q_2 \cdots q_i$ so that q_j appears first, then cancel p_1 against q_j, leaving

$$p_2 p_3 \cdots p_m = q_2' q_3' \cdots q_n',$$

where the accents denote the q's in their new order. Continue this process until no primes are left on one side of the resulting equation. There can then be no primes left on the other side, so that in the original factorization, $m = n$. We have caused the two factorizations to agree simply by rearranging the primes in the second factorization, as asserted in our uniqueness theorem, Q.E.D.

In the factorization of a number the same prime p may occur several times. Collecting these occurrences, we may write the decomposition as

(14) $a = \pm p_1^{e_1} p_2^{e_2} \cdots p_k^{e_k}$, $(1 < p_1 < p_2 < \cdots < p_k)$.

Here our uniqueness theorem asserts that the exponent e_i to which each prime p_i occurs is uniquely determined by the given number a.

EXERCISES

1. Describe a systematic process for finding the g.c.d. and the l.c.m. of two integers whose prime decompositions are known, illustrating with $a = 216$, $b = 360$, and $a = 144$, $b = 625$. (*Hint:* It is helpful to use "dummy" zero components for primes dividing one but not both of a or b.)

2. If $V_p(a)$ denotes the exponent of the highest power of the prime p dividing the non-zero integer a, prove the formulas
   (i) $V_p(a + b) \geqq \min \{V_p(a), V_p(b)\}$;
   (ii) $V_p((a, b)) = \min \{V_p(a), V_p(b)\}$;
   (iii) $V_p(ab) = V_p(a) + V_p(b)$;
   (iv) $V_p([a, b]) = \max \{V_p(a), V_p(b)\}$.

3. If $\| a \| = 2^{-V_p(a)}$, for V_p as in Ex. 2, prove that

   $$\| ab \| = \| a \| \cdot \| b \| \text{and}   \| a + b \| \leqq \max (\| a \|, \| b \|).$$

★4. Let $V(a)$ be a nonnegative function with integral values, defined for all non-zero integers a and having properties (i) and (iii) of Ex. 2. Prove that $V(a)$ is either identically 0 or a constant multiple of one of the functions $V_p(a)$ of Ex. 2. (*Hint:* First locate some p with $V(p) > 0$.)

5. Using the formulas of Ex. 2, show that for any positive integers a and b, $ab = (a, b)[a, b]$. (For a second proof, cf. Ex. 14(c), §7.)

6. Prove that the number of primes is infinite (Euclid). (*Hint:* If $p_1, \cdots, p_n$ are n primes, then the product $p_1 p_2 \cdots p_n + 1$ is divisible by none of these primes.)

★7. Define the function $e(n)$ (n any positive integer) as the g.c.d. of the exponents occurring in the prime factorization of n. Prove that (a) for given r and n in $\mathbf{Z}$, there is an integer x such that $x^r = n$, if and only if $r \mid e(n)$; (b) $e(n^r) = r \cdot e(n)$; (c) if $e(m) = e(n) = d$, then $d \mid e(mn)$.

8. If a product mn of positive integers is a square and if $(m, n) = 1$, show that both m and n are squares.

★9. The possible right triangles with sides measured by integers x, y, and z may be found as follows. Assume that x, y, and z have no common factors except ± 1.

(a) If $x^2 + y^2 = z^2$, show that x and y cannot both be odd.

(b) If y is even, apply Ex. 8 to show that $y = 2mn$, where m and n are integers with $x = m^2 - n^2$, $z = m^2 + n^2$. (*Hint:* Factor $z^2 - x^2$, and show $(z + x, z - x) = 2$.

9. Congruences

In giving the time of day, it is customary to count only up to 12, and then to begin over again. This simple idea of throwing away the multiples of a fixed number 12 is the basis of the arithmetical notion of congruence. We call two integers *congruent* "modulo 12" if they differ only by an integral multiple of 12. For instance, 7 and 19 are so congruent, and we write $7 \equiv 19 \pmod{12}$.

Definition. $a \equiv b \pmod{m}$ *holds if and only if* $m \mid (a - b)$.

One might equally well say that $a \equiv b \pmod{m}$ means that the difference $a - b$ lies in the set of all multiples of m. There is still another alternative definition, based on the fact that each integer a on division by m leaves a unique remainder (Corollary 1 of §7). This alternative we state as follows:

Theorem 13.   *Two integers* a *and* b *are congruent modulo* m *if and only if they leave the same remainder when divided by* $\mid m \mid$.

Since $a \equiv b \pmod{m}$ if and only if $a \equiv b \pmod{-m}$, it will suffice to prove this result for the case $m > 0$.

Proof.   Suppose first that $a \equiv b \pmod{m}$ according to our definition. Then $a - b = cm$, a multiple of m. On division by m, b leaves a remainder $b - qm = r$, where $0 \leqq r < m$. Then

$$a = b + cm = (qm + r) + cm = (q + c)m + r.$$

This equation indicates that r is the unique remainder of a on division by m; hence a and b do have the same remainder.

Conversely, suppose that $a = qm + r$, $b = q'm + r$, with the same remainder r. Then $a - b = (q - q')m$ is divisible by m, so that $a \equiv b \pmod{m}$, Q.E.D.

The relation of congruence for a fixed modulus m has for all integers a, b, and c the following properties, reminiscent of the laws of equality (§2):

Reflexive $a \equiv a$

Symmetric $a \equiv b$ implies $b \equiv a$ all taken $\pmod{m}$.

Transitive $a \equiv b$ and $b \equiv c$ imply $a \equiv c$

Each of these laws may be proved by reversion to the definition of congruence. The symmetric law, so translated, requires that $m \mid (a - b)$ imply $m \mid (b - a)$. The hypothesis here is $a - b = dm$, which gives the conclusion $m \mid (b - a)$ in the form $b - a = (-d)m$.

The relation of congruence for a fixed modulus m has a further "substitution property," reminiscent of equality also: sums of congruent integers are congruent, and products of congruent integers are congruent.

Theorem 14. *If $a \equiv b \pmod{m}$, then for all integers x,*

$$a + x \equiv b + x, \qquad ax \equiv bx, \qquad -a \equiv -b \qquad all \pmod{m}.$$

Here again the proofs rest on an appeal to the definition. Thus the hypothesis becomes $a - b = km$ for some k; from this we may derive the conclusions in the form

$$m \mid (a + x - b - x), \qquad m \mid (ax - bx), \qquad m \mid (-a + b).$$

The law of cancellation which holds for equations need not hold for congruences. Thus $2 \cdot 7 \equiv 2 \cdot 1 \pmod{12}$ does not imply that $7 \equiv 1 \pmod{12}$. This inference fails because the 2 which was cancelled is a factor of the modulus. At best, a modified cancellation law can be found:

Theorem 15. *Whenever c is relatively prime to m,*

$$ca \equiv cb \pmod{m} \qquad implies \qquad a \equiv b \pmod{m}.$$

Proof. By definition, the hypothesis states that $m \mid (ca - cb)$, or, in other words, that $m \mid c(a - b)$. But m is assumed relatively prime to the first factor c of this product, so Theorem 10 allows us to conclude that m divides the second factor $a - b$. This means that $a \equiv b \pmod{m}$, as asserted.

The study of linear equations may be extended to congruences.

Theorem 16. *If c is relatively prime to m, then the congruence $cx \equiv b$ $\pmod{m}$ has an integral solution x. Any two solutions x_1 and x_2 are congruent, modulo m.*

Proof. By hypothesis, the g.c.d. (c, m) is 1, so $1 = sc + tm$ for suitable integers s and t. Multiplying by b, $b = bsc + btm$. The final term here is a multiple of m, so that $b \equiv (bs)c \pmod{m}$. This states that $x = bs$ is the required solution of $b \equiv xc$.

On the other hand, two solutions x_1 and x_2 of this congruence must satisfy $cx_1 \equiv cx_2$, because congruence is a transitive and symmetric relation. Since c is supposed prime to m, we can cancel the c here, as in Theorem 15, obtaining the desired conclusion $x_1 \equiv x_2 \pmod{m}$, Q.E.D.

An important special case arises when the modulus m is a prime. In this case all integers not divisible by m are relatively prime to m. This fact gives the

Corollary.   *If p is a prime and if $c \not\equiv 0$ (mod p), then $cx \equiv b$ (mod p) has a solution which is unique, modulo p.*

Simultaneous congruences can also be treated.

Theorem 17.   *If the moduli m_1 and m_2 are relatively prime, then the congruences*

$$(15) \qquad\qquad x \equiv b_1 \ (mod \ m_1), \qquad x \equiv b_2 \ (mod \ m_2)$$

have a common solution x. Any two solutions are congruent modulo $m_1 m_2$.

Proof.   For any integer y, $x = b_1 + ym_1$ is a solution of the first congruence. Such an x satisfies the second congruence also if and only if $b_1 + ym_1 \equiv b_2$ (mod m_2), or $ym_1 \equiv b_2 - b_1$ (mod m_2). Since m_1 is relatively prime to the modulus m_2, this congruence can be solved for y by Theorem 16.

Conversely, suppose that x and x' are two solutions of the given simultaneous congruences (15). Then $x - x' \equiv 0$ (mod m_1) and also (mod m_2). Since m_1 and m_2 are relatively prime, this implies that the difference $x - x'$ is divisible by the product modulus $m_1 m_2$, so that $x \equiv x'$ (mod $m_1 m_2$), Q.E.D.

The same methods of attack apply to two or more congruences of the form $a_i x \equiv b_i$ (mod m_i), with $(a_i, m_i) = 1$ and with the various moduli relatively prime in pairs.

Theorem 18 (Fermat).   *If a is an integer and p a prime, then*

$$a^p \equiv a \ (mod \ p).$$

Proof.   For a fixed prime p, let $P(n)$ be the proposition that $n^p \equiv n$ (mod p). Then $P(0)$ and $P(1)$ are obvious. In the binomial expansion (Ex. 3, §5) for $(n + 1)^p$, every coefficient except the first and the last is divisible by p, hence $(n + 1)^p \equiv n^p + 1$ (mod p), whence $p(n)$ implies $(n + 1)^p \equiv n + 1$ (mod p), which is the proposition $P(n + 1)$.

EXERCISES

1. Solve the following congruences:
   (a) $3x \equiv 2$ (mod 5)   (b) $7x \equiv 4$ (mod 10),
   (c) $243x + 17 \equiv 101$ (mod 725),   (d) $4x + 3 \equiv 4$ (mod 5),
   (e) $6x + 3 \equiv 4$ (mod 10),   (f) $6x + 3 \equiv 1$ (mod 10).
2. Prove that the relation $a \equiv b$ (mod m) is reflexive and transitive.
3. Prove directly that $a \equiv b$ (mod m) and $c \equiv d$ (mod m) imply $a + c \equiv b + d$ (mod m) and $ac \equiv bd$ (mod m).

★4. (a) Show that the congruence $ax \equiv b$ (mod m) has a solution if and only if $(a, m) \mid b$.

(b) Show that if $(a, m) \mid b$, the congruence, has exactly (a, m) incongruent solutions modulo m. [*Hint:* Divide a, b, and m by (a, m).]

5. If m is an integer, show that $m^2 \equiv 0$, 1, or 4, modulo 8.

6. Prove $x^2 \equiv 35$ (mod 100) has no solutions.

★7. Prove that if $x^2 \equiv n$ (mod 65) has a solution then so does $x^2 \equiv -n$ (mod 65).

8. If x is an odd number not divisible by 3, prove that $x^2 \equiv 1$ (mod 24).

★9. (a) Show by tables that all numbers from 25 to 40 can be expressed as sums of four or fewer squares (the result is actually true for all positive numbers).

(b) Prove that no integer $m \equiv 7$ (mod 8) can be expressed as a sum of three squares. (*Hint:* Use Ex. 5.)

10. Solve the simultaneous congruences:

(a) $x \equiv 2$ (mod 5), $2x \equiv 1$ (mod 8);

(b) $3x \equiv 2$ (mod 5), $2x \equiv 1$ (mod 3).

11. On a desert island, five men and a monkey gather coconuts all day, then sleep. The first man awakens, and decides to take his share. He divides the coconuts into five equal shares, with one coconut left over. He gives the extra one to the monkey, hides his share, and goes to sleep. Later, the second man awakens and takes his fifth from the remaining pile; he too finds one extra and gives it to the monkey. Each of the remaining three men does likewise in turn. Find the minimum number of coconuts originally present. (*Hint:* Try -4 coconuts.)

★12. Show by induction that Theorem 17 can be generalized to n congruences with moduli relatively prime in pairs.

★13. Prove that if $(m_1, m_2) = (a_1, m_1) = (a_2, m_2) = 1$, then the simultaneous congruences $a_i x \equiv b_i$ (mod m_i) $(i = 1, 2)$ have a common solution, and any two solutions are congruent modulo $m_1 m_2$.

★14. Generalize Ex. 13 to n simultaneous congruences.

15. For what positive integers m is it true that whenever $x^2 \equiv 0$ (mod m) then also $x \equiv 0$ (mod m)?

16. If a and b are integers and p a prime, prove that $(a + b)^p \equiv a^p + b^p$ (mod p).

10. The Rings Z_n

From early antiquity, man has distinguished between the "even" integers 2, 4, 6, $\cdots$ and the "odd" integers 1, 3, 5, $\cdots$. The following laws for reckoning with even and odd integers are also familar:

$$(16) \quad \begin{aligned} \text{even} + \text{even} &= \text{odd} + \text{odd} = \text{even}, & \text{even} + \text{odd} &= \text{odd}, \\ \text{even} \cdot \text{even} &= \text{even} \cdot \text{odd} = \text{even}, & \text{odd} \cdot \text{odd} &= \text{odd}. \end{aligned}$$

These identities define a new integral domain Z_2, which consists of two elements 0 ("even") and 1 ("odd") alone, and having the addition and multiplication tables

$$0 + 0 = 1 + 1 = 0, \qquad 0 + 1 = 1 + 0 = 1,$$
$$0 \cdot 0 = 0 \cdot 1 = 1 \cdot 0 = 0, \qquad 1 \cdot 1 = 1.$$

We will now show that a similar construction can be applied to the remainders $0, 1, 2, \cdots, n - 1$ to any modulus n. Two such remainders can be added (or multiplied) by simply forming the sum (or product) in the ordinary sense (that is, in $\mathbf{Z}$), and then replacing the result by its remainder modulo n. Tables for the case $n = 5$ are displayed below.

+	0	1	2	3	4
0	0	1	2	3	4
1	1	2	3	4	0
2	2	3	4	0	1
3	3	4	0	1	2
4	4	0	1	2	3

·	0	1	2	3	4
0	0	0	0	0	0
1	0	1	2	3	4
2	0	2	4	1	3
3	0	3	1	4	2
4	0	4	3	2	1

In every case, the resulting system has properties (i)–(viii) of §1. That is, we have

Theorem 19.   *Under addition and multiplication modulo any fixed $n \geq 2$, the set of integers $0, 1, \cdots, n - 1$ constitutes a commutative ring $\mathbf{Z}_n$.*

Proof.   In the last section, we saw that the relation $x \equiv y \pmod{n}$ is reflexive, symmetric, and transitive, like ordinary equality. In fact, by Theorem 14, $a \equiv b \pmod{n}$ and $c \equiv d \pmod{n}$ together imply

$$(17) \qquad a + c \equiv b + d \pmod{n}, \qquad a \cdot c \equiv b \cdot d \pmod{n}.$$

That is, postulates (i)–(ii) hold, provided "equality" in $\mathbf{Z}$ is reinterpreted to mean "congruent modulo n." Again, 0 and 1 in $\mathbf{Z}$ act in $\mathbf{Z}_n$ as identities for addition and multiplication, respectively; while $n - k$ is an additive inverse of k, modulo n.

It remains to verify postulates (iii)–(v); consider the distributive law. Since $a(b + c) = ab + ac$ for any integers, one must by (17) have $a(b + c) \equiv ab + ac \pmod{n}$ when remainders are taken mod n. This is the distributive law in $\mathbf{Z}_n$; the proofs of the commutative and associative laws are the same. Q.E.D.

The only postulate for an integral domain not such an identity is the cancellation law of multiplication. According to Theorem 1 this law is equivalent to the assertion that there are no divisors of zero in $\mathbf{Z}_n$: $ab = 0$ implies $a = 0$ or $b = 0$. These equations in $\mathbf{Z}_n$ mean congruences for ordinary integers, so the law becomes the statement: $ab \equiv 0 \pmod{n}$ implies $a \equiv 0 \pmod{n}$ or $b \equiv 0 \pmod{n}$. This is equivalent to the assertion that $n \mid ab$ implies $n \mid a$ or $n \mid b$. This is true if n is a prime (Theorem

9). If n is not prime, n has a nontrivial factorization $n = ab$, so $n \mid ab$ although neither $n \mid a$ nor $n \mid b$, and Z_n has zero divisors. This proves

Theorem 20.   *The ring Z_n of integers modulo n is an integral domain if and only if n is a prime.*

There are other, more systematic ways to construct the algebra of integers modulo n. The device of replacing congruence by equality means essentially that all the integers which leave the same remainder on division by n are grouped together to make one new "number." Each such group of integers is called a "residue class." For the modulus 5 there are five such classes, corresponding to the possible remainders, 0, 1, 2, 3, and 4; some of these classes are

$$1_5 = \{ \cdots , -14, -9, -4, 1, 6, 11, 16, \cdots \},$$
$$2_5 = \{ \cdots , -13, -8, -3, 2, 7, 12, 17, \cdots \},$$
$$3_5 = \{ \cdots , -12, -7, -2, 3, 8, 13, 18, \cdots \}.$$

For any modulus n the residue class r_n determined by a remainder r with $0 \leqq r < n$ consists of all integers a which leave the remainder r on division by n. Each integer belongs to one and only one residue class, and two integers will belong to the same residue class if and only if they are congruent (Theorem 13). There are n residue classes, 0_n, 1_n, $\cdots$, $(n - 1)_n$.

The algebraic operations of Z_n can be carried out directly on these classes. For suppose that two residues r and s give in Z_n a remainder t as sum, $r + s \equiv t \pmod{n}$. The answer would be obtained if one used instead of the residues r and s any other elements in the corresponding classes. If a is in r_n, b in s_n, then $a + b$ is in the class t_n belonging to the sum t, for $a \equiv r$ and $b \equiv s$ give $a + b \equiv r + s \equiv t \pmod{n}$. In general, the algebra Z_n could be defined as the algebra of these residue classes: to add (or multiply) two classes, pick any representatives a and b of these classes, and find the residue class containing the sum (or the product) of these representatives. If a_n denotes the residue class which contains a, this rule may be stated as

$$(18) \qquad\qquad (a + b)_n = a_n + b_n, \qquad (ab)_n = a_n b_n.$$

For instance, the sum $1_5 + 2_5 = 3_5$ of the classes listed above may be found by adding any chosen representatives $6 + (-13)$ to get a result -7 which lies in the sum class 3_5. Other choices $-9 + (-3) = -12$, $11 + 7 = 18$, $-14 + 17 = 3$, all give the *same* sum, 3_5.

The residue classes which we have defined in terms of remainders may also be defined directly in terms of congruences, by a general method to be discussed in Chap. VI, §13.

EXERCISES

1. Construct addition and multiplication tables for $\mathbf{Z}_3$ and $\mathbf{Z}_4$.
2. Compute in $\mathbf{Z}_7$: $(3 \cdot 4) \cdot 5$, $3 \cdot (4 \cdot 5)$, $3 \cdot (4 + 5)$, $3 \cdot 4 + 3 \cdot 5$.
3. Find all divisors of zero in $\mathbf{Z}_{26}$, $\mathbf{Z}_{24}$.
4. Determine the exact set of all sums $x + y$ and that of all products xy, for x in 4_8, y in 4_8. How are these related to the sets $4_8 + 4_8$ and $4_8 \cdot 4_8$?
5. Verify the associative law for the addition of residue classes, as in the proof of Theorem 19.
6. For real numbers x and y, let $x \equiv y \pmod{2\pi}$ mean that $x = y + 2n\pi$ for some integer n. Show that addition of residue classes can then be defined as in (18), whereas multiplication of residue classes cannot be so defined.
★7. Show that, in $\mathbf{Z}_n$, any element c which is not a unit is a zero-divisor.
★8. (a) Enumerate the units of $\mathbf{Z}_{15}$.
    (b) Show that, if $n = 2m + 1$ is odd, then the number of units of $\mathbf{Z}_n$ is even.
★9. Show that k is a unit of $\mathbf{Z}_n$ if and only if $(k, n) = 1$ in $\mathbf{Z}$.

11. Some Basic Concepts of Logic

At this point we pause to discuss briefly the fundamental notions of class, binary operation, correspondence, and relation.

The words "class" and "set" are both used to refer to quite arbitrary collections of objects, such as the class of all odd numbers greater than 18, or the set of all points equidistant from two fixed points. These examples illustrate the principle that any *property* determines a *class;* namely, the class of all elements having that property. Conversely, any class C determines a property P_C, if an element is said to have the property P_C if and only if it belongs to the corresponding class C. It is often convenient to write "$x \, \epsilon \, C$" as shorthand for "x is in the class C." The *void* (or *empty*) *class* $\varnothing$, which contains no elements whatever, is a perfectly good set.

Two set A and B are equal if and only if they consist of the same elements, so $A = B$ if and only if every x in A is in B, and vice versa. Thus $A = B$ means $x \in A$ if and only if $x \in B$. This equality for sets does have the reflexive, symmetric, and transitive properties, as required for any equality in §2. A class A is called a *subset* (or subclass) of a set B if and only if every x in A is also in B. If A is a subset of B and B a subset of C, then A is a subset of C. Furthermore, $A = B$ if and only if A is a subset of B and B is a subset of A.

Operations on *pairs* of numbers arise in many instances—the addition of two integers, the addition of two residue classes in $\mathbf{Z}_n$, the multiplication of two real numbers, the subtraction of one integer from another, and the like. In such cases we speak of a "binary operation." In general, a *binary operation* "∘" on a set S of elements $a, b, c, \cdots$ is a rule which assigns to each ordered pair of elements a and b from S a uniquely defined third element $c = a \circ b$ in the same set S. To assert that this result is uniquely defined implies in particular that the element $c = a \circ b$ is unaltered if one replaces a or b by an equal element of S; in other words, $a = a'$ implies

$$(19) \qquad\qquad a \circ b = a' \circ b \qquad \text{and} \qquad b \circ a = b \circ a'$$

(the "substitution law"). By combination of the two parts of (19), one proves that

$$(20) \qquad\qquad a = a' \text{ and } b = b' \qquad \text{imply} \qquad a \circ b = a' \circ b'.$$

The special cases of this rule in which the operation $a \circ b$ is addition or multiplication have already been assumed as postulates in §1.

To each integer a corresponds a unique absolute value $|\,a\,|$, but any positive integer b is the absolute value of two different integers $\pm b$. This is expressed by the statement that $a \to |\,a\,|$ is a "many-one" correspondence. A *correspondence* (or *function*) $a \to a'$ is any rule which prescribes for each element a of set A a corresponding element a' in some other set B; it is said to be *many-one* from A onto B if each element a of A has one and only one correspondent in B, and if, conversely, each element of B is the correspondent of at least one element of A. For instance, in the choice of exchange names for a dial telephone system one may observe the many-one correspondence

between 25 letters and 9 digits. The correspondence $a \to a_n$ which sends each integer a into its residue class a_n modulo n is another many-one correspondence.

The one-one correspondences are especially important. A pairing $a \leftrightarrow a'$ is said to be a *one-one correspondence of a set A onto a set B* if each element a in A has one and only one correspondent a' in B, and if each element b in B is the correspondent $b = a'$ of one and only one element a in A. For instance, the correspondence $x \leftrightarrow x + 1$ is a one-one correspondence from $\mathbf{Z}$ onto $\mathbf{Z}$, while $x \leftrightarrow 2x$ is a one-one correspondence of the set of all integers with the set of all even integers. Another well-known example arises in analytic geometry. If a plane has fixed x and y coordinate axes, then the points of the plane are in one-one correspondence with the pairs of real numbers (x, y).

Two given integers may be "related" to each other in many ways, such as "$a = b$," "$a < b$," "$a \equiv b \pmod 7$," or "$a \mid b$." Each of these phrases is said to express a certain "binary relation" between a and b. One may readily mention many other relations between other types of mathematical objects; there are also nonmathematical relations, such as the relation "is a brother of" between people. To discuss relations in general we introduce a symbol R to stand for any relation ("R" stands for "$<$,"

"$\equiv$," or "$|$," etc.). Formally, "R" denotes a *binary relation* on a given set S of objects if, given two elements a and b in the set S, either a stands in the relation R to b (in symbols, aRb), or a does not stand in the relation R to b (in symbols, $aR'b$).

Especially important in mathematics are the relations R on a set S which, like congruence and equality, satisfy the following laws:

Reflexive: aRa,   for all a in S,
Symmetric: aRb implies bRa,   for all a, b in S,
Transitive: aRb and bRc imply aRc,   for all a, b, c in S.

Reflexive, symmetric, and transitive relations are known as *equivalence relations*. For example, the relation of congruence between triangles in the plane is such an equivalence relation.

EXERCISES

1. Which of the following binary operations $a \circ b$ on integers a and b are associative, and which ones are commutative: $a - b$, $a^2 + b^2$, $2(a + b)$, $-a - b$?
2. Which of the three properties "reflexive," "symmetric," and "transitive" apply to each of the following relations between integers a and b:
   $$a \leqq b, \qquad a < b, \qquad a \mid b, \qquad a^2 + a = b^2 + b, \qquad a < |b|.$$
3. Do the same for the following relations on the class of all people: "is a father of," "is a brother of," "is a friend of," "is an uncle of," "is a descendant of." Would any of your answers be changed if these relations are restricted to apply only to the class of all men?
★4. How is the relation "is an uncle of" connected with the relations "is a brother of" and "is a parent of"? Can you state any similar general rule for making a new relation out of two given ones?
5. A relation R is called "circular" if aRb and bRc imply cRa. Show that a relation is reflexive and circular if and only if it is reflexive, symmetric, and transitive.
★6. What is wrong with the following "proof" that the symmetric and transitive laws for a relation R imply the reflexive law? "By the symmetric law, aRb implies bRa; by the transitive law, aRb and bRa imply aRa."
7. Each of the following rules defines a correspondence from the class $\mathbf{Z}$ of all integers onto some subclass B of integers:
   (a) $a \to |a| + 1$,   (b) $a \to a^2$,
   (c) $a \to 2a + 5$,   (d) $a \to$ g.c.d. $(a, 6)$.
   In each case determine the subclass B, and state whether the correspondence is one-one.
8. Do Ex. 7, replacing $\mathbf{Z}$ by the class $\mathbf{Z}^+$ of positive integers.
9. For what integers n is the correspondence $x \to 6x + 7$ one-one on $\mathbf{Z}_n$?

12. Isomorphisms and Automorphisms

One of the most important concepts of modern algebra is that of isomorphism. We now define this concept for commutative rings as follows:

Definition. *An* isomorphism *between two commutative rings R and R', is a one-one correspondence $a \leftrightarrow a'$ of the elements a of R with the elements a' of R', which satisfies for all elements a and b the conditions*

$$(21) \qquad\qquad (a + b)' = a' + b', \qquad (ab)' = a'b'.$$

The rings R and R' are called isomorphic if there exists such a correspondence.

On account of the laws (21) one may say that the isomorphism $a \leftrightarrow a'$ "preserves sums and products." Loosely speaking, two commutative rings are isomorphic when they differ only in the notation for their elements. An appropriate example is the algebra of "even" and "odd" as compared with the integral domain $\mathbf{Z}_2$, as discussed in §10. The one-one correspondence

$$\text{even} \leftrightarrow 0 \quad \text{odd} \leftrightarrow 1$$

is an isomorphism between these domains, because corresponding elements are added and multiplied according to the same rules (cf. formula (16)).

Many integral domains have important isomorphisms with themselves. Such isomorphisms are called *automorphisms;* they are analogous to symmetries of geometrical figures (see Chap. VI, §1). Consider, for example, the domain $\mathbf{Z}[\sqrt{2}]$ described, in §1, as the set of all numbers $m + n\sqrt{2}$ for m and n in the domain $\mathbf{Z}$ of integers; it is isomorphic to itself under the nontrivial correspondence $m + n\sqrt{2} \leftrightarrow m - n\sqrt{2}$. This correspondence is an isomorphism, since for any $a = m + n\sqrt{2}$ and $b = m_1 + n_1\sqrt{2}$, we have

$$\begin{aligned}
(ab)' &= [(m + n\sqrt{2})(m_1 + n_1\sqrt{2})]' \\
&= [(mm_1 + 2nn_1) + (mn_1 + m_1 n)\sqrt{2}]' \\
&= (mm_1 + 2nn_1) - (mn_1 + m_1 n)\sqrt{2}, \\
a'b' &= (m - n\sqrt{2})(m_1 - n_1\sqrt{2}) \\
&= (mm_1 + 2nn_1) - (mn_1 + m_1 n)\sqrt{2}
\end{aligned}$$

and, similarly, $(a + b)' = a' + b'$.

Any isomorphism $a \leftrightarrow a'$ preserves not only sums and products, but also differences. By definition, $a - b$ is the solution of the equation $b + x = a$, so that $b + (a - b) = a$. Since the correspondence preserves sums, $b' + (a - b)' = a'$; this asserts that $(a - b)'$ is the (unique) solution of the equation $b' + x = a'$, or that

$$(a - b)' = a' - b'.$$

Other rules are

$$(22) \qquad\qquad 0' = 0, \qquad 1' = 1, \qquad (-a)' = -(a').$$

In words: the zero (unity) of R corresponds to the zero (unity) of R'.

We shall see later that the idea of isomorphism applies to algebraic systems in general. One may even describe abstract algebra as the study of those properties of algebraic systems which are preserved under isomorphism.

In describing the system of integers as an ordered domain in which each set of positive integers has a least element, we claimed that these postulates completely describe the integers for all mathematical purposes. We can now state this more precisely (it will be proved in Chap. II, §6). Any ordered domain in which the positive elements are well-ordered is isomorphic to the domain **Z** of integers. Such a characterization of **Z** "up to isomorphism" is the most that could be achieved with any postulate system of the type we have used. For it is clear, in general, that if a system S satisfies such a system of postulates, and if S' is another system isomorphic to S, then S' must also satisfy the postulates. Thus if S satisfies a commutative law for addition, then $a + b = b + a$ for all a and b in S. The corresponding elements in the given isomorphism must be equal, so $(a + b)' = (b + a)'$. Since the isomorphism preserves sums, $a' + b' = b' + a'$. This asserts that the commutative law also holds in S'. This argument is of a general character and applies to all our postulates.

EXERCISES

1. Prove that the properties (22) hold for any isomorphism.
2. Let $\mathbf{Z}[\sqrt{3}]$ be the domain of all numbers $m + n\sqrt{3}$ for $m, n \in \mathbf{Z}$. Exhibit a nontrivial isomorphism of $\mathbf{Z}[\sqrt{3}]$ with itself.
3. Prove that the correspondence $m + n\sqrt{2} \leftrightarrow m + n\sqrt{3}$ is not an isomorphism between the domains $\mathbf{Z}[\sqrt{2}]$ and $\mathbf{Z}[\sqrt{3}]$.
4. (a) Prove that under any isomorphism an element x satisfying an equation $x^2 = 1 + 1$ must correspond to an element $y = x'$ satisfying the equation $y^2 = 1' + 1'$.
   (b) Use (a) to show that no isomorphism is possible between $\mathbf{Z}[\sqrt{2}]$ and $\mathbf{Z}[\sqrt{3}]$.
5. Show that the domain **Z** of integers has no nontrivial isomorphisms with itself.
★6. Prove that an integral domain with exactly three elements is necessarily isomorphic to $\mathbf{Z}_3$.
7. Prove that isomorphism is an "equivalence relation" (i.e., a reflexive, symmetric, and transitive relation).

II. Rational Numbers and Fields

1. Definition of a Field

Both the integral domain **Q** of all rational numbers and the integral domain **R** of all real numbers have an essential algebraic advantage over the domain **Z** of integers: any equation $ax = b$ ($a \neq 0$) can be solved in them. Integral domains with this property are called *fields*. In §§1–2 below we will show that any integral domain can be extended to a field, in one and only one minimal way. The method of extension is illustrated by the standard representation of fractions as quotients of integers.

Definition. *A* field F *is an integral domain which contains for each element* $a \neq 0$ *an "inverse" element* a^{-1} *satisfying the equation* $a^{-1}a = 1$.

Theorem 1. *Division (except by zero) is possible and is unique in any field.*

Proof. We have to show that for given $a \neq 0$ and b in a field F the equation $ax = b$ has one and only one solution x in F. If $a \neq 0$, the inverse a^{-1} may be used to construct an element $x = a^{-1}b$ which on substitution proves to be a solution of $ax = b$. It is the only solution, for $ax = b$ and $ay = b$ together imply $ax = ay$, $(a^{-1}a)x = (a^{-1}a)y$, and hence $x = y$. The solution of $ax = b$ is also denoted by b/a (the *quotient* of b by a). In particular, $1/a = a^{-1}$. Q.E.D.

All the rules for algebraic manipulation which are listed in Chap. I, §2, are satisfied in fields, considered as integral domains. The usual rules for the manipulation of quotients can also be proved from the postulates for a field.

Theorem 2. *In any field, quotients obey the following laws (where $b \neq 0$ and $d \neq 0$),*

(i) $\qquad\qquad (a/b) = (c/d) \qquad$ *if and only if* $\qquad ad = bc$;

(ii) $\qquad\quad (a/b) \pm (c/d) = (ad \pm bc)/(bd)$;

(iii) $\qquad\qquad (a/b)(c/d) = (ac/bd)$;

(iv) $\qquad\quad (a/b) + (-a/b) = 0$;

(v) $\qquad\qquad (a/b)(b/a) = 1, \qquad$ *if* $(a/b) \neq 0$.

Proof of (i). The hypothesis $(a/b) = (c/d)$ means $ab^{-1} = cd^{-1}$. This gives $ad = a(b^{-1}b)d = cd^{-1}(bd) = cd^{-1}db = bc$. Conversely, if $ad = bc$, then $a/b = b^{-1}a = b^{-1}add^{-1} = b^{-1}bcd^{-1} = cd^{-1} = c/d$, as desired.

Proof of (ii).   Observe that $x = a/b$ and $y = c/d$ denote the solutions of $bx = a$ and $dy = c$. These equations may be combined to give

$$dbx = da, \qquad bdy = bc, \qquad bd(x \pm y) = ad \pm bc.$$

Thus $x \pm y$ is the unique solution $z = (ad \pm bc)/bd$ of the equation $bdz = ad \pm bc$.

Proof of (iii).   As above, the equations $bx = a$ and $dy = c$ can be combined to give

$$(bd)(xy) = (bx)(dy) = ac,$$

whence
$$xy = (ac)/(bd).$$

Proof of (iv).   Substituting in (ii), we have

$$(a/b) + (-a/b) = (ab - ba)/b^2 = 0/b^2 = 0 \cdot (b^2)^{-1} = 0.$$

Proof of (v).   Substituting in (iii), we have $(a/b)(b/a) = ab/ba$. But ab/ba is the unique solution of the equation $bax = ab$. Clearly $x = 1$ satisfies this equation; hence $ab/ba = 1$, Q.E.D.

Arguments similar to those just employed can be used to prove such other familiar laws as the following:

(1) $(bd)^{-1} = d^{-1}b^{-1}, \qquad (-b)^{-1} = -(b^{-1}), \qquad$ if $\qquad b \neq 0, d \neq 0,$
(2) $a \pm (b/c) = (ac \pm b)/c, \qquad a(b/c) = ab/c, \qquad\qquad c \neq 0,$
(3) $(a/b)/(c/d) = ad/bc, \qquad (a/b)/c = a/bc, \qquad\qquad a/1 = a,$
(4) $-(a/b) = (-a)/b = a/(-b), \qquad\qquad (-a)/(-b) = a/b,$

where in (3) and (4), $b \neq 0$, $c \neq 0$, and $d \neq 0$. The proofs will be left to the reader as exercises.

If one assumes that the real numbers form a field, one can easily construct other examples of fields by using the notion of a *subfield*.

Definition.   *A subfield of a given field F is a subset of F which is itself a field under the operations of addition and multiplication in F.*

All identities (viz., the commutative, associative, and distributive laws) which hold in F hold *a fortiori* in any subset of F, provided the operations in question can be performed. In testing a subset S of F for being a subfield, one can therefore ignore the postulates which are identities and test only those which involve some "existence" assertion, such as the existence of an inverse. This gives the following result:

Theorem 3.   *A subset S of a field F is a subfield if S contains the zero and unity of F, if S is closed under addition and multiplication, and if each a of S has its negative and (provided $a \neq 0$) its inverse a^{-1} in S.*

Theorem 3 may now be applied to show that the set of all real numbers of the form $a + b\sqrt{2}$, with rational coefficients a and b, is a subfield of the field of all real numbers. This subfield is customarily denoted by $Q(\sqrt{2})$, where Q designates the field of rationals. Theorem 3 does apply, for the sum of any two numbers of $Q(\sqrt{2})$ is another one of the same sort, and similarly the product is

$$(a + b\sqrt{2})(c + d\sqrt{2}) = (ac + 2bd) + (bc + ad)\sqrt{2}.$$

Again, $Q(\sqrt{2})$ contains $0 = 0 + 0\sqrt{2}, 1 = 1 + 0\sqrt{2}$, and $-(a + b\sqrt{2})$ $= -a - b\sqrt{2}$ if it contains $a + b\sqrt{2}$. Finally, an inverse $(a + b\sqrt{2})^{-1}$ of any non-zero element may be found by "rationalizing the denominator,"

$$\frac{1}{a + b\sqrt{2}} = \frac{1}{a + b\sqrt{2}}\left(\frac{a - b\sqrt{2}}{a - b\sqrt{2}}\right) = \left(\frac{a}{a^2 - 2b^2}\right) - \left(\frac{b}{a^2 - 2b^2}\right)\sqrt{2}.$$

The new denominator $a^2 - 2b^2$ is never zero (as is proved in Chap. III, §6), and the resulting inverse does have the required form $a' + b'\sqrt{2}$ with rational coefficients $a' = a/(a^2 - 2b^2)$, $b' = -b/(a^2 - 2b^2)$. One may easily verify that this inverse does indeed satisfy the equation

$$(a' + b'\sqrt{2})(a + b\sqrt{2}) = 1.$$

Similarly, the set $Q(\sqrt[3]{5})$ of all real numbers $a + b\sqrt[3]{5} + c\sqrt[3]{25}$ with rational a, b, c is a field. Addition, subtraction, and multiplication are performed within this set much as in $Q(\sqrt{2})$, using this time the fact that $(\sqrt[3]{5})^3 = 5$ is a rational number. Finally, $(a + b\sqrt[3]{5} + c\sqrt[3]{25})^{-1}$ may be computed by showing that the equation

$$(a + b\sqrt[3]{5} + c\sqrt[3]{25})(x + y\sqrt[3]{5} + z\sqrt[3]{25}) = 1 + 0 \cdot \sqrt[3]{5} + 0 \cdot \sqrt[3]{25}$$

is equivalent to a system of simultaneous linear equations. These equations can always be solved for x, y, and z, unless $a = b = c = 0$.

We may construct still other subfields if we assume that there is a field of *complex* numbers $a + bi$, where $i = \sqrt{-1}$ and a and b are real. The quadratic equation

$$\omega^2 + \omega + 1 = 0$$

will have a root $\omega = (-1 + \sqrt{-3})/2 = -1/2 + (\sqrt{3}/2)i$ in the field. (Note that since $\omega^3 - 1 = (\omega - 1)(\omega^2 + \omega + 1) = 0$, ω is an "imaginary" cube root of unity!) All $a + b\omega$ (a, b rational) form a subfield $Q(\omega)$ of the field of all complex numbers. For,

$$(a + b\omega) + (c + d\omega) = (a + c) + (b + d)\omega,$$
$$(a + b\omega)(c + d\omega) = ac + (bc + ad)\omega + bd\omega^2$$
$$= (ac - bd) + (bc + ad - bd)\omega,$$

where the equation $\omega^2 = -\omega - 1$ has been used to get rid of the higher powers of ω. Furthermore, any $a + b\omega \neq 0$ has an inverse in the set, for

$$(a + b\omega)\left[\frac{-(b - a + b\omega)}{a^2 - ab + b^2}\right] = \frac{a^2 - ab + b^2}{a^2 - ab + b^2} = 1.$$

The denominator $a^2 - ab + b^2$ appearing in this inverse is never zero, for $a^2 - ab + b^2 = (a^2 + b^2)/2 + (a - b)^2/2$ is certainly positive unless $a = b = 0$.

EXERCISES

1. Prove formulas (1)–(4) from the postulates for a field.
2. Prove the cancellation law for multiplication from the other postulates for a field. (*Hint:* See the proof of Rule 4 in Chap. I, §2.)
3. If the set of real numbers is assumed to be a field, which of the following subsets of reals are fields: (a) all positive integers, (b) all numbers $a + b\sqrt{3}$, with a, b rational, (c) all numbers $a + b\sqrt[3]{5}$, with a, b rational, (d) all rational numbers which are not integers, (e) all numbers $a + b\sqrt{5}$, with a and b rational.
4. Show that in Theorem 3 the conditions $0 \in S$ and $1 \in S$ can be replaced by the condition "S contains at least two elements." (*Hint:* Consider $ax = a$.)
★5. Prove that the commutative law for addition of an integral domain can be replaced by the assumption that $y + a = 0$ has a solution. (*Hint:* Expand $(a + b)(1 + 1)$ in two ways, and add inverses.)
6. Is every integral domain isomorphic to a field itself a field? Why?
7. Prove that the only subfield of the field Q of rational numbers is Q itself.
8. State and prove an analogue of Theorem 3 for subdomains.
9. Show that a subfield of $Q(\sqrt{2})$ which contains all rational numbers is either R itself or the whole field $Q(\sqrt{2})$.
10. If S and S' are two subfields of a given field F, show that the set of elements common to S and S' is also a subfield.
11. Can you state a general theorem on the possible subdomains of Z? of Z_n?
★12. Construct addition and multiplication tables for a field of four elements, assuming that $1 + 1 = 0$ (addition is mod 2) and that there is an element x such that $x^2 = x + 1$.
★13. Find all subfields of the field of Ex. 12.

2. Construction of the Rationals

We will now prove rigorously that the (ordered) field Q of rational numbers can be constructed from the well-ordered domain Z of all integers, whose existence was postulated in Chap. I. Indeed, we will prove more: that a similar construction can be applied to *any* integral domain.

The integers alone do not form a field; the construction of the rational numbers from the integers is essentially just the construction of a field which will contain the integers. Clearly, this field must also contain solutions for all equations $bx = a$ with integral coefficients a and $b \neq 0$. To abstractly construct the "rational numbers" which solve these equations we simply introduce certain new symbols (or couples) $r = (a, b)$, each of which is intended to stand for a solution of an equation $bx = a$. To realize this intention we must specify that these new objects shall be added, multiplied, and equated exactly as are the quotients a/b in a field (Theorem 2, rules (i)–(iii)).

The preceding specification makes good sense whether we start with the domain of integers $\mathbf{Z}$, or from some other integral domain D. It can be formulated precisely as follows.

Definition. *Let D be any integral domain. The "field of quotients" $Q(D)$ of D consists of all couples (a, b) with $a, b \in D$ and $b \neq 0$. The "equality" of such couples is governed by the convention that*

(5) $(a, b) \equiv (a', b')$ *if and only if* $ab' = a'b$,

while sums and products are defined respectively by

(6) $(a, b) + (a', b') = (ab' + a'b, bb')$,
(7) $(a, b) \cdot (a', b') = (aa', bb')$.

Note that since $\mathbf{Z}$ contains no "divisors of zero" (Chap. I, Theorem 1), the product $bb' \neq 0$ in (6) and (7), and so $\mathbf{Q}$ is closed under addition and multiplication.

We wish to regard the relation "$\equiv$" of "congruence" between couples as an equality. Since this relation is not formal identity ((a, b) identical to (a', b') would mean $a = a'$ and $b = b'$), we must prove that this congruence has the properties of equality listed in §2 of Chap. I (for formal identity these properties would have been trivial). In the first place, we may check by straightforward argument that "$\equiv$" is reflexive, symmetric, and transitive. And then, the sum and product are uniquely determined in the sense of this congruence. For instance, $(a, b) \equiv (a', b')$ implies $(a, b) + (a'', b'') \equiv (a', b') + (a'', b'')$. For, each sum in the conclusion is given by a formula like (6), and these two results are congruent in the sense (5) if and only if $(ab'' + a''b)b'b'' = (a'b'' + a''b')bb''$. But this equation follows from the hypothesis $(a, b) \equiv (a', b')$ (i.e., $ab' = a'b$). A similar uniqueness assertion holds for the product. We conclude that the equality defined by (5) has the desired properties.

Various algebraic laws in $Q(D)$ may now be checked. Thus, for the distributive law one can reduce each side of the law systematically, according to definitions (6) and (7), in the following way, where r, r', and r'' are any three couples:

$$
\begin{array}{ll}
r(r' + r'') & rr' + rr'' \\
(a, b)[(a', b') + (a'', b'')] & (a, b)(a', b') + (a, b)(a'', b'') \\
(a, b)(a'b'' + a''b', b'b'') & (aa', bb') + (aa'', bb'') \\
(aa'b'' + aa''b', bb'b'') & (aa'bb'' + aa''bb', bb'bb'').
\end{array}
$$

These two results give equal couples in the sense of (5), as the second result differs from the first only in the presence of an extra factor b in all terms. Such an extra factor in a couple always gives an equal couple, $(bx, by) \equiv (x, y)$, for by (5) this equality amounts simply to the identity $bxy = byx$.

This explicit proof of the distributive law in $Q(D)$ is but an illustration.

By the same straightforward use of the definitions and the laws for D one proves the associative and commutative laws. An identity element for addition (a zero) is the couple $(0, 1)$, for

$$(0, 1) + (a, b) = (0 \cdot b + 1 \cdot a, 1 \cdot b) = (a, b).$$

The cancellation law holds, and the couple $(1, 1)$ is an identity for multiplication. The negative of (a, b) is $-(a, b) = (-a, b)$. This verifies all the postulates listed in §1 of Chap. I for an integral domain.

Theorem 4. *The "field of quotients" $Q(D)$ is a field, for any integral domain D.*

It remains only to prove that every equation $rx = 1$ with $r \neq 0$ has a solution x in $Q(D)$—that is, the existence for every $r \neq 0$ in $Q(D)$ of an inverse for r. We can even show the possibility of division in general, for an equation

$$(8) \qquad\qquad (a, b)(x, y) \equiv (c, d) \qquad \text{with} \qquad (a, b) \not\equiv (0, 1)$$

does in fact have a solution, suggested by (3):

$$(8') \qquad\qquad\qquad (x, y) = (bc, ad).$$

For, by direct substitution, $(a, b)(bc, ad) = (abc, bad)$, and $(abc, bad) \equiv (c, d)$ because $abcd = badc$. The hypothesis $(a, b) \not\equiv (0, 1)$ insures that $a \neq 0$, hence that (x, y) has a second term ad not zero, as required by our definition of a rational number, Q.E.D.

We now wish to show that $Q(D)$ actually contains our original integral domain D as a subdomain—in other words, that $Q(D)$ is actually an *extension* of D. This is not strictly possible, since a couple (a, b) can't be the same thing as an element of D. However, we can associate with each $a \in D$ a couple $(a, 1)$ which behaves under equality, addition, and multiplication exactly like a itself, as shown by

$$(a, 1) + (b, 1) = (a \cdot 1 + b \cdot 1, 1 \cdot 1) = (a + b, 1),$$
$$(a, 1) \cdot (b, 1) = (ab, 1 \cdot 1) = (ab, 1),$$
$$(a, 1) \equiv (b, 1) \qquad \text{if and only if } a = b.$$

One may conclude that the one-one correspondence $a \leftrightarrow (a, 1)$ is an isomorphism of the given integral domain D to a subdomain of the field $Q(D) = F$. Moreover equations (8) and (8') show that any couple $r = (a, b) \in Q(D)$ is the solution of an equation $(b, 1)r = (a, 1)$, or $br = a$; hence $r = (a, b)$ is the quotient a/b. This proves

Theorem 5. *Any integral domain D can be embedded isomorphically in a field $Q(D)$, each element of which is a quotient of two elements of D.*

The preceding theorem applies in particular to the domain $\mathbf{Z}$; indeed, it is suggestive to follow through the preceding arguments thinking of the special case that $D = \mathbf{Z}$, so that $Q(D) = Q(\mathbf{Z})$ is the set of all ordinary fractions. Hence we have the

Corollary. *The integral domain* $\mathbf{Z}$ *can be embedded as a subdomain in a field* $\mathbf{Q} = Q(\mathbf{Z})$, *each element of which is a quotient* a/b *of integers,* $b \neq 0$.

We now show that the rational field $\mathbf{Q} = Q(\mathbf{Z})$ is in fact exactly characterized (up to isomorphism) by the preceding statement. Since $\mathbf{Z}$ is defined by its postulates only up to an isomorphism, this is as complete a characterization as we can hope for. We will, in fact, prove the analogous result for any domain D.

Theorem 6. *Let an integral domain* D *be contained as a subdomain in any field* F. *Then the set of all those elements of* F *of the form* a/b, $a, b \in D$, $b \neq 0$, *is a subfield* S *of* F; *moreover this subfield* S *is isomorphic to* $Q(D)$ *under the correspondence* $a/b \leftrightarrow (a, b)$.

Note. An isomorphism between two fields F and F' means an isomorphism between F and F' regarded as commutative rings. Specifically, it is a one-one correspondence between F and F' such that if $x \leftrightarrow x'$ and $y \leftrightarrow y'$, then

$$(x + y) \leftrightarrow (x' + y') \qquad \text{and} \qquad (xy) \leftrightarrow (x'y').$$

Proof. The field F contains quotients a/b which are solutions of equations $bx = a$ with coefficients a and $b \neq 0$ in D. The set S of all these quotients contains all the integers $a/1 = a$; by the rules of Theorem 2, S is closed under addition, subtraction, multiplication, and division, so that S might be described as the closure of D under these operations in F. In any event, S is a field (Theorem 3).

The way in which these quotients a/b add, multiply, and become equal is described by rules (i)–(iii) of Theorem 2. Exactly the same rules are used for the couples (a, b). Hence the correspondence $a/b \leftrightarrow (a, b)$ is an isomorphism of the closure S of D onto $Q(D)$, Q.E.D.

Observe, in particular, that this correspondence maps each a in D onto $a/1 \leftrightarrow (a, 1) = a$.

Combining Theorem 6 with the preceding corollary, we get

Theorem 7. *The integral domain* $\mathbf{Z}$ *can be embedded in one and only one way in a field* $\mathbf{Q} = Q(\mathbf{Z})$ *so that each element of* $\mathbf{Q}$ *is a quotient of integers.*

This completes the construction of the rational field $\mathbf{Q}$ from the integers.

EXERCISES

1. Prove in detail the commutative and the associative laws for multiplication of couples.

2. Prove that the "equality" relation defined by (5) is reflexive, symmetric, and transitive.

3. Let $Z[i]$ be the set of all complex numbers $a + bi$, where a and b are integers and $i^2 = -1$. (a) State explicitly how to add and multiply two such numbers. (b) Prove that they form an integral domain. (c) Describe its quotient field.

4. Can the ring Z_6 of integers modulo 6 be embedded in a field? Why?

5. Describe the field of quotients of the ring Z_5 of integers modulo 5.

6. What is the field of quotients of the field Q? Generalize.

7. Show that under any isomorphism $F \leftrightarrow F'$ between two fields, $a \leftrightarrow a'$, $b \leftrightarrow b'$, and $c \leftrightarrow c'$ imply $c^{-1} \leftrightarrow c'^{-1}$ and $(a - b)/c \leftrightarrow (a' - b')/c'$, provided $c \neq 0$. (Cf. Ex. 1 of Chap. I, §12.)

8. Prove that the correspondence $a + b\sqrt{7} \leftrightarrow a + b\sqrt{11}$ (a, b rational) is *not* an isomorphism.

★9. Prove that there is no isomorphism between the field $Q(\sqrt{7})$ of numbers of the form $a + b\sqrt{7}$ and that of numbers of the form $a + b\sqrt{11}$ (a, b rational). (*Hint:* Show that nothing can correspond to $\sqrt{7}$.)

10. What can one say about the fields of quotients a/b and a'/b' from isomorphic integral domains D and D'? Prove your statements.

★11. Prove that any rational number not 0 or ± 1 can be expressed uniquely in the form $(\pm 1)p_1^{e_1} \cdots p_r^{e_r}$, where the p_i are positive primes with $p_1 < p_2 < \cdots < p_r$ and the exponents e_i are positive or negative integers.

★12. Prove that any rational number $r/s \neq 0$ can be expressed uniquely in the form $r/s = b_1 + b_2/2! + b_3/3! + \cdots + b_n/n!$, where n is a suitable integer, and each b_k is an integer, with $0 \leqq b_k < k$ if $k > 1$, and $b_n \neq 0$.

13. For a fixed prime p, show that the set $Z_{(p)}$ of all rationals m/n with n prime to p is an integral domain. Identify its field of quotients.

14. Find the smallest integral domain contained in Q and containing the rational numbers $1/6$ and $1/5$.

★15. Describe all possible integral domains which are subdomains of Q.

16. Show that any field with exactly two elements is isomorphic to Z_2.

17. Show that the integral domain $Z[\sqrt{3}]$, consisting of all $a + b\sqrt{3}$ for integers a and b, has a field of quotients isomorphic to the set of all real numbers of the form $r + s\sqrt{3}$, r and s rational, and obtain an explicit isomorphism.

3. Simultaneous Linear Equations

A field need not consist of ordinary "numbers"; for instance, if p is a prime, the integers modulo p form a field containing only a finite number of distinct (i.e., incongruent) elements. The fact that the domain Z_p is a field is a corollary of

Theorem 8. *Any finite integral domain D is a field.*

Proof. The assumption that D is finite means that the elements of D can be completely enumerated in a list $b_1, b_2, \cdots, b_n$, where n is some positive integer. (A set is by definition finite precisely when it can be so enumerated). To prove D a field, we need only provide an inverse for any specified element $a \neq 0$ in D. Try *all* the products

$$ab_1, \ ab_2, \ \cdots \ , \ ab_n \qquad (b_1, \ \cdots \ , \ b_n \text{ the elements of } D).$$

This gives n elements in D which are all distinct, because $ab_i = ab_j$ for $i \neq j$ would by the cancellation law entail $b_i = b_j$, counter to the assumption that the b's are distinct. Since this list exhausts all of D, the unity element 1 of D must somewhere appear in the list as $1 = ab_i$. The corresponding element b_i is then the desired inverse of a, Q.E.D.

To actually find an inverse in $\mathbf{Z}_p$ by the proof, one proceeds by trial of all possible numbers b_i in $\mathbf{Z}_p$. Inverses can also be computed directly, for the equation $ax = 1$ with $a \neq 0$ in $\mathbf{Z}_p$ is simply another form of the congruence $ax \equiv 1 \pmod{p}$ with $a \not\equiv 0$, and the latter can be solved for the integer x by the Euclidean Algorithm methods, as in Theorem 16 of Chap. I. Incidentally, the corollary of this theorem gives a direct proof of Theorem 8 for the case of the domain $\mathbf{Z}_p$.

The most important thing about fields is the fact that the entire theory of simultaneous linear equations applies to fields in general. Thus, consider the two simultaneous equations

$$(9) \qquad\qquad ax + by = e, \qquad cx + dy = f,$$

where the letters $a, \ \cdots \ , f$ stand for arbitrary elements of the field F. Multiplying the first equation by d, the second by b and subtracting, we get $(ad - bc)x = de - bf$; multiplying the second equation by a, the first by c and subtracting, we get $(ad - bc)y = af - ce$. Hence, if we define the *determinant* of the coefficients of (9) as (cf. Chap. X)

$$\Delta = \begin{vmatrix} a & b \\ c & d \end{vmatrix} = ad - bc,$$

and

$$\Delta \neq 0,$$

then equations (9) have the solution

$$(9') \qquad x = \frac{de - bf}{\Delta}, \qquad y = \frac{af - ce}{\Delta} \qquad (\Delta = ad - bc),$$

and no other solution. Whereas if $\Delta = 0$, then equations (9) either have no solutions or many solutions (the latter eventuality arises when $c = ka$, $d = kb$, $f = ke$, so that the two equations are "proportional").

Gauss elimination. The preceding device of *elimination* can be extended to m simultaneous linear equations in n unknowns $x_1, \ \cdots \ , x_n$, of the form

$$
\begin{aligned}
a_{11}x_1 + a_{12}x_2 + \cdots + a_{1n}x_n &= b_1, \\
a_{21}x_1 + a_{22}x_2 + \cdots + a_{2n}x_n &= b_2,
\end{aligned}
$$

(E)

$$
\cdot
$$

$$
\cdot
$$

$$
\cdot
$$

$$
a_{m1}x_1 + a_{m2}x_2 + \cdots + a_{mn}x_n = b_m.
$$

Here both the known coefficients a_{ij}, b_i and the unknowns x_j are restricted to a specified field F. We will now describe a general process, known as "Gauss elimination," for finding all solutions of the given set (system) of equations. The idea is to replace the given system by a simpler system, which is *equivalent* to the given system in the sense of having precisely the same solutions. (Thus, the degenerate equation $0 \cdot x_1 + \cdots + 0 \cdot x_n = b_i$ is "equivalent" to $0 = b_i$, which cannot be satisfied.)

In a more compact notation, we write down only the ith equation, indicating its form by a sample term $a_{ij}x_j$ and the statement that the equation is to be summed over $j = 1, \cdots, n$ by writing

(E') $$\sum_{j=1}^{n} a_{ij}x_j = b_j \qquad \text{for } i = 1, \cdots, m; \qquad \text{all } a_{ij} \in F.$$

We argue by induction on n, the number of unknowns, distinguishing two cases.

Case 1. Every $a_{i1} = 0$. Then, trivially, the system (E') is equivalent to a "smaller" system of m equations in the $n - 1$ unknowns $x_2, \cdots, x_n$; x_1 is arbitrary, for any solution of the smaller system.

Case 2. Some $a_{i1} \neq 0$. By interchanging two equations (if necessary), we get an equivalent system with $a_{11} \neq 0$. Multiplying the first equation by a_{11}^{-1}, we then get an equivalent system in which $a_{11} = 1$. Then subtracting a_{i1} times the first equation from each ith equation in turn ($i = 1, 2, \cdots, m$), we get an equivalent system of the form

(E'')

$$
\begin{aligned}
x_1 + a_{12}'x_2 + a_{13}'x_3 + \cdots + a_{1n}'x_n &= b_1' \\
a_{22}'x_2 + a_{23}'x_3 + \cdots + a_{2n}'x_n &= b_2' \\
\cdots\cdots\cdots\cdots\cdots\cdots\cdots\cdots \\
a_{m2}'x_2 + a_{m3}'x_3 + \cdots + a_{mn}'x_n &= b_n'
\end{aligned}
$$

For example, over the field $\mathbf{Z}_{11}$ this would reduce

$$
\begin{array}{ccc}
3x + 5y + 7z \equiv 6 & & x + 9y + 6z \equiv 2 \\
5x + 9y + 6z \equiv 7 & \text{to} & 8y + 9z \equiv 8 \\
2x + \;\; y + 4z \equiv 3 & & 5y + 3z \equiv 10,
\end{array}
$$

where all equations are understood to be modulo 11.

Proceeding by induction on m, we obtain

Theorem 9. *Any system* (E) *of* m *simultaneous linear equations in* n *unknowns can be reduced to an equivalent system whose* i*th equation has the form*

(F) $$x_i + c_{i,i+1}x_{i+1} + c_{i,i+2}x_{i+2} + \cdots + c_{in}x_n = d_i,$$

for some subset of r *of the integers* $i = 1, \cdots, m$*, plus* $m - r$ *equations of the form* $0 = d_k$*.*

Proof. If Case 2 always arises, we get m equations of the form (E''). If Case 1 arises, then we may get degenerate equations of the form $0 = d_k$. If all $d_k = 0$, these can be ignored; if one $d_k \neq 0$, the original system (E) is *incompatible* (has no solutions), Q.E.D.

Written out in full, the system (F) looks like the display written below

$$x_1 + d_{12}x_2 + d_{13}x_3 + \cdots \cdots + d_{1n}x_n = b_1'',$$
$$x_2 + d_{23}x_3 + \cdots \cdots + d_{2n}x_n = b_2'',$$
$$x_3 + \cdots \cdots + d_{3n}x_n = b_3'',$$

$$\vdots$$

$$x_r + \cdots + d_{rn}x_n = b_r'', \qquad (r \leqq m),$$

which is said to be in *echelon* form.

Solutions of any system of the echelon form (F) are easily described. Consider $x_n, x_{n-1}, x_{n-2}, \cdots, x_1$ in succession. If a given x_i in this sequence is the first variable in an equation of (F), then it is determined by $x_n, \cdots, x_{i+1}$ from the relation

(F') $$x_i = d_i - c_{i,i+1} - c_{i,i+2}x_{i+2} - \cdots - c_{in}x_n.$$

If it does not, then this x_i can be chosen arbitrarily. This proves the

Corollary. *In the* compatible *case of Theorem 9, the set of all solutions of* (E) *is determined as follows. The* $m - r$ *variables* x_k *not occurring in* (F) *can be chosen arbitrarily (they are free parameters). For any choice of these* x_k*, the remaining* x_i *can be computed recursively by substituting in* (F')*.*

In the numerical example displayed, $8y + 9z \equiv 8 \pmod{11}$ would first be reduced to $y + 8z \equiv 1 \pmod{11}$. Subtracting five times this equation from $5y + 3z \equiv 10 \pmod{11}$, we get $7z \equiv 5 \pmod{11}$, whence $z \equiv 7 \pmod{11}$. The echelon form of the given system is thus

$$\left. \begin{array}{r} x + 9y + 6z \equiv 2 \\ y + 8z \equiv 1 \\ z \equiv 7 \end{array} \right\} \pmod{11}.$$

Solving, we get $y \equiv 1 - 8z \equiv 0 \pmod{11}$, and $x \equiv 2 - 9y - 6z \equiv 4$

(mod 11). The solution $x = 4$, $y = 0$, $z = 7$ can be checked by substituting into the original equation. *

A system of equations (E) is *homogeneous* if the constants b_i on the right are all zero. Such a system always has a (trivial) solution $x_1 = x_2 = \cdots = x_n = 0$. There may be no further solutions, but if the number of variables exceeds the number of equations, the last equation of (E'') will always contain an extra variable which can be chosen at will. Furthermore, the possible inconsistent equations $0 = b_i''$ can never arise for homogeneous equations. Hence,

Theorem 10. *A system of m homogeneous linear equations in n variables, with $m < n$, always has a solution in which not all the unknowns are zero.*

EXERCISES

1. Solve the following simultaneous congruences:
   (a) $3x + 2y \equiv 1 \pmod 7$, $\quad\quad\quad 4x + 6y \equiv 3 \pmod 7$;
   (b) $2x + 7y \equiv 3 \pmod{11}$, $\quad\quad 3x + 4z \equiv 6 \pmod{11}$,
   $\quad\quad\quad\quad\quad\quad\quad\quad\quad\quad\quad\quad\quad\quad 4x + 7y + z \equiv 0 \pmod{11}$;
   (c) $x - 2y + z \equiv 5 \pmod{13}$, $\quad 2x + 2y \equiv 7 \pmod{13}$,
   $\quad\quad\quad\quad\quad\quad\quad\quad\quad\quad\quad\quad\quad\quad 5x - 3y + 4z \equiv 1 \pmod{13}$.

2. Solve the equations (a) and (b) of Ex. 1, with moduli deleted, in the field **Q** of rational numbers.

3. Solve in $\mathbf{Q}(\sqrt{2})$ the simultaneous equations

   $$(1 + \sqrt{2})x + (1 - \sqrt{2})y = 2, \quad\quad (2 - \sqrt{2})x + (3 - \sqrt{2})y = 1.$$

4. Find all incongruent solutions of the simultaneous congruences

   $$x + y + z \equiv 0 \pmod 5, \quad\quad 3x + 2y + 4z \equiv 0 \pmod 5.$$

5. Find all incongruent solutions of the simultaneous congruences:
   (a) $x + 2y - z + 5t \equiv 4$, $\quad\quad 2x + 5y + z + 2t \equiv 1$,
   $\quad\quad\quad\quad\quad\quad\quad\quad\quad\quad\quad x + 3y + 2z + 6t \equiv 2$, all mod 7;
   (b) $x + y + z \equiv 1 \pmod 5$, $\quad\quad 3x + 3y + 3z \equiv 4 \pmod 5$.

6. Prove that two equations $a_1x_1 + \cdots + a_nx_n = c$, $b_1x_1 + \cdots + b_nx_n = d$ always have a solution for coefficients in a given field, provided there are no constants $k \neq 0$ and $m \neq 0$ with $ka_i = mb_i$ for $i = 1, \cdots, n$.

7. Prove that if $(x_1, \cdots, x_n)$ is any solution of a system of homogeneous linear equations, then $(-x_1, \cdots, -x_n)$ is another solution. What can be said about the sum of two solutions?

★8. (a) Prove that the *three* simultaneous equations

   $$ax + by + cz = d, \quad\quad a'x + b'y + c'z = d', \quad\quad a''x + b''y + c''z = d'',$$

   have one and only one solution in any field F if the 3×3 determinant

   $$\Delta = ab'c'' + a'b''c + a''bc' - a''b'c - a'bc'' - ab''c' \neq 0.$$

   (b) Compute a formula for x in (a).

4. Ordered Fields

A field F is said to be *ordered* if it contains a set P of "positive" elements with the additive, multiplicative, and trichotomic properties listed in §3 of Chap. I; in other words, a field is ordered if, when considered as a domain, it is an ordered integral domain. We know by experience that the rational numbers do constitute such an ordered field; we shall now prove this from our construction of rationals as couples of integers, and shall show further that the "natural" method of ordering is the only way of making the rational numbers into an ordered field.

First recall that in any ordered domain a non-zero square b^2 is always positive. If a quotient a/b is positive, the product $(a/b)b^2 = ab$ must therefore also be positive, and conversely. Hence in any ordered field,

$$(11) \qquad a/b > 0 \qquad \text{if and only if} \qquad ab > 0.$$

But the rational number (a, b) was intended to represent the quotient a/b. Hence we define a rational number (a, b) to be *positive* if and only if the product ab is positive in $\mathbf{Z}$.

Theorem 11. *The rational numbers form an ordered field if $(a, b) > 0$ is defined to mean that the integer ab is positive.*

Proof. Since we have defined equality by convention, we must prove that equals of positive elements are positive: $(a, b) > 0$ and $(a, b) \equiv (c, d)$ imply $(c, d) > 0$. This is true, since cd has the same sign as b^2cd, ab the same sign as abd^2, and since $abd^2 = b^2cd$ in virtue of the hypothesis $ad = bc$. Positiveness also has the requisite additive, multiplicative, and trichotomic properties. For instance, the sum of two positive couples (a, b) and (c, d) is positive, since $ab > 0$ and $cd > 0$ imply $d^2ab > 0$ and $b^2cd > 0$, whence

$$bd(ad + bc) = d^2ab + b^2cd > 0,$$

which is to say that the sum $(ad + bc, bd)$ is positive. Finally, the definition of "positive" for fractions agrees with the natural order of the special fractions $(a, 1)$ which represent integers, for $(a, 1)$ is positive by the definition (11) only if $1 \cdot a > 0$, Q.E.D.

Since the proof of Theorem 11 involves only the assumption that the integers are an ordered domain, it in fact establishes the following more general result:

Theorem 12. *The field Q of quotients of an ordered integral domain D may be ordered by the stipulation that a quotient a/b of elements a and b of D is positive if and only if ab is positive. This is the only way in which the order of D may be extended to an order of Q.*

There are many other ordered fields: the field of real numbers, the field $\mathbf{Q}(\sqrt{2})$ of numbers $a + b\sqrt{2}$ (see §1), and other subfields of the real number field. In any such field an absolute value can be introduced as in §3 of Chap. I, and all the usual properties of inequalities may be established. In any ordered field in addition to the rules valid in any ordered domain, one may prove

(12)	$0 < 1/a$	if and only if	$a > 0$,
(13)	$a/b < c/d$	if and only if	$abd^2 < b^2cd$,
(14)	$0 < a < b$	implies	$0 < 1/b < 1/a$,
(15)	$a < b < 0$	implies	$0 > 1/a > 1/b$,

$$(16) \qquad a_1^2 + a_2^2 + \cdots + a_n^2 \geqq 0.$$

The two rules (14) and (15) are the usual ones for the division of inequalities. The rule (16) that a sum of squares is never negative (Theorem 2, Chap. I) is especially useful. For instance, if $a \neq b$, then $(a - b)^2 > 0$, so $a^2 - 2ab + b^2 > 0$, which gives $a^2 + b^2 > 2ab$. In this, set $x = a^2$ and $y = b^2$ and divide by 2. Then

$$(x + y)/2 > \sqrt{xy} \qquad (x \neq y).$$

This states that the arithmetic mean of two distinct positive real numbers exceeds the geometric mean $\sqrt{xy}$.

EXERCISES

1. Assuming that the integers form an ordered domain, prove that the product of two positive rational numbers is positive.
2. Prove similarly that if $(a, b) \neq 0$, then just one of the two alternatives $(a, b) > 0$ and $-(a, b) > 0$ holds.
3. Prove $|xx' + yy'| \leqq \sqrt{(x^2 + y^2)(x'^2 + y'^2)}$ in any ordered field in which all positive numbers have square roots. (*Hint:* Square both sides.)
4. Prove formulas (12)–(16) of the text.
5. If n is a positive integer, and a and b positive rational numbers, prove that $(a^n + b^n)/2 \geqq ((a + b)/2)^n$. (*Hint:* Set $(a + b)/2 = r$, $a = r + d$, $b = r - d$.)
6. (a) Prove: any subfield of an ordered field is an ordered field.
   (b) Is any subdomain of an ordered field an ordered domain?
7. For the rational numbers (or, more generally, in any ordered field) prove that, if $a < b$, there are infinitely many x satisfying $a < x < b$.
8. Prove that in no ordered field do the positive elements form a well-ordered set.
9. A common mistake in arithmetic is the assumption that $a/b + a/c = a/(b + c)$.
   (a) Show that, in any field, $a/b + a/c = a/(b + c)$ implies $a = 0$ or $b^2 + bc + c^2 = 0$.
   (b) Show that in an ordered field, it implies $a = 0$.

III. Polynomials

1. Polynomial Forms

Let D be any integral domain, and let x be any element of a larger integral domain E which contains D as a subdomain. In E, one can form sums, differences and products of x with the elements of D and with itself.

By performing these operations repeatedly, one evidently gets all expressions of the form

$$(1) \quad a_0 + a_1 x + \cdots + a_n x^n \qquad (a_0, \cdots, a_n \in D; \quad a_n \neq 0 \text{ if } n > 0),$$

where x^n (n any positive integer) is defined as $xx \cdots x$ to n factors. But conversely, using only the postulates for an integral domain, one can add, subtract, or multiply any two expressions of the form (1), obtaining a third such expression. For example, if D is the domain of integers,

$$
\begin{aligned}
f(x) &= (0 + 1 \cdot x + (-2)x^2)(2 + 3 \cdot x) \\
&= 0 \cdot 2 + 0 \cdot 3 \cdot x + 1 \cdot x \cdot 2 + 1 \cdot x \cdot 3 \cdot x + (-2)x^2 \cdot 2 \\
&\qquad\qquad\qquad\qquad\qquad\qquad\qquad\qquad + (-2)x^2 \cdot 3 \cdot x \\
&= 0 + 0 \cdot x + 2x + 3x^2 + (-4)x^2 + (-6)x^3 \\
&= 0 + (0 + 2)x + (3 + (-4))x^2 + (-6)x^3 \\
&= 0 + 2x + (-1)x^2 + (-6)x^3,
\end{aligned}
$$

by the generalized distributive law, the commutative and associative law, and finally the distributive law.

This argument can be generalized. Indeed, let

$$
\begin{aligned}
p(x) &= a_0 + a_1 x + \cdots + a_m x^m \qquad \text{and} \\
q(x) &= b_0 + b_1 x + \cdots + b_n x^n
\end{aligned}
$$

be any two expressions of the form (1). If $m > n$, then we have

$$(2) \quad p(x) \pm q(x) = (a_0 \pm b_0) + \cdots + (a_n \pm b_n)x^n + a_{n+1}x^{n+1} + \cdots + a_m x^m.$$

A similar formula holds if $m \leqq n$. Again, by the distributive law,

$$p(x)q(x) = \sum_{i=0}^{m} \sum_{j=0}^{n} a_i b_j x^{i+j}.$$

47

Collecting terms with the same exponent and adding coefficients, we have

(3) $p(x)q(x) = a_0b_0 + (a_0b_1 + a_1b_0)x + \cdots + a_mb_nx^{m+n}.$

In this formula, the coefficient of x^k is clearly a sum

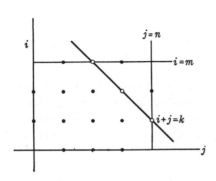

Figure 1

$$\sum_i a_ib_{k-i}$$

for all i with $0 \leq i \leq m$ and $0 \leq k - i \leq n$ — cf. Figure 1.

We have thus proved the following result:

Theorem 1. *Assume there exists an integral domain E containing a subdomain isomorphic with the given domain D, and an element x not in D. Then the polynomials (1) in this element x are added, subtracted, and multiplied by formulas (2)–(3), and so form a subdomain of E.*

In order to prove that there always does exist such an integral domain E, one wants the following definition.

Definition. *By a polynomial in x over an integral domain D is meant an expression of the form (1). The integer n is called the* degree *of the form (1). Two polynomials are called equal if they have the same degree and if corresponding coefficients are equal.*

Since nothing is assumed known about the symbol x, the expression (1) is also often called a polynomial *form* (to distinguish it from a polynomial function; see §2), and the symbol x itself is called an *indeterminate*.

Theorem 2. *If addition and multiplication are defined by formulas (2)–(3), then the different polynomial forms in x over any integral domain D form a new integral domain D[x] containing D.*

Proof.   The absence of zero-divisors (cancellation law of multiplication) follows from (3), since the leading coefficient a_mb_n of the product of two non-zero polynomial forms is the (non-zero) product of the non-zero leading coefficients a_m and b_n of its factors. The properties of 0 and 1 and the existence of additive inverses follow readily from (2)–(3).

To prove the commutative, associative, and distributive laws it is convenient to introduce "dummy" zero coefficients. This changes (2) and

(3) to the simpler forms

(2′)
$$\sum_{k=0}^{\infty} a_k x^k + \sum_{k=0}^{\infty} b_k x^k = \sum_{k=0}^{\infty} (a_k + b_k) x^k,$$

(3′)
$$\left(\sum_{k=0}^{\infty} a_k x^k\right)\left(\sum_{k=0}^{\infty} b_k x^k\right) = \sum_{k=0}^{\infty} \left(\sum_{i+j=k} a_i b_j x^k\right),$$

where all but a finite number of coefficients are zero. Any law such as the distributive law may then be verified simply by multiplying out both sides of the law by rules (2′)–(3′), as

$$\left(\sum_k a_k x^k\right)\left(\sum_k b_k x^k + \sum_k c_k x^k\right) = \sum_k \left[\sum_{i+j=k} a_i(b_j + c_j)\right] x^k,$$

$$\left(\sum_k a_k x^k\right)\left(\sum_k b_k x^k\right) + \left(\sum_k a_k x^k\right)\left(\sum_k c_k x^k\right)$$
$$= \sum_k \left[\left(\sum_{i+j=k} a_i b_j\right) + \left(\sum_{i+j=k} a_i c_j\right)\right] x^k,$$

and showing that the coefficient of each power x^k of x is the same in both expressions. By the distributive law in the domain D, the coefficient of the k-th power of x is the same in both expressions. Similar arguments complete the proof of Theorem 2.

Now recalling Theorem 7 of Chap. II, we see that if we define a *rational form* in the indeterminate x over D as a formal *quotient*

$$\frac{p(x)}{q(x)} = \frac{a_0 + a_1 x + \cdots + a_m x^m}{b_0 + b_1 x + \cdots + b_n x^n} \quad (a_i, b_j \text{ in } D; a_m \neq 0 \text{ if } m > 0, b_n \neq 0)$$

of polynomial forms with non-zero denominator, and define equality, addition, and multiplication by (5), (6), and (7) of the Definition of §2, Chap. II, we get a field.

Corollary.   *The rational forms in an indeterminate x over any integral domain D constitute a field. This field is denoted by $D(x)$.*

EXERCISES

1. Reduce to the form (1): $x^2 - 5x(3x + 7)^2$,
   $(x^3 + 5x - 4)(x^2 - 2x + 3)$, $(3x^2 + 7x - 1/2)(x^3 - x/2 + 1)$.
2. Compute similarly $(3x^3 + 5x - 4)(4x^3 - x + 3)$, where the coefficients are the integers mod 7.
3. Is $x^3 + 5x - 4$ of the form (1)? Reduce it to this form. Reduce $(1 + x + 2x^2 + 3x^3) - (0 + x + x^2 + 3x^3)$ to the form (1), stating which postulates are used at each step.
4. (a) Is $1/2 + 3 \cdot x^{1/2} + 5x$ a polynomial form over the rational field?
   (b) Why is $x^3 \cdot x^4$ not equal to x^2 in the domain of polynomial forms with coefficients in $\mathbf{Z}_5$?

5. Discuss the following statements:
   (a) the degree of the product of two polynomial forms is the sum of the degrees of the factors;
   (b) the degree of the sum of two polynomials is the larger of the degrees of the summands.
6. Prove that the associative laws for addition and multiplication hold in $D[x]$.
7. The "formal derivative" of $p(x) = a_0 + a_1x + \cdots + a_nx^n$ is defined as $p'(x) = a_1 + 2a_2x + \cdots + na_nx^{n-1}$. Prove, over any integral domain,
   (a) $(cp)' = cp'$ (b) $(p + q)' = p' + q'$,
   (c) $(pq)' = pq' + p'q$,   (d) $(p^n)' = np^{n-1}p'$.
★8. If $p(y)$ and $q(x)$ are polynomial forms in indeterminates y and x, show that the substitution $y = q(x)$ yields a polynomial $p(q(x))$. For the formal derivative of Ex. 7, prove that $[p(q(x))]' = p'(q(x)) \cdot q'(x)$.
★9. For given D show how to construct an integral domain $D\{t\}$ consisting of all "formal" infinite power series $a_0 + a_1t + a_2t^2 + \cdots$ in a symbol t, with coefficients a_i in D.
★10. (a) If D is an ordered domain, show that the polynomial forms (1) constitute an ordered domain $D[x]$, if $p(x) > 0$ is defined to mean that the first non-zero coefficient a_k in $p(x)$ is positive in D.
   (b) Show that $D[x]$ is also an ordered domain if we define $p(x) > 0$ to mean that $a_n > 0$ in (1).
★11. Setting $D = \mathbf{Z}$ in Ex. 10(b), show that 1 is the least "positive" polynomial in $\mathbf{Z}[x]$, though $\mathbf{Z}[x]$ fails to satisfy the well-ordering principle.

2. Polynomial Functions

As before, let D be any integral domain, and let

$$f(x) = a_0 + a_1x + \cdots + a_mx^m$$

be any polynomial form in x over D. If the indeterminate x is replaced by an element $c \in D$, $f(x)$ no longer remains an empty expression: it can be evaluated as a definite member $a_0 + a_1c + \cdots + a_mc^m$ of D. In other words, if x is regarded as an independent *variable* in the sense of the calculus, instead of as an abstract symbol outside of D, $f(x)$ becomes an ordinary *function*: "If x is given (as c), then $f(x)$ is determined (as $f(c)$)." By abstraction, we shall define generally a "function" f of a variable on D as a rule assigning to each element x of D a "value" $f(x)$, also in D. We shall define two such functions to be *equal* (in symbols, $f = g$) if and only if $f(x) = g(x)$ for all x. The *sum* $h = f + g$, the *difference* $q = f - g$, and the *product* $p = fg$ of two functions are defined by the rules $h(x) = f(x) + g(x)$, $q(x) = f(x) - g(x)$, and $p(x) = f(x)g(x)$ for all x. A *constant* function is one whose value b is independent of x; the *identity* function is the function j with $j(x) = x$ for all x.

Definition. *A polynomial function is a function which can be written in the form* (1).

Since the only rules used in deriving formulas (2)–(3) are valid in any integral domain, they hold no matter what value c (in D) is assigned to the indeterminate† x. That is, they are *identities*, and therefore sums and products of polynomial functions can also be computed by formulas (2)–(3).

By definition, each form (1) determines a unique polynomial function, and each polynomial function is determined by at least one such form. Therefore there is certainly a *many-one* correspondence, which preserves sums and products, between the polynomial forms and the polynomial functions over any given integral domain D. (Such correspondences are called homomorphisms onto; see §3.)

If we could be certain that the correspondence was *one-one*, we would know that it was an *isomorphism*. Hence, from the point of view of abstract algebra, it would be permissible to forget the distinction between polynomial forms and polynomial functions. Unfortunately, such is not the case. Indeed, over the field $\mathbf{Z}_3$ of integers mod 3, the distinct forms $f(x) = x^3 - x$ and $g(x) = 0$ determine the same function—the function which is identically zero. By Fermat's Theorem (Chap. I, Theorem 18), the same is true over $\mathbf{Z}_p$ for $x^p - x$ and 0. Hence, over any $\mathbf{Z}_p$, equality has an effectively different meaning for functions than it does for forms.

We shall now show that it is no accident that the domain of coefficients in the preceding example is finite. We could not construct such an example over the field of rationals. But before doing this, we recall some elementary definitions. By the *degree* of a non-zero form (1), we mean n, its biggest exponent. The term $a_n x^n$ of biggest degree is called its *leading term*, a_n its *leading coefficient*, and if $a_n = 1$, the polynomial is termed *monic*.

Theorem 3. *A polynomial form $r(x)$ over a domain D is divisible by $x - a$ if and only if $r(a) = 0$.*

Here the statement "$r(x)$ is divisible by $x - a$" means that $r(x) = (x - a)s(x)$ for some polynomial form $s(x)$ over D.

Proof. Set $r(x) = c_0 + c_1 x + \cdots + c_n x^n$ $(c_n \neq 0)$. For every a, we have, by high school algebra,

$$\sum_{k=0}^{n} c_k x^k - \sum_{k=0}^{n} c_k a^k = \sum_{k=0}^{n} c_k (x^k - a^k)$$

$$= \sum_{k=1}^{n} c_k [(x - a)(x^{k-1} + x^{k-2}a + \cdots + a^{k-1})].$$

Therefore $r(x) - r(a) = (x - a)s(x)$, where $s(x)$ is a polynomial form of degree $n - 1$. Conversely, if $r(x) = (x - a)s(x)$, substituting a for x gives $r(a) = 0$.

---

† Indeed, this is the secret of solving equations by letting "x be the unknown quantity": every manipulation allowed on x must be true for every possible value of x.

Corollary. *A polynomial form $r(x)$ of degree n over an integral domain D has at most n zeros in D.*

(By a zero of $r(x)$ is meant a root of the equation $r(x) = 0$; that is, an element $a \in D$ such that $r(a) = 0$.)

Proof. If a is a zero, then by the theorem $r(x) = (x - a)s(x)$, where $s(x)$ has degree $n - 1$. By induction, $s(x)$ has at most $n - 1$ zeros; but $r(x) = 0$ by Theorem 1 of Chap. I if and only if $x = a$ or $s(x) = 0$. Hence $r(x)$ has at most n zeros.

Theorem 4. *If an integral domain D is infinite, then two polynomial forms over D which define the same function have identical coefficients.*

Proof. As in (1), let $p(x)$ and $q(x)$ be two given forms in the indeterminate x. If they determine the same function, then $p(a) = q(a)$ for every element a chosen from D; the desired conclusion is then that $p(x)$ and $q(x)$ have the same degree and have corresponding coefficients equal. In terms of the difference $r(x) = p(x) - q(x)$, this is to say that $r(a) = c_0 + c_1 a + \cdots + c_n a^n = 0$ for all a in D implies that $c_0 = c_1 = \cdots = c_n = 0$. This conclusion follows by Theorem 3, for unless the coefficients c_i are all zero, the polynomial $r(x)$ is zero for at most n values of x—whence, since D is infinite, there will be remaining values of x on which $r(x) \neq 0$.

Thus, if D is infinite, the concepts of polynomial function and polynomial form are equivalent (technically, the ring of polynomial functions is *isomorphic* to that of polynomial forms).

On the other hand, Theorem 4 never holds if D is a *finite* integral domain, with elements $a_1, \cdots, a_n$. For example, the monic polynomial form $(x - a_1)(x - a_2) \cdots (x - a_n)$ of degree n determines the same function as the form 0, in this case.

Since any system isomorphic with an integral domain is itself an integral domain, Theorem 4 implies the following corollary:

Corollary. *The polynomial functions on any infinite integral domain themselves form an integral domain.*

If D is an *infinite field*, distinct rational forms define distinct rational functions, and the rational *functions* on D form a field. (Caution: A rational function is not defined at all points, but only where the denominator is not zero. Thus it is defined, if D is a field, at all but a finite number of points.)

It is often desired to find a polynomial $p(x)$ of minimum degree which assumes given values $y_0, y_1, \cdots, y_n$ in a field F at $n + 1$ given points $a_0, a_1, \cdots, a_n \in F$, so that

(4) $\qquad p(a_i) = y_i \qquad (i = 0, 1, \cdots, n; \qquad a_i \neq a_j \text{ if } i \neq j)$.

This is called the problem of polynomial interpolation.

To solve this problem, consider the polynomials

$$q_i(x) = \prod_{j \neq i} (x - a_j) = (x - a_0) \cdots (x - a_{i-1})(x - a_{i+1}) \cdots (x - a_n).$$

Evidently $q_i(a_j) = 0$ if $j \neq i$, while

$$C_i = q_i(a_i) = \prod_{j \neq i} (a_i - a_j) \neq 0.$$

Hence C_i^{-1} exists, and the following polynomial of degree n or less

$$(5) \qquad p(x) = \sum_{i=0}^{n} C_i^{-1} y_i q_i(x) = \sum_{i=0}^{n} \frac{y_i \prod\limits_{j \neq i} (x - a_j)}{\prod\limits_{j \neq i} (a_i - a_j)}$$

satisfies equations (4). Formula (5) is called Lagrange's Interpolation Formula.

In view of Theorem 3, at *most* one polynomial of degree n or less can satisfy equations (4): the difference of two such polynomials would have $n + 1$ zeros, and so would be the polynomial form zero. This proves the following result.

Theorem 5.   *There is exactly one polynomial form of degree n or less which assumes given values at $n + 1$ distinct points.*

EXERCISES

1. In the domain $\mathbf{Z}_5$, find a second polynomial form determining the same function as $x^2 - x + 1$.
2. Show that $x^2 - 1$ has four zeros over $\mathbf{Z}_{15}$. Why doesn't this contradict the corollary of Theorem 3?
3. Show that, if $a_0 = a_1 - h$, $a_2 = a_1 + h$, and $1 + 1 \neq 0$, then (4) can be solved for $n = 2$ by the parabolic interpolation formula:

$$p(x) = y_1 + \frac{1}{2} (y_2 - y_0) \left(\frac{x - a_1}{h}\right) + \frac{1}{2} (y_2 - 2y_1 + y_0) \left(\frac{x - a_1}{h}\right)^2.$$

4. Find a cubic polynomial $f(x) = a + bx + cx^2 + dx^3$ satisfying $f(0) = 0$, $f(1) = 1$, $f(2) = 0$, $f(3) = 1$, by treating a, b, c, d as unknowns in four equations, of which the last is $a + 3b + 9c + 27d = 1$. (This is the method of undetermined coefficients.)
5. Use the interpolation formula (5) to show that every function on any finite field (such as $\mathbf{Z}_p$) is equal to a polynomial function.
★6. Let D be a finite integral domain with n elements $a_1, \cdots, a_n$. Let $m(x)$ denote the fixed polynomial form $(x - a_1) \cdots (x - a_n)$.
   (a) Show that if two polynomial forms $f(x)$ and $g(x)$ determine the same function, then $m(x)$ is a divisor of the form $f(x) - g(x)$.
   (b) Compute $m(x)$ for the domains $\mathbf{Z}_3$ and $\mathbf{Z}_5$.
   (c) Show that $m(x) = x^p - x$ in case $D = \mathbf{Z}_p$. (*Hint:* Use Fermat's Theorem.)

7. Prove that over an infinite field, distinct rational forms which determine the same functions are formally equal in the sense of Chap. II, §2.

8. (a) If D and D' are isomorphic domains, prove that $D[x]$ is isomorphic to $D'[y]$, where $D[x]$ and $D'[y]$ are the domains of polynomial forms in indeterminates x and y over D and D', respectively.

   (b) How about $D(x)$ and $D'(y)$?

9. If Q is the field of quotients of a domain D (Chap. II), prove that the field $D(x)$ is isomorphic to the field $Q(x)$.

3. Zero-divisors and Commutative Rings

Let D be any finite integral domain, and let $D\langle x \rangle$ denote the system of polynomial functions over D. For all $x \in D$, $f(x) + g(x) = g(x) + f(x)$, $0 + f(x) = f(x)$, $1 \cdot f(x) = f(x)$, and so on. Hence addition and multiplication are commutative, associative, and distributive; identity elements exist for addition and multiplication; and inverses exist for addition. In summary, $D\langle x \rangle$ satisfies all the postulates for an integral domain *except* the cancellation law of multiplication. This breaks down, as we have seen, because there exists a zero product $(x - a_1)(x - a_2) \cdots (x - a_n)$ of non-zero factors.

In other words, $D\langle x \rangle$ is a *commutative ring* in the sense defined in Chap. I, §1. For convenience, we recapitulate this definition here.

Definition. *A commutative ring is a set closed under two binary, commutative, and associative operations, called addition and multiplication, in which further:*

   (i) *multiplication is distributive over addition;*

   (ii) *an additive identity (zero) 0 and additive inverses exist;*

   (iii) *a multiplicative identity (unity) 1 exists.*†

It will be recalled that Rules 1–9 in Chap. I, §2, were proved to be valid in any commutative ring. Also, an interesting family of *finite* commutative rings Z_m was constructed in Chap. I, Theorem 19.

Another instance of a commutative ring is furnished by the system D^* of *all* functions on any D, where addition and multiplication are defined as in §2. There are zero-divisors in the domain D^* of all functions even on infinite integral domains D. Thus, if D is any *ordered* domain, and if we define $f(x) = |x| + x$ and $g(x) = |x| - x$, then $fg = h$ is $h(x) = |x|^2 - x^2 = 0$ for all x, yet $f \neq 0$, $g \neq 0$. On the other hand, D^* has every other defining property of an integral domain. One can prove each law for D^* from the corresponding law for D by the simple device of writing "for all x" in the right places. Thus $f(x) + g(x) = g(x) + f(x)$ for all x implies $f + g = g + f$. Again, if we define e as the constant

---

† Some authors omit condition (iii) in defining commutative rings. The *noncommutative* ring of quaternions will be discussed in Chap. VIII, §10.

function $e(x) = 1$ for all x, then $e(x)f(x) = 1 \cdot f(x) = f(x)$ for all x and f, whence $ef = f$ for all f. (See why the cancellation law of multiplication cannot be proved in this way.) Since the cancellation law for multiplication was nowhere used in the above, we may assert:

Lemma 1. *The functions on any commutative ring A themselves form a commutative ring.*

Now let us define (by analogy with "subdomain") a *subring* of a commutative ring A as a subset of A which contains, with any two elements f and g, also $f \pm g$ and fg, and which also contains the unity of A.

By Theorem 1, the set $D\langle x \rangle$ of polynomial functions on any integral domain D is (1) a subring of the ring D^* of all functions on D, which (2) contains all constant functions and the identity function, and (3) is contained in any other such subring. In this sense $D\langle x \rangle$ is the subring of D^* *generated* by the constant functions and the identity function. This gives a simple algebraic characterization of the concept of a polynomial function.

Deeper insight into polynomials can be gained by generalizing the notion of isomorphism as follows.

Definition. *A function $\phi\colon a \to a\phi$ from a commutative ring R into a commutative ring R' is called a* homomorphism *if and only if it satisfies, for all $a, b \in R$,*

$$(6) \qquad\qquad (a + b)\phi = a\phi + b\phi,$$
$$(7) \qquad\qquad (ab)\phi = (a\phi)(b\phi),$$

and carries the unity of R into the unity of R'.

These conditions state that the homomorphism preserves addition and multiplication. Evidently, an isomorphism is just a homomorphism which is one-one and onto.

One easily verifies that the function from n to the residue class containing n, for any fixed modulus m, is a homomorphism $\mathbf{Z} \to \mathbf{Z}_m$ mapping the domain of integers onto the ring $\mathbf{Z}_m$ of Chap. I, Theorem 19. We now prove another easy result

Lemma 2. *Let ϕ be a homomorphism from a commutative ring R into a commutative ring R'. Then 0ϕ is the zero of R', and $(a - b)\phi = a\phi - b\phi$ for all $a, b \in R$.*

Proof. By (6), $0\phi = (0 + 0)\phi = 0\phi + 0\phi$, which proves that 0ϕ is the zero of R'. Likewise, if $x = a - b$ in R, then $b + x = a$ and so $a\phi = (b + x)\phi = b\phi + x\phi$, whence $x\phi = a\phi - b\phi$ in R'.

Theorem 6. *The correspondence $p(x) \to f(x)$ from the domain $D[x]$ of polynomial forms over any integral domain D to the ring $D\langle x \rangle$ of polynomial functions over D is a homomorphism.*

Proof. For any element x in D, the addition and multiplication of the *numbers* $p(x)$ and $q(x)$ in D must conform to identities (2)–(3), since the derivation of these identities in §1 used only the postulates for an integral domain.

The result of Theorem 4 states that, if D is infinite, then the homomorphism of Theorem 6 is an isomorphism.

EXERCISES

1. (a) Show that there are only four different functions on the field $\mathbf{Z}_2$, and write out addition and multiplication tables for this ring of functions.
   (b) Express each of these functions as a polynomial function.
   (c) Is this ring of functions isomorphic with the ring of integers modulo 4?
2. How many different functions are there on the ring $\mathbf{Z}_n$ of integers modulo n?
3. Are the following sets of functions commutative rings with unity:
   (a) all functions f on a domain D for which $f(0) = 0$;
   (b) all functions f on D with $f(0) = f(1)$;
   (c) all functions f on D with $f(0) \neq 0$;
   (d) all functions f on $\mathbf{Q}$ (the rational field) with $-7 \leqq f(x) \leqq 7$ for all x;
   (e) all f on $\mathbf{Q}$ with $f(x + 1) = f(x)$ for all x (such an f is periodic)?
4. Construct two commutative rings of functions not included in the examples of Ex. 3.
5. Let D^* be defined as in the text. Prove the associative law for sums and products in D^*.
6. (a) If D and D' are isomorphic domains, prove that $D\langle x \rangle$ and $D'\langle x \rangle$ are isomorphic.
   (b) How about D^* and $(D')^*$?
7. Show that one cannot embed in a field the ring $\mathbf{Z}_p\langle x \rangle$ of all polynomial functions over $\mathbf{Z}_p$.
8. Show that if ϕ with (b) and (7) maps a commutative ring R *onto* a commutative ring R', then the unity of R is carried by ϕ into the unity of R'.

*4. Polynomials in Several Variables

The discussion of §§1–3 dealt with polynomials in a *single* variable (indeterminate) x. But most of the results extend without difficulty to the case of *several* variables (resp. indeterminates) $x_1, \cdots, x_n$.

Definition. *A* polynomial form *over* D *in indeterminates* $x_1, \cdots, x_n$ *is defined recursively as a form in* x_n *over the domain* $D[x_1, \cdots, x_{n-1}]$ *of polynomial forms in* $x_1, \cdots, x_{n-1}$ *(in short,* $D[x_1, \cdots, x_n] = D[x_1, \cdots, x_{n-1}][x_n]$*). A polynomial function of variables* $x_1, \cdots, x_n$ *on an integral domain* D *is one which can be built up by addition, subtraction, and multiplication from the constant function* $f(x_1, \cdots, x_n) = c$ *and the* n *identity functions* $f_i(x_1, \cdots, x_n) = x_i$ $(i = 1, \cdots, n)$.

Thus, in the case of two variables x, y, one such form would be $p(x, y) = (3 + x^2) + 0 \cdot y + (2x - x^3)y^2$—often written in the more flexible form $3 + x^2 + 2xy^2 - x^3y^2$.

A corollary of Theorem 4 and induction on n is

Theorem 7. *Each polynomial function in $x_1, \cdots, x_n$ can be expressed in one and only one way as a polynomial form, if D is infinite. Whether D is infinite or not, $D[x_1, \cdots, x_n]$ is an integral domain.*

It is obvious from the definition that every permutation of the subscripts induces a natural automorphism of the commutative ring $D\langle x_1, \cdots, x_n \rangle$ of polynomial functions of n variables. It follows by Theorem 7 that if D is infinite, the same is true of polynomial forms (whose definition is not symmetrical in the variables). We shall now show that this result is true for *any* integral domain D.

Theorem 8. *Every permutation of the subscripts induces a different automorphism on $D[x_1, \cdots, x_n]$.*

Proof. Consider the case of two indeterminates x, y. Each form

$$p(y, x) = \sum_i \left(\sum_j a_{ij} y^j \right) x^i$$

of $D[y, x]$ can be rearranged by the distributive, commutative, and associative laws in $D[y, x]$ to give an expression of the form

$$p(y, x) = \sum_j \left(\sum_i a_{ij} x^i \right) y^j.$$

This result has the proper form, and can be interpreted as if it were a polynomial $p'(x, y)$ in the domain $D[x, y]$ (x first, then y). The correspondence $p(y, x) \to p'(x, y)$ thus set up is one-one—every finite set of non-zero coefficients a_{ij} corresponds to just one element of $D[y, x]$ and just one of $D[x, y]$. Finally, since rules (2)–(3) for addition and multiplication can be deduced from the postulates for an integral domain, which both $D[y, x]$ and $D[x, y]$ are, we see that the correspondence preserves sums and products.

The case of n indeterminates can be treated similarly with a more elaborate general notation—or deduced by induction from the case of two variables.

Thus $D[x_1, \cdots, x_n]$ in fact depends *symmetrically* on $x_1, \cdots, x_n$. This suggests framing a definition of $D[x_1, \cdots, x_n]$ from which this symmetry is immediately apparent. This may be done in the case $n = 2$, for the domain $D'' = D[x, y]$, roughly as follows. Firstly, D'' is generated by x, y, and elements of D (every element of D'' may be obtained from x, y, and D by repeated sums and products); in the second place, the generators x and y are *simultaneous indeterminates* over D (or, are *alge-*

braically independent over D). By this we mean that a finite sum

$$\sum_{i,j} a_{ij} x^i y^j$$

with coefficients a_{ij} in D can be zero if and only if all coefficients a_{ij} are zero. These two properties uniquely determine the domain $D[x, y]$ in a symmetrical manner (see Ex. 9 below).

EXERCISES

1. Represent as polynomials in y with coefficients in $D[x]$:
   (a) $p(x, y) = y^3 x + (x^2 - xy)^2$,
   (b) $q(x, y) = (x + y)^3 - 3yx(x^2 + x - 1)$.
2. Compute the number of possible functions of two variables x, y on the domain $\mathbf{Z}_2$.
3. Rearrange the following expression as a polynomial in x with coefficients which are polynomials in y (as in the proof of Theorem 8):

$$(3x^2 + 2x + 1)y^3 + (x^4 + 2)y^2 + (2x - 3)y + x^4 - 3x^2 + 2x.$$

4. Let D be any integral domain. Prove that the correspondence which carries each $p(x)$ into $p(-x)$ is an automorphism of $D[x]$. Is it also one of $D\langle x \rangle$?
5. Is the correspondence $p(x) \to p(x + c)$, where c is a constant, an automorphism of $D[x]$? Illustrate by numerical examples.
6. If F is a field, show that the correspondence $p(x) \to p(ax)$ is an automorphism of $F[x]$ for any constant $a \neq 0$.
7. Exhibit automorphisms of $D[x, y]$ other than those described in Theorem 8.
8. Prove Theorem 7, (a) for $n = 2$; (b) for any n.
9. (a) Prove in detail that the domain $D[x, y]$ (first x, then y) is indeed generated over D by two "simultaneous indeterminates" x and y.
   (b) Let D' and D'' be two domains each generated over D by two simultaneous indeterminates x', y' and x'', y'', respectively. Prove that D' is isomorphic to D'' under a correspondence which maps x' on x'', y' on y'', and each element of D on itself.
   (c) Use parts (a) and (b) to give another proof of Theorem 8, for $n = 2$.

5. The Division Algorithm

The Division Algorithm for polynomials (sometimes called "polynomial long division") provides a standard scheme for dividing one polynomial $b(x)$ by a second one $a(x)$ so as to get a quotient $q(x)$ and remainder $r(x)$ of degree less than that of the divisor $a(x)$. We shall now show that this Division Algorithm, although usually carried out with rational coefficients, is actually possible for polynomials with coefficients in any field.

Theorem 9. *If F is any field, and $a(x) \neq 0$ and $b(x)$ are any polynomials over F, then we can find polynomials $q(x)$ and $r(x)$ over F so that*

$$(8) \qquad\qquad b(x) = q(x)a(x) + r(x),$$

where $r(x)$ is either zero or has a degree less than that of $a(x)$.

Informal proof. Eliminate successively the highest terms of the dividend $b(x)$ by subtracting from it products of the divisor $a(x)$ by suitable monomials cx^k. If $a(x) = a_0 + a_1x + \cdots + a_mx^m$ ($a_m \neq 0$) and $b(x) = b_0 + b_1x + \cdots + b_nx^n$ ($b_n \neq 0$), and if the degree n of $b(x)$ is not already less than that m of $a(x)$, we can form the difference

$$(9) \qquad \begin{aligned} b_1(x) &= b(x) - (b_n/a_m)x^{n-m}a(x) \\ &= 0 \cdot x^n + (b_{n-1} - a_{m-1}b_n/a_m)x^{n-1} + \cdots , \end{aligned}$$

which will be of degree less than n, or zero. We can then repeat this process until the degree of the remainder is less than m.

A formal proof for this Division Algorithm can be based on the Second Induction Principle, as formulated in §5 of Chap. I. Let m be the degree of $a(x)$. Any polynomial $b(x)$ of degree $n < m$ then has a representation $b(x) = 0 \cdot a(x) + b(x)$, with a quotient $q(x) = 0$. For a polynomial $b(x)$ of degree $n \geq m$, transposition of (9) gives

$$(10) \qquad\qquad b(x) = b_1(x) + (b_n/a_m)x^{n-m}a(x),$$

where the degree k of $b_1(x)$ is less than n unless $b_1(x) = 0$. By the Second Induction Principle, we can assume the expansion (8) to be possible for all $b(x)$ of degree $k < n$, so that we have

$$(11) \qquad\qquad b_1(x) = q_1(x)a(x) + r(x),$$

where the degree of $r(x)$ is less than m, unless $r(x) = 0$. Substituting (11) in (10), we get the desired equation (8), as

$$b(x) = [q_1(x) + (b_n/a_m)x^{n-m}]a(x) + r(x).$$

In particular, if the polynomial $a(x) = x - c$ is monic and linear, then the remainder $r(x)$ in (8) is a constant $r = b(x) - (x - c)q(x)$. Setting $x = c$, this equation gives $r = b(c) - 0q(c) = b(c)$. Hence we have

Corollary 1. *The remainder of a polynomial $p(x)$, when divided by $x - c$, is $p(c)$. (Remainder Theorem.)*

When the remainder $r(x)$ in (8) is zero, we say that $b(x)$ is divisible by $a(x)$. More exactly, if $a(x)$ and $b(x)$ are two polynomial forms over an integral domain D, then $b(x)$ is *divisible* by $a(x)$ *over* D or *in* $D[x]$ if and only if $b(x) = q(x)a(x)$ for some polynomial form $q(x) \in D[x]$.

EXERCISES

1. Show that $q(x)$ and $r(x)$ are unique for given $a(x)$ and $b(x)$ in (8).
2. Compute $q(x)$, $r(x)$ if $b(x) = x^5 - x^3 + 3x - 5$ and $a(x) = x^2 + 7$.
3. The same as Ex. 2 if $a(x)$ is respectively $x - 2$, $x + 2$, $x^3 + x - 1$.
4. (a) Do Ex. 2 for the field Z_5.
   (b) Do Ex. 3 for the field Z_3.
5. Is $x^3 + x^2 + x + 1$ divisible by $x^2 + 3x + 2$ over any of the domains Z_3, Z_5, Z_7?
6. Find all possible rings Z_n over which $x^5 - 10x + 12$ is divisible by $x^2 + 2$.
7. (a) If a polynomial $f(x)$ over any domain has $f(a) = 0 = f(b)$, where $a \neq b$, show that $f(x)$ is divisible by $(x - a)(x - b)$.
   (b) Generalize this result.
8. In the application of the Second Induction Principle to the Division Algorithm, what specifically is $P(n)$ (see Chap. I, §5)?

6. Units and Associates

One can get a complete analogue for polynomials of the fundamental theorem of arithmetic. In this analogue, the role of prime numbers is played by "irreducible" polynomials, defined as follows.

Definition. *A polynomial form is called "reducible" over a field F, if it can be factored into polynomials of lower degree with coefficients in F; otherwise, it is called "irreducible" over F.*

Thus the polynomial $x^2 + 4$ is irreducible over the field of rationals. For suppose instead $x^2 + 4 = (x + a)(x + b)$. Substituting $x = -b$ this gives $(-b)^2 + 4 = (-b + a)(-b + b) = 0$, hence $(-b)^2 = -4$. This is clearly impossible, as a square cannot be negative. Since the same reasoning holds in any ordered field, we conclude that $x^2 + 4$ is also irreducible over the real field or any other ordered field.

To clarify the analogy between irreducible polynomials and prime numbers, we now define certain divisibility concepts for an arbitrary integral domain D, be it the polynomial domain $Q[x]$, the domain Z of integers, or something else.

An element a of D is divisible by b (in symbols, $b \mid a$) if there exists some c in D such that $a = cb$. Two elements a and b are *associates* if both $b \mid a$ and $a \mid b$. An associate of the unity element 1 is called a *unit*. Since $1 \mid a$ for all a, an element u is a unit in D if and only if it has in D a multiplicative inverse u^{-1} with $1 = uu^{-1}$. Elements with this property are also called *invertible*.

If a and b are associates, $a = cb$ and $b = c'a$, hence $a = cc'a$. The cancellation law gives $1 = cc'$, so both c and c' are units. Conversely, $a = ub$ is an associate of b if u is a unit. Hence two elements are associates if and only if each may be obtained from the other by introducing a unit factor.

EXAMPLE 1.   In a field, every $a \neq 0$ is a unit.

EXAMPLE 2.   In the domain $\mathbf{Z}$ of integers, the units are ± 1; hence the associates of any a are $\pm a$.

EXAMPLE 3.   In a polynomial domain $D[x]$ in an indeterminate x, the degree of a product $f(x) \cdot g(x)$ is the sum of the degrees of the factors. Hence any element $b(x)$ with a polynomial inverse, $a(x)b(x) = 1$ must be a polynomial $b(x) = b$ of degree 0. Such a constant polynomial b has an inverse only if b already has an inverse in D. Therefore the units of $D[x]$ are the units of D.

If F is a field, the units of the polynomial domain $F[x]$ are thus exactly the non-zero constants of F, so that two polynomials $f(x)$ and $g(x)$ are associates in $F[x]$ if and only if each is a constant multiple of the other.

EXAMPLE 4.   In the domain $\mathbf{Z}[\sqrt{2}]$ of all numbers $a + b\sqrt{2}$ (a, b integers), $(a + b\sqrt{2})(x + y\sqrt{2}) = 1$ implies $x = a/(a^2 - 2b^2)$, $y = -b/(a^2 - 2b^2)$—and these are integers if and only if $a^2 - 2b^2 = \pm 1$. Thus, $1 \pm \sqrt{2}$ and $3 \pm 2\sqrt{2}$ are units, whereas $2 + \sqrt{2}$ is not a unit in $\mathbf{Z}[\sqrt{2}]$.

An element b of an arbitrary integral domain D is divisible by all its associates and by all units. These are called "improper" divisors of b. An element not a unit with no proper divisors is called *prime* or *irreducible* in D.

EXAMPLE 5.   Over any field F, a linear polynomial $ax + b$ with $a \neq 0$ is irreducible, for its only factors are constants (units) or constant multiples of itself (associates).

EXAMPLE 6.   Consider the domain $\mathbf{Z}[\sqrt{-1}]$ of "Gaussian integers" of the form $a + b\sqrt{-1}$, with $a, b \in \mathbf{Z}$. If $a + b\sqrt{-1}$ is a unit, then, for some $c + d\sqrt{-1}$, we have

$$1 = (a + b\sqrt{-1})(c + d\sqrt{-1}) = (ac - bd) + (ad + bc)\sqrt{-1}.$$

Hence $ac - bd = 1$, $ad + bc = 0$, and

$$1 = (ac - bd)^2 + (ad + bc)^2 = (a^2 + b^2)(c^2 + d^2),$$

as can easily be checked. Since $a^2 + b^2$, $c^2 + d^2$ are non-negative integers, we infer $a^2 + b^2 = c^2 + d^2 = 1$; the only possibilities are thus 1, -1, $\sqrt{-1}$, and $-\sqrt{-1}$, giving four units.

Lemma.   *In any integral domain D, the relation "a and b are associates" is an equivalence relation.*

The proof will be left to the reader. (See also Exercises 1–3 below.)

EXERCISES

1. In any integral domain D, prove that
   (a) the relation "$b \mid a$" is reflexive and transitive,
   (b) if $c \neq 0$, then $b \mid a$ if and only if $bc \mid ac$,
   (c) any two elements have a common divisor and a common multiple,
   (d) if $a \mid b$ and $a \mid c$, then $a \mid (b \pm c)$.
2. Prove that the units of Z_m are the integers relatively prime to Z_m.
3. In any integral domain, let "$a \sim b$" mean "a is associate to b." Prove that
   (a) if $a \sim b$, then $c \mid a$ if and only if $c \mid b$,
   (b) if $a \sim b$, then $a \mid c$ if and only if $b \mid c$,
   (c) if $a \mid c$ if and only if $b \mid c$, then $a \sim b$,
   (d) if p is prime and $p \sim q$, then q is prime.
4. Show that if $a \sim a'$ and $b \sim b'$, then $ab \sim a'b'$—whereas in general $a + b \sim a' + b'$ fails.
5. Prove the "generalized law of cancellation": if $ax \sim by$, $a \sim b$, and $a \neq 0$, then $x \sim y$.
6. List all associates of $x^3 + 2x - 1$ in $Z_5[x]$.
7. Find all units in the domain $D[x, y]$ of polynomials in two indeterminates.
8. For which elements a of an integral domain D is the correspondence $p(x) \to p(ax)$ an automorphism of $D[x]$?
9. Find all the units in the domain D which consists of all rational numbers m/n with m and n integers such that n is not divisible by 7.
10. Where $\alpha = a + b\sqrt{3}$, define $N(\alpha) = a^2 - 3b^2$. Prove
    (a) $N(\alpha\alpha') = N(\alpha)N(\alpha')$, and
    (b) If α is a unit in $Z[\sqrt{3}]$, then $N(\alpha) = \pm 1$.
11. Let $Z[\sqrt{5}]$ be the domain of all numbers $\alpha = a + b\sqrt{5}$ (a, b integers), and set $N(\alpha) = a^2 - 5b^2$.
    (a) Prove that $9 + 4\sqrt{5}$ is a unit in this domain. (Cf. Ex. 10.)
    (b) Show that $1 - \sqrt{5}$ and $3 + \sqrt{5}$ are associates, but are not units.
    (c) Show generally that α is a unit if and only if $N(\alpha) = \pm 1$.
    (d) If $N(\alpha)$ is a prime in Z, show that α is a prime in $Z[\sqrt{5}]$.
    (e) Show that $4 + \sqrt{5}$ and $4 - \sqrt{5}$ are primes.
    (f) Show that 2 and $3 + \sqrt{5}$ are primes. (*Hint:* $x^2 \equiv 2 \pmod 5$ is impossible for $x \in Z$.)
    (g) Use $2 \cdot 2 = (3 + \sqrt{5})(3 - \sqrt{5})$ to show that $Z[\sqrt{5}]$ is not a unique factorization domain (§9).
12. Prove in detail the lemma of the text.

7. Irreducible Polynomials

A basic problem in polynomial algebra consists in finding effective tests for the irreducibility of polynomials over a given field. The nature of such tests depends entirely on the field F in question. Thus over the complex field C, $x^2 + 1$ can be factored as $x^2 + 1 = (x + \sqrt{-1})(x - \sqrt{-1})$. In fact, as will be shown in Chap. V, the only irreducible polynomials of $C[x]$ are linear. Yet $x^2 + 1$ is irreducible over the real field R.

Again, since $x^2 - 28 = (x - \sqrt{28})(x + \sqrt{28})$, the polynomial $x^2 - 28$ is reducible over the real field. The same polynomial is irreducible over the rational field, as we shall now prove rigorously.

Lemma.   *A quadratic or cubic polynomial $p(x)$ is irreducible over a field, F, unless $p(c) = 0$ for some $c \in F$.*

Proof.   In any factorization of $p(x)$ into polynomials of lower degree, one factor must be linear since the degree of a product of polynomials is the sum of the degrees of the factors.

Theorem 10.   *Let $p(x) = a_0 x^n + a_1 x^{n-1} + \cdots + a_n$ be a polynomial with integral coefficients. Any rational root of the equation $p(x) = 0$ must have the form r/s, where $r \mid a_n$ and $s \mid a_0$.*

Proof.   Suppose $p(x) = 0$ for some fraction $x = b/c$. By dividing out the g.c.d. of b and c one can express b/c in "lowest terms" as a quotient r/s of relatively prime integers r and s. Substitution of this value in $p(x)$ gives,

$$(12) \qquad 0 = s^n p(r/s) = a_0 r^n + a_1 r^{n-1} s + \cdots + a_n s^n,$$

whence

$$-a_0 r^n = s(a_1 r^{n-1} + a_2 r^{n-2} s + \cdots + a_n s^{n-1}), \qquad \text{and} \qquad s \mid a_0 r^n.$$

But $(s, r) = 1$; hence, by successive applications of Theorem 10 of Chap. I, $s \mid a_0 r^{n-1}, \cdots, s \mid a_0$. Similarly, as $-a_n s^n = r(a_0 r^{n-1} + \cdots + a_{n-1} s^{n-1})$, $r \mid a_n$.

Corollary.   *Any rational root of a monic polynomial having integral coefficients is an integer.*

It is now easy to prove that $x^2 - 28$ is irreducible over **Q**. By the Corollary, $x^2 = 28$ implies that $x = r/s$ is an integer. But $x^2 - 28 > 0$ if $|x| \geq 6$, and $x^2 - 28 < 0$ if $|x| \leq 5$. Hence no integer can be a root of $x^2 - 28 = 0$, and (by the Lemma), $x^2 - 28$ is irreducible over the rational field.

There is no easy general test for irreducibility of polynomials over the rational field **Q**.

EXERCISES

1. Test the following equations for rational roots:
   (a) $3x^3 - 7x = 5$,   (b) $5x^3 + x^2 + x = 4$,
   (c) $8x^5 + 3x^2 = 17$,   (d) $6x^3 - 3x = 18$.
2. Prove that $30x^n = 91$ has a rational root for no integer $n > 1$. (*Hint:* Use the fundamental theorem of arithmetic.)

3. For which rational numbers x is $3x^2 - 7x$ an integer? Find necessary and sufficient conditions.
4. For what integers a between 0 and 250 does $30x^n = a$ have a rational root for some $n > 1$?
5. Is $x^2 + 1$ irreducible over $\mathbf{Z}_3$? over $\mathbf{Z}_5$? How about $x^3 + x + 2$?
6. Find a finite field over which $x^2 - 2$ is (a) reducible, (b) irreducible.
7. Find all monic irreducible quadratic polynomials over the field $\mathbf{Z}_5$.
8. Find all monic irreducible cubic polynomials over $\mathbf{Z}_3$.
9. Prove that if $a_0 + a_1x + a_2x^2 + \cdots + a_nx^n$ is irreducible, then so is $a_n + a_{n-1}x + a_{n-2}x^2 + \cdots + a_0x^n$.
10. Decompose into irreducible factors the polynomial $x^4 - 5x^2 + 6$ over the field of rationals, over the field $\mathbf{Q}(\sqrt{2})$ of Chap. II, §1, and also over the field of reals.
⋆11. Show that, if $4ac > b^2$, then $ax^2 + bx + c$ is irreducible over any ordered field.

8. Unique Factorization Theorem

Throughout §8, we shall be considering factorization in the domain $F[x]$ of polynomial forms in one indeterminate x over a *field F*. The main result is that factorization into irreducible (prime) factors is unique, the proof being a virtual repetition of that of the analogous fundamental theorem of arithmetic (Chap. I). The analogy involves the following fundamental notion, which plays a fundamental role in the general theory of rings.

Definition.   *A nonvoid subset C of a commutative ring R is called an ideal when $a \in C$ and $b \in C$ imply $(a \pm b) \in C$, and $a \in C$, $r \in R$ imply $ra \in C$.*

Remark.   For any $a \in R$, the set of all multiples ra of a is an ideal, since

$$ra \pm sa = (r \pm s)a \qquad \text{and} \qquad s(ra) = (sr)a, \qquad s, r \in R.$$

Such an ideal is called a *principal ideal*. We will now show that all ideals in any $F[x]$ are principal.

Theorem 11.   *Over any field F, any ideal C of $F[x]$ consists either (i) of 0 alone, or (ii) of the set of multiples $q(x)a(x)$ of any non-zero member $a(x)$ of least degree.*

Proof.   Unless $C = 0$, it contains a non-zero polynomial $a(x)$ of least degree $d(a)$, and, with $a(x)$, all its multiples $q(x)a(x)$. In this case, if $b(x)$ is *any* polynomial of C, by Theorem 9 some $r(x) = b(x) - q(x)a(x)$ has degree less than $d(a)$. But by hypothesis C contains $r(x)$, and by construction no non-zero polynomial of degree less than $d(a)$. Hence $r(x) = 0$ and $b(x) = q(x)a(x)$, proving the theorem.

Now let $a(x)$ and $b(x)$ be any two polynomials, and consider the set C of all the "linear combinations" $s(x)a(x) + t(x)b(x)$ which can be formed from them with any polynomial coefficients $s(x)$ and $t(x)$. This set C is obviously nonvoid, and contains any sum, difference, or multiple of its members, since (in abbreviated notation)

$$(sa + tb) \pm (s'a + t'b) = (s \pm s')a + (t \pm t')b,$$
$$q(sa + tb) = (qs)a + (qt)b.$$

Hence by Theorem 11, the ideal C of linear combinations consists of the multiples of some polynomial $d(x)$ of least degree.

This polynomial $d(x)$ will divide both $a(x) = 1 \cdot a(x) + 0 \cdot b(x)$ and $b(x) = 0 \cdot a(x) + 1 \cdot b(x)$, and will be divisible by any common divisor of $a(x)$ and $b(x)$, since $d(x) = s_0(x)a(x) + t_0(x)b(x)$. Our conclusion is

Theorem 12. *In $F[x]$, any two polynomials a and b have a "greatest common divisor" d satisfying* (i) $d \mid a$ *and* $d \mid b$, (i') $c \mid a$ *and* $c \mid b$ *imply* $c \mid d$. *Moreover,* (ii) d *is a "linear combination"* $d = sa + tb$ *of a and b.*

We remark that the "Euclidean Algorithm" described in detail in Chap. I, §7, can be used to compute d explicitly from a and b. (This is because our "Division Algorithm" allows us to compute remainders of polynomials explicitly.)

Also, if d satisfies (i)–(i')–(ii), then so do all associates of d. Incidentally, (i) and (ii) imply (i').

The g.c.d. $d(x)$ is unique except for unit factors, for if d and d' are two greatest common divisors of the same polynomials a and b, then by (i) and (i'), $d \mid d'$ and $d' \mid d$, so that d and d' are indeed associates. Conversely, if d is a g.c.d., so is every associate of d. It is sometimes convenient to speak of the unique monic polynomial associate to d as "the" g.c.d.

Two polynomials $a(x)$ and $b(x)$ are said to be *relatively prime* if their greatest common divisors are unity and its associates. This means that polynomials are relatively prime if and only if their only common factors are the non-zero constants of F (the units of the domain $F[x]$).

Theorem 13. *If $p(x)$ is irreducible, then $p(x) \mid a(x)b(x)$ implies that $p(x) \mid a(x)$ or $p(x) \mid b(x)$.*

Proof. Because $p(x)$ is irreducible, the g.c.d. of $p(x)$ and $a(x)$ is either $p(x)$ or the unity 1. In the former case, $p(x) \mid a(x)$; in the latter case, we can write $1 = s(x)p(x) + t(x)a(x)$ and so

$$b(x) = 1 \cdot b(x) = s(x)p(x)b(x) + t(x)[a(x)b(x)].$$

Since $p(x)$ divides the product $a(x)b(x)$, it divides both terms on the right, hence does divide $b(x)$, as required for the theorem.

Theorem 14. *Any nonconstant polynomial $a(x)$ in $F[x]$ can be expressed as a constant c times a product of monic irreducible polynomials. This expression is unique except for the order in which the factors occur.*

First, such a factorization is possible. If $a(x)$ is a constant or irreducible, this is trivial. Otherwise, $a(x)$ is the product $a(x) = b(x)b'(x)$ of factors of lower degree. By the Second Induction Principle, we can assume

$$b(x) = cp_1(x) \cdots p_m(x), \qquad b'(x) = c'p_1'(x) \cdots p_n'(x),$$

whence $a(x) = (cc')p_1(x) \cdots p_m(x)p_1'(x) \cdots p_n'(x)$, where cc' is a constant and the $p_i(x)$ and $p_j'(x)$ are irreducible and monic polynomials.

To prove the uniqueness, suppose $a(x)$ has two possible such "prime" factorizations,

$$a(x) = cp_1(x) \cdots p_m(x) = c'q_1(x) \cdots q_n(x).$$

Clearly, $c = c'$ will be the leading coefficient of $a(x)$ (since the latter is the product of the leading coefficients of its factors). Again, since $p_1(x)$ divides $c'q_1(x) \cdots q_n(x) = a(x)$, it must by Theorem 13 divide some (nonconstant) factor $q_i(x)$; since $q_i(x)$ is irreducible, the quotient $q_i(x)/p_1(x)$ must be a constant; and since $p_1(x)$ and $q_i(x)$ are both monic, it must be 1. Hence $p_1(x) = q_i(x)$. Cancelling, $p_2(x) \cdots p_m(x)$ equals the product of the $q_k(x)$ [$k \neq i$], and has a lower degree than $a(x)$. Therefore, again by the Second Induction Principle, the $p_j(x)$ [$j \neq 1$] and $q_k(x)$ [$k \neq i$] are equal in pairs, completing the proof.

It is a corollary (cf. Chap. I, §8, last paragraph) that the exponent e_i to which each (monic) irreducible polynomial $p_i(x)$ occurs as a factor of $a(x)$ is uniquely determined by $a(x)$, and is the biggest e such that $p_i(x)^e \mid a(x)$.

If a polynomial $a(x)$ is decomposed into irreducible factors $p_i(x)$ which are not necessarily monic, the factors are no longer absolutely unique, as in Theorem 14. However, each factor $p_i(x)$ divided by its leading coefficient gives a (unique) monic irreducible factor, and therefore is associate to this irreducible in $F[x]$. Hence any two such factorizations can be made to agree with each other simply by reordering terms and replacing each factor by a suitable associate factor. This situation is summarized by the statement that the decomposition of a polynomial in $F[x]$ is unique to *within order and unit factors* (or, to within order and replacement of factors by associates).

EXERCISES

1. Show that, if ϕ is any homomorphism from a ring R to a ring R', then the antecedents of the additive zero 0 of R' form an ideal in R.

2. (a) Find the g.c.d. of $x^3 - 1$ and $x^4 + x^3 + 2x^2 + x + 1$.

(b) Express this g.c.d. as a linear combination $d(x) = s(x)a(x) + t(x)b(x)$ of the given polynomials. (*Caution:* The coefficients need not be integers.)

(c) The same for $x^{18} - 1$, $x^{33} - 1$.

3. Find the g.c.d. of $2x^3 + 6x^2 - x - 3$, $x^4 + 4x^3 + 3x^2 + x + 1$.

4. Do Ex. 3, assuming that the polynomials have coefficients in Z_3.

5. Show that $x^3 + x + 1$ is irreducible modulo 5.

6. Find the decomposition of the following polynomials in Z_3:

(a) $x^2 + x + 1$,   (b) $x^3 + x + 2$,   (c) $2x^3 + 2x^2 + x + 1$,
(d) $x^4 + x^3 + x + 1$,   (★e) $x^4 + x^3 + x + 2$.

7. List (to within associates) all divisors of $x^4 - 1$ in the domain of polynomials with rational coefficients, proving that every divisor of $x^4 - 1$ is associate to one on your list.

8. Do the same for $x^6 - 1$, $x^8 - 1$.

9. Prove that two polynomial forms $q(x)$ and $r(x)$ over Z represent the same function on Z_p if and only if $(x^p - x) \mid [q(x) - r(x)]$. (*Hint:* Use Ex. 6 of §2.)

10. Prove that any finite set of polynomials over a field has a g.c.d., which is a linear combination of the given polynomials.

11. (a) Prove that the set of all common multiples of any two given polynomials over a field is an ideal.

(b) Infer that the polynomials have a l.c.m.; illustrate by finding the l.c.m. of $x^3 + 3x + 2$ and $(x + 1)^2$.

12. If a given polynomial $p(x)$ over F has the property that $p(x) \mid a(x)b(x)$ always implies either $p(x) \mid a(x)$ or $p(x) \mid b(x)$, prove $p(x)$ irreducible over F.

13. If $p(x)$ is a given polynomial such that any other polynomial is either relatively prime to $p(x)$ or divisible by $p(x)$, prove $p(x)$ irreducible.

14. If $m(x)$ is a power of an irreducible polynomial, show that $m(x) \mid a(x)b(x)$ implies either $m(x) \mid a(x)$ or $m(x) \mid (b(x))^e$ for some e.

15. If $h(x)$ is relatively prime to both $f(x)$ and $g(x)$, prove $h(x)$ relatively prime to $f(x)g(x)$.

16. If $h(x) \mid f(x)g(x)$ and $h(x)$ is relatively prime to $f(x)$, prove that $h(x) \mid g(x)$.

17. If $f(x)$ and $g(x)$ are relatively prime polynomials in $F[x]$, and if F is a subfield of K, prove that $f(x)$ and $g(x)$ are relatively prime also in $K[x]$.

★18. If two polynomials with rational coefficients have a real root in common, prove that they have a common divisor with rational coefficients which is not a constant.

19. The following descriptions give certain sets of polynomials with rational coefficients. Which of these sets are ideals? When the set is an ideal, find in it a polynomial of least degree.

(a) All $b(x)$ with $b(3) = b(5) = 0$;
(b) All $b(x)$ with $b(3) \neq 0$ and $b(2) = 0$;
(c) All $b(x)$ with $b(3) = 0$, $b(6) = b(7)$;
(d) All $b(x)$ such that some power of $b(x)$ is divisible by $(x + 1)^4(x + 2)$.

20. Let S be any set of polynomials over F which contains the difference of any two of its members and contains with any $b(x)$ both $xb(x)$ and $ab(x)$ for each constant a in F. Show that S is an ideal.

IV. Real Numbers

1. Dilemma of Pythagoras

A completely geometric approach to real numbers was used by the Greeks. For them, a number was simply a ratio $(a\!:\!b)$ between two line segments a and b. They gave direct geometric constructions for equality between ratios, and for addition, multiplication, subtraction, and division of ratios. The postulates stating that the real numbers form an *ordered field* (Chap. II, §4) appeared to the Greeks as a series of geometric theorems, to be proved from postulates for plane geometry (including the parallel postulate).

The ancient Greek philosopher Pythagoras knew that the ratio $r = d/s$ between the length d of a diagonal of a square and the length s of its side must satisfy the equation

$$(1) \qquad d^2 = (rs)^2 = s^2 + s^2 \qquad \text{(Pythagorean Theorem)}.$$

So, he reasoned, there is a "number" r satisfying $r^2 = 1 + 1 = 2$.

On the other hand, he found r could not be represented as a quotient $r = a/b$ of integers. For $(a/b)^2 = 2$ would imply $a^2 = 2b^2$. By the prime factorization theorem, 2 divides a^2 just twice as often as it divides a—hence an even number of times; similarly, it divides $2b^2$ an odd number of times. Therefore, $a^2 = 2b^2$ has no solution in integers.

From this "dilemma of Pythagoras" one can escape only by creating *irrational* numbers: numbers which are not quotients of integers.

Similar arguments show that both the ratio $\sqrt{3}$ of the length of a diagonal of a cube C to the length of its side, and the ratio $\sqrt[3]{2}$ of the length of a side of C to the side of a cube having half as much volume, are irrational numbers. These results are special cases of Theorem 10 of Chap. III.

Further irrational numbers are π (which thus cannot be exactly $\frac{22}{7}$ or even 3.1416), e, and many others. Indeed, it can be demonstrated that the vast majority of real numbers not only are irrational, but also (unlike $\sqrt{2}$) even fail to satisfy any algebraic equation. To answer the fundamental question *"what is a real number?"* we shall need to use entirely new ideas.

One such idea is that of *continuity*: the idea that if the real axis is divided into two segments, then these segments must touch at a common frontier point. A second such idea is that the ordered field **Q** of rational numbers is *dense* in the real field, so that every real number is a *limit* of one or more sequences of rational numbers (e.g., of finite decimal approximations correct to n places). This idea can also be expressed in the statement

(2)   If $x < y$, then there exists $m/n \, \epsilon \, \mathbf{Q}$ such that $x < m/n < y$.

This property of real numbers was first recognized by the Greek mathematician Eudoxus. Thinking of $x = a:b$ and $y = c:d$ as ratios of lengths of line segments, integral multiples $n \cdot a$ of which could be formed geometrically, Eudoxus stipulated that $(a:b) = (c:d)$ if, and only if, for all positive integers m and n,

(3) $na > mb$ implies $nc > md$, $na < mb$ implies $nc < md$.

The two preceding ideas can be combined into a single postulate of *completeness*, which also permits one to construct the real field as a natural extension of the ordered field $\mathbf{Q}$. This "completeness" postulate is analogous to the well-ordering postulate for the integers (Chap. I, §4): both deal with properties of infinite sets, and so are *nonalgebraic*. As we shall see, this completeness postulate is needed to establish certain essential algebraic properties of the real field (e.g., that every positive number has a square root).

EXERCISES

1. Give a direct proof that $\sqrt{3}$ is irrational.
2. Prove that $\sqrt[n]{a}$ is irrational unless the integer a is the nth power of some integer.
3. Prove that $\log_{10} 3$ is irrational. (*Hint:* Use the definition of the logarithm.)
4. Show that, if $a \neq 0$ and b are rational, then $au + b$ is rational if and only if u is rational.
★5. Prove that $\sqrt{2} + \sqrt{5}$ is irrational. (*Hint:* Find a polynomial equation for $x = \sqrt{2} + \sqrt{5}$, starting by squaring both sides of $x - \sqrt{2} = \sqrt{5}$.)
★6. Prove that e, as defined by the convergent series $\sum\limits_{k=0}^{\infty} 1/k!$ is irrational.

   (*Hint:* If e were rational, then $(n!)e$ would be an integer for some n.)

2. Upper and Lower Bounds

The real field can be most simply characterized as an ordered field in which arbitrary bounded sets have greatest lower and least upper bounds. We now define these two notions, which are analogous to the concepts of greatest common divisor and least common multiple in the theory of divisibility.

Definition. *By an* upper bound *to a set S of elements of an ordered domain D is meant an element b (which need not itself be in S) such that* $b \geq x$ *for every x in S. An upper bound b of S is* a least upper bound *if no smaller element of D is an upper bound for S, that is, if for any* $b' < b$ *there is an x in S with* $b' < x$. *The concepts of* lower bound *and* greatest lower bound *of S are defined dually, by interchanging* $>$ *with* $<$ *throughout, in the above definition.*

It follows directly from the definition that a subset S of D has at most one least upper bound and at most one greatest lower bound (why?).

Intuitively, think of the real numbers as the points of a continuous line (the x-axis), and imagine the rational numbers as sprinkled densely on this line in their natural positions. From this picture, one readily concludes that every real number a can be characterized as the least upper bound of the set S of all rational numbers $r = m/n$ ($n > 0$) such that $r < a$. For example, $\sqrt{2}$ is the least real number greater than all ratios m/n ($m > 0, n > 0$) such that $m^2 < 2n^2$. That is, the number $\sqrt{2}$ is the least upper bound of the set of positive rational numbers m/n such that $m^2 < 2n^2$.

The concept of real numbers as least upper bounds of sets of rationals is directly involved in the familiar representation of real numbers by unlimited decimals. Thus we can write $\sqrt{2}$ as both a least upper bound (l.u.b.) and a greatest lower bound (g.l.b.),

$$
\begin{aligned}
\text{(4)} \qquad \sqrt{2} &= \text{l.u.b. } (1.4, 1.41, 1.414, 1.4142, \cdots) \\
&= \text{g.l.b. } (1.5, 1.42, 1.415, 1.4143, \cdots).
\end{aligned}
$$

Assuming the familiar properties of this decimal representation, it is very easy to "see" that every nonempty set T of positive real numbers has a greatest lower bound, as follows.

Consider the n-place decimals which express members of T to the first n places: there will be a least among them, because there are only a finite number of nonnegative n-place decimals less than any given member of T. Let this least n-place decimal be $k + 0.d_1 d_2 \cdots d_n$, where k is some integer and each d_i is a digit. The least $(n + 1)$-st place decimal coincides with this through the first n places, so has the form $k + 0.d_1 d_2 \cdots d_n d_{n+1}$, with one added digit. Our construction hence defines a certain unlimited decimal $c = k + 0.d_1 d_2 d_3 \cdots$. By construction, this is a lower bound to T (since its decimal expansion is greater than that of no x in T), and even a *greatest* lower bound (any bigger decimal would lose this property).

However, if the real numbers are defined as unlimited decimals, it is very hard to prove what is implicitly assumed in high-school algebra: that the system of unlimited decimals is an ordered field.†

† For details, see J. F. Ritt, *Theory of Functions*, (New York: Kings Crown Press, 1947). The difficulty begins with equations like $.19999 \cdots = .20000 \cdots$ between different decimals.

EXERCISES

1. Prove that $x = .12437437437 \cdots$ represents a rational number. (*Hint:* Compute $1000x - x$.)
2. Do the same for $y = 1.23672367 \cdots$.
★3. Prove that *any* "repeating decimal," like those of Exs. 1–2, represents a rational number. Define your terms carefully.
★4. Prove conversely that the decimal expansion of any rational number is "repeating." (*Suggestion:* Show that if the same remainder occurs after m as after $m - k$ divisions by 10, the block of k digits between gets repeated indefinitely.)
★5. Does the result of Ex. 4 hold in the duodecimal scale?
6. Find three successive approximations to $\sqrt{2}$ in the domain of all rational numbers with denominators powers of 3.
7. Describe two different sets of rational numbers which both have the same l.u.b. 2.
★8. Define the sequence $(2, 3/2, 17/12, 577/408, \cdots)$ recursively by $x_1 = 2$, $x_{k+1} = (x_k/2) + (1/x_k)$.
   (a) Show that, for $k > 1$, $x_k = m_k/n_k$, where $m_k{}^2 = 2n_k{}^2 + 1$.
   (b) Defining $\epsilon_k = x_k - \sqrt{2}$, show that $0 < \epsilon_{k+1} < \epsilon_k{}^2/2\sqrt{2}$.
   (c) Show that g.l.b. $(2, 3/2, 17/12, \cdots) = \sqrt{2}$.

3. Postulates for Real Numbers

We shall now describe the real numbers by a brief set of postulates. Subsequently we shall see (Theorem 6) that these postulates determine the real numbers uniquely, up to an isomorphism.

Definition. *An ordered domain D is* complete *if and only if every non-empty set S of positive elements of D has a greatest lower bound in D.*

Postulate for the real numbers. The real numbers form a complete ordered field **R**.

From the properties of the real numbers given by this postulate one can actually deduce all the known properties of the real numbers, including such a result as Rolle's Theorem, which is known to be fundamental in the proof of Taylor's Theorem and elsewhere in the calculus.

However, we shall confine our attention to a few simple applications.

Theorem 1. *In the field $\mathbf{R}$ of real numbers every nonempty subset S which has a lower bound has a greatest lower bound, and, dually, every nonempty subset T which has an upper bound has a least upper bound.*

Proof. Suppose S has a lower bound b. If $1 - b$ is added to each number x of S, there results a set S' of positive numbers $x - b + 1$. By our postulate, this set S' has a g.l.b. c'. Consequently, the number

$c = c' + b - 1$ is then a g.l.b. for the original set S, as may be readily verified.

Dually, if the set T has an upper bound a, the set of all negatives $-y$ of elements of T has a lower bound $-a$, hence, by the previous proof, has a greatest lower bound b^*. The number $a^* = -b^*$ then proves to be a least upper bound of the given set T, Q.E.D.

Our postulates make the real numbers an ordered field **R**. On the other hand, it can be shown† that, in any ordered field, the subfield generated by 1 is a copy of (i.e., isomorphic to) the rational field **Q**. Since **Q** is defined only up to isomorphism, we may refer to elements of this subfield as "rational numbers," and the multiples of 1 in **R** as integers. With this understanding, it is easy to prove the following property of the reals (often called the Archimedean law).

Theorem 2. *For any two numbers $a > 0$ and $b > 0$ in the field* **R** *of all real numbers (as defined by our postulates) there exists an integer n for which $na > b$.*

Proof. Suppose the conclusion false for two particular real numbers a and b, so that, for every n, $b \geq na$. The set S of all the multiples na then has the upper bound b so that it has also a least upper bound b^*. Therefore $b^* \geq na$ for every n, so that also $b^* \geq (m + 1)a$ for every m. This implies $b^* - a \geq ma$ so that $b^* - a$ is an upper bound for the set S of all multiples of a, although it is smaller than the given least upper bound.

Corollary. *Given real numbers a and b, with $b > 0$, there exists an integer q such that $a = bq + r$, $0 \leq r < b$.*

The proof of this extension of the Division Algorithm will be left to the reader.

The so-established "Archimedean property" may be used to justify the condition of Eudoxus (cf. §1, (3)).

Theorem 3. *Between any two real numbers $c > d$, there exists a rational number m/n such that $c > m/n > d$.*

As before, this is to be proved simply from the postulate that the reals form a complete ordered field. By hypothesis, $c - d > 0$, so the Archimedean law yields a positive integer n such that $n(c - d) > 1$, or $1/n < c - d$. Now let m be the smallest integer such that $m > nd$; then $(m - 1)/n \leq d$, so that

$$m/n = (m - 1)/n + 1/n < d + (c - d) = c.$$

Since $m/n > d$, this completes the proof.

† See for example G. Birkhoff and S. Mac Lane, *A Survey of Modern Algebra*, Chap. II, Thm. 18, Cor. 2.

We can visualize the above proof as follows. The various fractions 0, $\pm 1/h$, $\pm 2/h$, $\cdots$ with a fixed denominator h are spaced along the real axis at intervals of length $1/h$. To be sure that one such point falls between c and d, we need only make the spacing $1/h$ less than the given difference $c - d$.

This theorem may be used to substantiate formally the idea used intuitively in a representation like (4) of a real number as a l.u.b. of rationals.

Corollary. *Every real number is the l.u.b. of a set of rationals.*

Proof. For a given real number c, let S denote the set of all rationals $m/n \leqq c$. Then c is an upper bound of S; by the theorem no smaller real number d could be an upper bound of S, hence c is the *least* upper bound of S.

EXERCISES

1. Prove that there is no ordered domain D in which *every* nonempty set has a l.u.b. (*Hint:* Show that D itself can have no upper bound.)
2. Show that the ordered domain $\mathbf{Z}$ is complete.
3. State in geometrical language a postulate on points of the real axis which asserts that bounded sets have l.u.b. and g.l.b. (use the words "left" and "right").
4. Exhibit the l.u.b. of each of the following sets of rational numbers:
   (a) $1/3$, $4/9$, $13/27$, $40/81$, $\cdots$;
   (b) $1/2$, $3/4$, $7/8$, $15/16$, $\cdots$.
5. Let a set S have a l.u.b. a^* and a g.l.b. b^*.
   (a) Show in detail why the set of all numbers $-3x$, for x in S, has the l.u.b. $-3b^*$ and the g.l.b. $-3a^*$.
   (b) In the same way, find the l.u.b. and the g.l.b. of the set of all numbers $x + 5$, for x in S.
6. In Ex. 5, what is the l.u.b. (a) of the set of all numbers $7x + 2$, for x in S; (b) of the set of all numbers $1/x$, for $x \neq 0$ in S, if $b^* > 0$?
7. Let S_1 and S_2 be sets of real numbers with the respective least upper bounds b_1 and b_2. What is the least upper bound (a) of the set $S_1 + S_2$ of all sums $s_1 + s_2$ (for s_1 in S_1, and s_2 in S_2); (b) of the set of all elements belonging either to S_1 or to S_2?
8. Collect in one list a complete set of postulates for the real numbers.
★9. Construct a system of postulates for the positive real numbers. (*Hint:* Define the relation $a < b$ to mean that $a + x = b$ has a solution x.)
10. Show that an element a^* in an ordered field is a least upper bound for a set S if and only if (i) $x \leqq a^*$ for all $x \in S$; (ii) for each positive e in the field, there is an x in S with $|x - a^*| < e$.
11. Show that between any two real numbers $c < d$, there exists a rational cube $(m/n)^3$ such that $c < (m/n)^3 < d$. Is this true for rational squares?
12. If $h > 1$ is an integer, prove that between any two real numbers $c > d$, there lies a rational number of the form m/h^k, where m and k are suitable integers.

13. Let a, b, c, and d be positive elements of a complete ordered field. Show that $a/b = c/d$ if and only if the condition (3) of Eudoxus is satisfied.

14. Prove in detail the corollary to Theorem 2.

4. Roots of Polynomial Equations

We shall now show how to use the existence of least upper bounds to prove various properties of the real number system **R**, including first the existence of solutions for equations such as $x^2 = 2$.

Theorem 4. *If $p(x)$ is a polynomial with real coefficients, if $a < b$, and if $p(a) < p(b)$, then for every constant C satisfying $p(a) < C < p(b)$, the equation $p(x) = C$ has a root between a and b.*

Geometrically, the hypothesis means that the graph of $y = p(x)$ meets the horizontal line $y = p(a)$ at $x = a$ and the line $y = p(b)$ at $x = b$; the conclusion asserts that the graph must also meet each intermediate horizontal line† $y = C$ at some point with an x-coordinate between a and b.

The proof depends upon two lemmas.

Lemma 1. *For any real x and h, we have $p(x + h) - p(x) = hg(x, h)$, where $g(x, h)$ is a polynomial depending only on $p(x)$.*

Proof. (Cf. Theorem 3, Chap. III.) For each monomial term $a_k x^k$ of $p(x)$ this is true by the binomial theorem. Now summing over k and taking out the common factor h, we get the desired result.

Lemma 2. *For given a, b and $p(x)$ there exists a real constant M, such that $|p(x + h) - p(x)| \leq Mh$ for all x and all positive h satisfying $a \leq x \leq b$, $a \leq x + h \leq b$.*

Proof. By Lemma 1, it suffices to show that $|g(x, h)| \leq M$ whenever $|x| \leq |a| + |b|$, $|h| \leq |b - a|$. But if we replace each term in $g(x, h)$ by its absolute value, we increase $|g(x, h)|$ or leave it undiminished, by formula (3) of Chap. I and induction. We do the same again if we replace $|x|$ and $|h|$ by $|a| + |b|$ and $|b - a|$, respectively. This substitution gives us, however, a real constant M, depending only on the coefficients of $p(x)$ and the interval $a \leq x \leq b$.

Having Lemma 2 at our disposal we are ready to prove Theorem 4. Let S denote the set of real numbers between a and b satisfying $p(x) \leq C$. Since $p(a) < C$, S is nonvoid, and it has b as upper bound; hence it has a real *least* upper bound c. We shall show that $p(c) = C$.

For this purpose, it is clearly sufficient to exclude the possibilities $p(c) < C$ and $p(c) > C$. But $p(c) < C$ would imply that $p(c + h) \leq C$, for $h = [C - p(c)]/M$, by Lemma 2, whence $(c + h) \in S$. This would con-

---

† There is a general theorem of analysis which asserts this conclusion, not only for polynomial functions $p(x)$, but for any continuous function.

tradict our definition of c, as an upper bound to S. (Lemma 2 applies because $c + h \geqq b$ is evidently also impossible.)

There remains the possibility $p(c) > C$. But in this case, again by Lemma 2, $p(c - h) > C$ for all positive $h \leqq [p(c) - C]/(2M)$. This would contradict our definition of c as the *least* upper bound of S: $c - [p(c) - C]/(2M)$ would give a smaller upper bound. There remains only the possibility $p(c) = C$, Q.E.D.

From the theorem one readily proves:

Corollary 1.   *If $p(x)$ is a polynomial with positive coefficients and no constant term, and if $C > 0$, then $p(x) = C$ has a positive real root.*

Corollary 2.   *If $p(x)$ is of odd degree, then $p(x) = C$ has a real root for every real number C.*

Theorem 4 does not give a construction for actually computing a root of $p(x) = C$ in decimal form, but this is easy to do. For example, one can let $c_1 = (a + b)/2$; then either $p(c_1) = C$, $p(c_1) > C$, or $p(c_1) < C$. In the first case the root is found; in the second and third cases there is a root in an interval ($a \leqq x \leqq c_1$, respectively $c_1 \leqq x \leqq b$) half as long as before. Repeating this construction a root of $p(x) = C$ can be found to any desired approximation.

Convergence would be much faster if one used linear interpolation and set

$$c_1 = a + [C - p(a)][b - a][p(b) - p(a)]^{-1}.$$

Other efficient methods of calculating roots of equations are studied in analysis. For example, one may use an infinite series such as

$$(5) \quad \sqrt{1 + x} = 1 + \frac{1}{2}x + \frac{1}{2}\left(-\frac{1}{2}\right)\frac{x^2}{2!} + \frac{1}{2}\left(-\frac{1}{2}\right)\left(-\frac{3}{2}\right)\frac{x^3}{3!} + \cdots .$$

Appendix. Trigonometric Solution of Cubic.   In the case of a cubic equation

$$(6) \qquad a_3x^3 + a_2x^2 + a_1x + a_0 = 0, \qquad a_3 \neq 0,$$

the real roots can be found as follows. Dividing through by a_3, we reduce (6) to the case $a_3 = 1$. Now, by making the substitution $x = y - a_2/3$ and transposing the constant term, we reduce (6) to

$$(7) \qquad\qquad y^3 + py = q.$$

If $p = 0$, the solution is immediate.

Otherwise, setting $y = hz$ and multiplying (7) through by k, where $h = \sqrt{4 \mid p \mid / 3}$, $k = 3/(h \mid p \mid)$, we can reduce it to one of the forms

$$(8) \qquad\qquad 4z^3 + 3z = C \qquad \text{or} \qquad 4z^3 - 3z = C.$$

To solve the first equation one can use the familiar trigonometric identity

$\sinh 3\theta = 4 \sinh^3 \theta + 3 \sinh \theta$, whence

(9a) $z = \sinh [(1/3) \sinh^{-1} C]$.

To solve the second equation, if $C \geq 1$, we use the analogous formula
$\cosh 3\theta = 4 \cosh^3 \theta - 3 \cosh \theta$ to get

(9b) $z = \cosh [(1/3) \cosh^{-1} C]$.

If $C \leq -1$, the same method applies after changing the sign of z. To solve
the second equation when $|C| < 1$ (this is the so-called irreducible case),
use similarly $\cos 3\theta = 4 \cos^3 \theta - 3 \cos \theta$, to get

(9c) $z = \cos [(1/3) \cos^{-1} C]$.

In this case z assumes *three* values, because $(\frac{1}{3}) \cos^{-1} C$ has three values,
differing by multiples of $120°$.

EXERCISES

1. Prove that every positive real number has a real square root.
2. Show that, for any positive real number a and any integer n, the equation
   $x^n - a$ has one and only one positive real root $\sqrt[n]{a}$.
3. Show that $x^4 - x = C$ has two real roots for every $C > -3/8$.
4. Find $\sqrt{5}$ to four decimal places, using (5) and $(\sqrt{5}/2)^2 = 1 + \frac{1}{4}$.
5. Find $\sqrt{2}$ to six places using (5) and $(5\sqrt{2}/7)^2 = 1 + 1/49$.
6. Show that a monic polynomial of even degree assumes a least value K, and
   every value $C > K$ twice.
7. (a) If a and b are positive reals, show that $ax^{n+1} > bx^n$ for all sufficiently
       large positive values of x.
   (b) Given a polynomial $p(x)$ with a positive leading coefficient, find a real
       number M such that $p(x) > 0$ for all $x > M$.
8. Prove Corollary 1.
9. Prove Corollary 2.
10. Find to three decimal places the real roots of
    (a) $3x^3 - x = 1/9$,   (b) $x^3 - 3x^2 + 6x = 7$,
    (c) $x^3 + 3x^2 + 2 = 0$.

V. Complex Numbers

1. Definition

Especially in algebra, but also in the theory of analytic functions and differential equations, many algebraic theorems have much simpler statements if one extends the real number system **R** to a larger field **C** of "complex" numbers. This we shall now define, and show that it is what one gets from the real field if one desires to make every polynomial equation have a root.

Definition. *A "complex number" is a couple (x, y) of real numbers—x being called the real and y the imaginary component of (x, y). Complex numbers are added and multiplied by the rules:*

(1) $$(x, y) + (x', y') = (x + x', y + y'),$$
(2) $$(x, y) \cdot (x', y') = (xx' - yy', xy' + yx').$$

The system of complex numbers so defined is denoted by **C**.

We owe the above definition not to divine revelation, but to simple algebraic experimentation. First, it was observed that the equation $x^2 = -1$ had no real root (x^2 being never negative). This suggested inventing an *imaginary* number i, satisfying $i^2 = -1$, and otherwise satisfying the ordinary laws of algebra. Stated in precise language, it suggested the plausible hypothesis that there was an integral domain D containing such an element i and the real field **R** as well.

In D, any expression of the form $x + yi$ (x, y real numbers) would represent an element. Moreover, by the definition of an integral domain (laws of ordinary algebra),

(1') $$(x + yi) \pm (x' + y'i) = (x \pm x') + (y \pm y')i,$$
(2') $$(x + yi) \cdot (x' + y'i) = xx' + (xy' + yx')i + yy'i^2.$$

Since $i^2 = -1$, we get from (2')

(2'') $$(x + yi) \cdot (x' + y'i) = (xx' - yy') + (xy' + yx')i.$$

It is a corollary that the subdomain of D generated by **R** and i contains all elements of the form $x + yi$ and no others.

Again, $(x + yi) = (x' + y'i)$ implies $(x - x') = (y' - y)i$; hence squaring both sides, $(x - x')^2 = -(y' - y)^2$. And since $(x - x')^2 \geqq 0$, $-(y' - y)^2 \leqq 0$, this is impossible unless $x = x'$, $y = y'$. In summary, distinct couples (x, y) of real numbers determine distinct elements $x + yi$ of D. This establishes a one-one correspondence of the form $(x, y) \leftrightarrow x + yi$ between the elements of $\mathbf{C}$ and those of the subdomain of D generated by $\mathbf{R}$ and i. Finally, comparing formulas (1′)–(2″) with (1)–(2), we see that the correspondence preserves sums and products, hence is an isomorphism. This proves

Theorem 1. *Let D be any integral domain containing the real number system $\mathbf{R}$ and a square root i of -1. Then the subdomain of D generated by $\mathbf{R}$ and i is isomorphic with $\mathbf{C}$.*

We now prove our conjecture that there does indeed exist an integral domain D which contains the real numbers and a square root of -1.

Theorem 2. *The complex number system, as defined above, is a field containing a subfield isomorphic to $\mathbf{R}$ and a root of $x^2 + 1 = 0$.*

Proof. For the couples (x, y), the commutative and associative laws of addition, the fact that $(0, 0)$ is an additive identity, and the fact that $(-x, -y)$ is an additive inverse of (x, y) are immediate consequences of the fact that *real* and *imaginary* components are added independently, while the corresponding laws hold for them.

Similarly, the commutative and associative laws of multiplication, the facts that $(1, 0)$ is a multiplicative identity, and that every $(x, y) \neq (0, 0)$ has a multiplicative inverse

$$(3) \qquad (x, y)^{-1} = (x/(x^2 + y^2), -y/(x^2 + y^2))$$

follow from the fact to be established in §2, that "arguments" and "absolute values" of complex numbers combine independently under multiplication and themselves satisfy the same laws. But at the present stage, it is preferable to check these laws by direct substitution in the definition (2)—only the calculation for the associative law is long-winded. We omit the details.

Finally, we can check the distributive law by similar direct substitution. Thus let $z = (x, y)$, $z' = (x', y')$, $z'' = (x'', y'')$. Then substituting in (1)–(2),

$$z(z' + z'') = (x, y)(x' + x'', y' + y'')$$
$$= (x(x' + x'') - y(y' + y''), x(y' + y'') + y(x' + x'')),$$
$$zz' + zz'' = (xx' - yy', xy' + yx') + (xx'' - yy'', xy'' + yx'')$$
$$= (xx' - yy' + xx'' - yy'', xy' + yx' + xy'' + yx'');$$

from this $z(z' + z'') = zz' + zz''$ can be checked directly.

In this field $\mathbf{C}$ of couples of numbers one may find a subfield of real numbers by exploiting the correspondence $(x, y) \leftrightarrow x + yi$, used in Theorem 1, in which the real numbers x correspond to couples with second term zero and the couple $(0, 1)$ to i. Specifically, if the second components y and y' in the definitions (1) and (2) are both zero, then the first components x and x' add and multiply just as do the real numbers x and x'. This is just the recognition that the correspondence $x \leftrightarrow (x, 0)$ is an isomorphism of the field $\mathbf{R}$ of reals to a subset of $\mathbf{C}$. We agree, as in previous cases, that each such special complex number $(x, 0)$ is simply to be identified with the corresponding real number x.

Finally, the desired square root of -1 is presumably the couple $(0, 1)$; and in fact, a special case of the definition (2) shows that $(0, 1)^2 = (-1, 0) = -1$. Hence we *define* i to be the couple $(0, 1)$. Any couple (x, y) then has the form

$$(4) \qquad (x, y) = (x, 0) + (0, y) = (x, 0) + (y, 0)(0, 1) = x + yi$$

The notation $x + yi$ is so suggestive that we shall usually employ it instead of (x, y) in the sequel. For brevity, we shall also often write $z = (x, y) = x + yi$, $w = (u, v) = u + vi$, $c = (a, b) = a + bi$, and so on—in other words, we use a single letter to denote a complex number, and the two immediately preceding letters of the alphabet for its real and imaginary components.

EXERCISES

1. Check that complex multiplication is commutative and associative.
2. Check that $(x, y)(x, y)^{-1} = (1, 0)$ holds if formula (3) is used.
3. Solve $(1, 1)(x, y) = (2, 1)$:
    (a) as a pair of simultaneous linear equations in x and y;
    (b) using (3).
4. Find complex numbers $z = x + yi$ and $w = u + vi$ which satisfy
    (a) $z + iw = 1$, $iz + w = 1 + i$,
    (b) $(1 + i)z - iw = 3 + i$, $(2 + i)z + (2 - i)w = 2i$.
5. Find all complex roots of $z^2 = -a$, where a is any positive real number. Justify your answer.
6. Describe the subfield of $\mathbf{C}$ which is generated by i and the *rational* numbers.
7. Is Theorem 1 still true if D is a commutative ring? Give details.
8. (a) Show that $z^2 = a + ib$ has solutions $z = x + iy$ with

    $$x = [(1/2)(a + \sqrt{a^2 + b^2})]^{1/2}, \qquad y = b/(2x).$$

    (b) Show also that $y = [(1/2)(\sqrt{a^2 + b^2} - a)]^{1/2}$, $x = b/(2y)$. (Note that the formulas (b) are more accurate for numerical computation when a is negative and b/a small.)
9. The equation $z^3 + 3iz = 3 + i$ has $-i$ for one root. Compute one other root in decimal form.
★10. Show that if F is any ordered field, then there exists a larger field F^* containing a subfield isomorphic to F and a square root of -1.

★11. Using the methods of Theorems 1 and 2, show without recourse to the real numbers that the rational field **Q** can be extended to a larger field $\mathbf{Q}(\sqrt{2})$ containing **Q** and a square root of 2.

12. Show that there is no possible definition of "positive complex number" which would make **C** an ordered field.

2. The Complex Plane

There is a fundamental one-one mapping of the complex numbers onto the points of a Cartesian plane. Namely, each complex number $z = x + iy$ is mapped onto the point $P = (x, y)$ with the real component x of z as abscissa and the imaginary component y as ordinate.

Polar coordinates may be used in this plane. We may recall that each point P of the plane and hence each complex number z is uniquely determined by the two polar coordinates r and θ, where r is the (nonnegative) length of the segment $\overline{Oz}$ joining the point P to the origin, while θ is the angle from the x-axis to this segment (Figure 1), so

Figure 1

$$(5) \qquad \begin{aligned} |z| &= r = (x^2 + y^2)^{1/2}, \\ \arg z &= \theta = \tan^{-1} y/x. \end{aligned}$$

One calls r the *absolute value* of the complex number z and θ the *argument* of z. They determine x and y by

$$(6) \qquad x = r \cos \theta, \qquad y = r \sin \theta, \qquad z = r(\cos \theta + i \sin \theta),$$

the usual laws for the transformation from polar to rectangular coordinates. One also writes (6) in the form $z = re^{i\theta}$, since the usual Taylor series expansion gives

$$e^{i\theta} = 1 + i\theta + \frac{(-1)\theta^2}{2!} + \frac{(-i)\theta^3}{3!} + \cdots$$
$$= \cos \theta + i \sin \theta.$$

The importance of the absolute values and arguments rests largely on de Moivre's formulas, which may be stated as follows:

Theorem 3. *The absolute value of a product of complex numbers is the product of the absolute values of the factors; the argument is the sum of the arguments of the factors; in other words,*

$$(7) \qquad |zz'| = |z| \cdot |z'|, \qquad \arg zz' = \arg z + \arg z'.$$

Proof.　As in (6), $z = r(\cos \theta + i \sin \theta)$, $z' = r'(\cos \theta' + i \sin \theta')$. Substituting in the definition (2), we get

$$zz' = rr'[(\cos \theta \cos \theta' - \sin \theta \sin \theta') + i(\cos \theta \sin \theta' + \sin \theta \cos \theta')];$$

by well-known trigonometric formulas this is equivalent to

$$zz' = rr'[\cos (\theta + \theta') + i \sin (\theta + \theta')].$$

This gives the result (7).

Not only the multiplicative, but the additive properties of (inequalities on) absolute values are valid for complex as well as real numbers. That is,

(8) $$|z| > 0 \quad \text{unless } z = 0, \quad |0| = 0;$$
(9) $$|z + z'| \le |z| + |z'|.$$

To prove these, note that formula (1) means that the sum $z + z'$ may be found by drawing (Figure 2) the parallelogram with three vertices at z, 0, and z'; the fourth vertex will be $z + z'$. Formulas (8)–(9) now follow from the identity between absolute values and geometrical lengths.

Complex nth roots of unity may be found using trigonometry. From de Moivre's formulas (7) one sees immediately that

$$[r(\cos \theta + i \sin \theta)]^{-1} = (1/r)[\cos (-\theta) + i \sin (-\theta)].$$

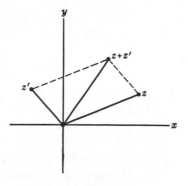

Figure 2

Further, one sees that $z^n = 1$ if and only if $|z|^n = 1$ and $n \cdot \arg z$ is an integral multiple $2k\pi$ of 2π. Since $|z| \ge 0$, $|z| = 1$. Since $\arg z$ is single-valued on $0 \le \theta < 2\pi$, there are thus precisely n solutions for $z^n = 1$; in rectangular coordinates they are 1, $\cos 2\pi/n + i \sin 2\pi/n$, $\cdots$, $\cos 2\pi(n - 1)/n + i \sin 2\pi(n - 1)/n$. If we denote $\cos 2\pi/n + i \sin 2\pi/n$ by ω, we obtain another representation of these nth roots of unity as 1, ω, ω^2, $\cdots$, ω^{n-1}. Geometrically stated, this is

Theorem 4.　*The complex nth roots of unity are the vertices of a regular polygon of n sides inscribed in the unit circle $|z| = 1$.*

Consider more generally the equation $z^n = c$, where $c \ne 0$ is any complex number. In polar coordinates, one solution of this is

$$z_0 = |c|^{1/n}(\cos \theta + i \sin \theta), \quad \text{with} \quad \theta = (1/n) \arg c.$$

Furthermore, wz_0 is also a root of $x^n = c$ if and only if $c = (wz_0)^n = w^n z_0^n = w^n c$, whence $w^n = 1$. Thus the nth roots of c are z_0, ωz_0, $\omega^2 z_0$, $\cdots$,

$\omega^{n-1}z_0$, where ω is as defined above. In particular, they are also represented by the vertices of a regular polygon.

One can easily compute the nth roots z_0, ωz_0, $\cdots$, $\omega^{n-1}z_0$ of $c = a + bi$ numerically, with the aid of logarithmic and trigonometric tables. From the identity

$$\log |z_0| = \log |c|^{1/n} = (1/n) \log (a^2 + b^2)^{1/2} = (1/2n) \log (a^2 + b^2)$$

one can compute $|z_0|$. By de Moivre's formula (7), arg z_0 equals $(1/n)$ $\tan^{-1} (b/a)$, and arg $\omega^k z_0 = (1/n) \tan^{-1} (b/a) + 360k/n$ in degrees. The computation is completed by the formula

$$z = r(\cos \theta + i \sin \theta) = |z| \cos (\arg z) + i |z| \sin (\arg z).$$

Each complex nth root of unity ω satisfies a polynomial equation with rational coefficients irreducible over the field of rationals. These equations, known as the "cyclotomic" equations, play an important role in the theory of equations.

By definition, every nth root of unity satisfies $z^n - 1 = 0$; moreover, all except $z = 1$ satisfy

$$(10) \quad q_n(z) = (z^n - 1)/(z - 1) = z^{n-1} + z^{n-2} + \cdots + z + 1 = 0.$$

An argument which will not be given here shows that $q_p(z)$ is irreducible if $n = p$ is a prime.

If n is not a prime, the facts are less simple. Thus, if $n = 4$, $z^3 + z^2 + z + 1 = (z + 1)(z^2 + 1)$ is reducible. In general, we can factor out from (10) the cyclotomic polynomials satisfied by kth roots of unity, where k runs through the proper divisors of n. The nth roots of unity which are not also kth roots of unity for some $k < n$ are called *primitive nth roots of unity*. (Thus, the primitive fourth roots of unity are i and $-i$.) They are the ω^m with m relatively prime to n, and they all satisfy the same irreducible equation over the rational field. But the proof of this result, and the computation of the degree of this equation, involve more number theory than is desirable here.

EXERCISES

1. Prove the commutative and associative laws of multiplication and the existence of multiplicative inverses from de Moivre's formulas.
2. Describe geometrically the correspondence $z \rightarrow zi$.
3. Find to 4 decimal places (using trigonometric tables) the real and imaginary components of the cube roots and the fifth roots of unity.
4. Find to 4 decimal places the cube and fourth roots of $2 + 2i$.
5. List the primitive twelfth roots of unity, and plot them on graph paper, drawing a large "unit circle."

6. Describe geometrically the effect of transformations $z \to cz + d$ $(c, d \in \mathbf{C}$, $c \neq 0)$. What if $|c| = 1$? (*Hint:* Use the words "translation," "rotation," and "expansion.")

7. Find the irreducible factors of $z^6 - 1$ over $\mathbf{Q}$ (the rationals).

8. (a) Prove that $\omega = \cos{(2\pi/n)} + i\sin{(2\pi/n)}$ is a primitive nth root of unity.
   (b) Prove that ω^m is a primitive nth root of unity if and only if m is relatively prime to n.

3. Fundamental Theorem of Algebra

We saw in §1 that the complex number system is obtained by adjoining to the real number system $\mathbf{R}$ an imaginary root i of the equation $z^2 + 1 = 0$. But why stop here? Why not try to add "imaginary" roots of other polynomial equations so as to get still larger fields?

The answer is contained in the so called "Fundamental Theorem of Algebra": as soon as i is adjoined, every polynomial equation *has* actual (complex) roots, so that one does not need to invent imaginary ones to solve equations.

Theorem 5 (Euler-Gauss). *Every polynomial $p(z)$ of positive degree with complex coefficients has a complex root.*

Many proofs of this celebrated theorem are known.[†] All proofs involve nonalgebraic concepts like those introduced in Chap. IV; we have selected one whose nonalgebraic part is especially plausible intuitively. We do not prove the nonalgebraic part in detail from the relevant axioms of Chap. IV.

Proof. Since $p(z) = a_m z^m + a_{m-1} z^{m-1} + \cdots + a_0$, with $a_m \neq 0$, has the same roots as

$$\begin{aligned} q(z) &= z^m + (a_{m-1}/a_m)z^{m-1} + \cdots + (a_0/a_m) \\ &= z^m + c_{m-1} z^{m-1} + \cdots + c_0, \end{aligned}$$

only the case where the leading coefficient is unity need be discussed.

In this case let us picture *two* complex planes, labeling one the "z-plane," and the other the "w-plane." The given function $q(z)$ maps each point $z_0 = (x_0, y_0)$ of the z-plane onto a point $w_0 = q(z_0)$ of the w-plane. Moreover if z describes a continuous curve on the z-plane, then $q(z)$ (being differentiable) will describe a continuous curve on the w-plane. Our object is to show that the origin 0 of the w-plane is the "image" $q(z)$ of some z on the z-plane—or, what is the same thing, that the image of some circle on the z-plane passes through 0.

For each fixed $r > 0$, the function $w = q(re^{i\theta})$ defines a closed curve γ_r' in the w-plane: the image of the circle γ_r: $|z| = r$ $(z = re^{i\theta})$ of radius r and center 0 in the z-plane. For each fixed r, consider the Riemann

---

[†] Cf., for example, L. E. Dickson, *New First Course in the Theory of Equations* (New York: Wiley, 1939), Appendix, or L. Weisner, *Introduction to the Theory of Equations,* (New York: Macmillan, 1938), p. 145.

integral†

$$\phi(r, \theta) = \int_0^\theta d(\arg w) = \int_0^\theta (u\,dv - v\,du)/(u^2 + v^2);$$

this is defined for any γ_r' *not* passing through the origin $w = 0$. (If γ_r'

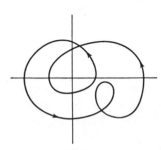

passes through $w = 0$, the conclusion of Theorem 5 is immediate.) It is geometrically obvious that $\phi(r, 2\pi) = 2\pi n(r)$, where the *winding number* $n(r)$ is the number of times that γ_r' winds counterclockwise around the origin.

Now consider the variation of $n(r)$ with r. Since $q(re^{i\theta})$ is a continuous function, $n(r)$ varies continuously with r except when γ_r' passes through the origin. Again, $n(0) = 0$ (unless $c_0 = 0$ in which case 0 is a root). Now

Figure 3

assume $c_0 \neq 0$. We shall now show that if r is large enough, $n(r)$ is the *degree m* of $q(z)$. Indeed, let

$$q(z) = z^m + c_{m-1}z^{m-1} + \cdots + c_1 z + c_0 = z^m \left(1 + \sum_{k=1}^m c_{m-k}z^{-k}\right).$$

By de Moivre's formulas (7),

$$\arg q(z) = m \arg z + \arg \left(1 + \sum_{k=1}^m c_{m-k}z^{-k}\right).$$

Hence, as z describes the circle γ_r counterclockwise, the net change in $\arg q(z)$ is the sum of m times the change in $\arg z$ (which is $m \cdot 2\pi$) plus the change in

$$\arg \left(1 + \sum_k c_{m-k}z^{-k}\right).$$

But if $|z| = r$ is sufficiently large, by formulas (8) and (9)

$$1 + \sum_k c_{m-k}z^{-k} = u$$

stays in the circle $|u - 1| < 1/2$, and so goes around the origin zero times (make a figure to illustrate this).

We conclude that, if r is large enough, $n(r) = m$: the total change in $\arg q(z)$ is $2\pi m$. But as r changes, γ_r' is deformed continuously (since $q(z)$ is continuous). It is geometrically evident,‡ however, that a curve which winds around the origin $n \neq 0$ times cannot be continuously deformed into a point without being made to pass through the origin at some stage

---

† In proving the existence of Riemann integrals, essential use is made of the *completeness* of **R**. The identity $(d \arg w) = (u\,dv - v\,du)/(u^2 + v^2)$ holds since $\arg w = \arctan(v/u)$.
‡ This is proved as a theorem in plane topology; cf., for example, S. Lefschetz, *Introduction to Topology* (Princeton University Press, 1949), p. 127.

of the deformation. It follows that, for some r, $\gamma_r{}'$ must pass through the origin; where this happens, $q(z) = 0!$ Q.E.D.

As a corollary, we note that if $p(z_1) = 0$, then by the Remainder Theorem (Chap. III) we can write $p(z) = (z - z_1)r(z)$. If the degree m of $p(z)$ exceeds 1, the quotient $r(z)$ has positive degree, hence also has a complex root $z = z_2$. Proceeding thus, we find m linear factors for $p(z)$, as

$$(11) \qquad p(z) = c(z - z_1)(z - z_2) \cdots (z - z_m).$$

It follows that *the only irreducible polynomials over* **C** *are linear.* A corollary of this and the unique factorization theorem of Chap. III is

Theorem 6. *Any polynomial with complex coefficients can be written in one and only one way in the form (11).*

The roots of $p(z)$ are evidently the z_i in (11)—since a product vanishes if and only if one of its factors is zero. If a factor $(z - z_i)$ occurs repeatedly, the number of its occurrences is called the *multiplicity* of the root z_i. It can also be defined, using the calculus, as the "order" to which $p(z)$ vanishes at z_i: the greatest integer ν such that $p(z)$ and its first $(\nu - 1)$ derivatives all vanish at z_i.

EXERCISES

1. Prove the uniqueness of the decomposition (11) without using the general uniqueness theorem of Chap. III.
2. Prove that any rational complex function which is finite for all z is a polynomial.
3. Do couples (w, z) of complex numbers when added and multiplied by rules (1)–(2) form a commutative ring? A field?
4. Show that any quadratic polynomial can be brought to one of the forms $cz(z - 1)$ or cz^2 by a suitable automorphism of **C**$[z]$.
5. (a) Using the MacLaurin series, show formally that $e^{ix} = \cos x + i \sin x$.
   (b) Show that every complex number can be written as $re^{i\theta}$.
   (c) Derive the identities $\cos z = (e^{iz} + e^{-iz})/2$, $\sin z = (e^{iz} - e^{-iz})/2i$.
6. Use partial fractions to show that any rational function over the field **C** can be written as a sum of a polynomial plus rational functions in which each numerator is a constant and each denominator a power of a linear function.
7. Factor $z^2 + z + 1 + i$.

4. Conjugate Numbers and Real Polynomials

In the complex field **C**, the equation $z^2 = -1$ has two roots i and $-i = 0 + (-1)i$. The correspondence $x + yi \rightarrow x + y(-i) = x - yi$ carries the first of these roots into the second and conversely, while leaving all real numbers unchanged. Furthermore, this correspondence carries sums into sums and products into products, as may be checked either by direct substitution in formulas (1) and (2) or by application of Theorem 1. In other words, the correspondence is an *automorphism* of **C** (an isomorphism of **C** with itself).

We can state this more compactly as follows. By the "conjugate" z^* of a complex number $z = x + yi$, we mean the number $x - yi$. The correspondence $z \rightarrow z^*$ is an automorphism of period two of **C**, in the sense that

$$(12) \qquad (z_1 + z_2)^* = z_1^* + z_2^*, \qquad (z_1 z_2)^* = z_1^* z_2^*, \qquad (z^*)^* = z.$$

It amounts geometrically to a reflection of the complex plane in the x-axis; the only numbers which are equal to their conjugates are the real numbers.

Conjugate complex numbers are very useful in mathematics and physics (especially in wave mechanics). In using them, it is convenient to memorize such simple formulas as

$$|z|^2 = zz^*, \qquad z^{-1} = z^*/|z|^2.$$

Their use enables one to derive the factorization theory of real polynomials easily out of Theorem 6.

Lemma. *The nonreal complex roots of a polynomial equation with real coefficients occur in conjugate pairs.*

This generalizes the well-known fact that a quadratic $ax^2 + bx + c$ with *discriminant* $b^2 - 4ac < 0$ has two roots $x = (-b \pm \sqrt{b^2 - 4ac})/2a$ which are complex conjugates.

Proof. Let $p(z)$ be the given polynomial; we can write it in the form (11), where the z_i are complex (not usually real). Since the correspondence $z_i \rightarrow z_i^*$ applied to these roots z_i is an automorphism, it carries $p(z)$ into another polynomial $p^*(z) = c^*(z - z_1^*)(z - z_2^*) \cdots (z - z_n^*)$ in which each coefficient is the conjugate of the corresponding coefficient of $p(z)$. But since the coefficients of $p(z)$ are real, $p(z) = p^*(z)$. Hence, the expansion (11) being unique, $c = c^*$ is real, and the z_i are also real or complex conjugate in pairs.

Theorem 7. *Any polynomial with real coefficients can be factored into (real) linear polynomials and (real) quadratic polynomials with negative discriminant.*

Proof. The real z_i in the lemma give (real) linear factors $(z - z_i)$. A pair of conjugate complex roots $a + bi$ and $a - bi$ with $b \neq 0$ may be combined as in

$$(z - (a + bi))(z - (a - bi)) = z^2 - 2az + (a^2 + b^2)$$

to give a quadratic factor of $p(z)$ with real coefficients and with a real discriminant $4a^2 - 4(a^2 + b^2) = -4b^2 < 0$. Q.E.D.

Conversely, linear polynomials and quadratic polynomials with negative discriminant are irreducible over the real field (the latter since it has only complex roots, and hence no linear factors). It is a corollary that the factorization described in Theorem 7 is unique.

EXERCISES

1. Solve

$$\text{(a)} \ (1 + i)z + 3iz^* = 2 + i,$$
$$\text{(b)} \ zz^* + 2z = 3 + i,$$
$$\text{(c)} \ zz^* + 3(z - z^*) = 4 - 3i.$$

2. Solve $\quad zz^* + 3(z + z^*) = 7, \quad zz^* + 3(z + z^*) = 3i.$

3. Solve simultaneously

$$iz + (1 + i)w = 3 + i, \qquad (1 + i)z^* - (6 + i)w^* = 4.$$

4. Give an independent proof of Corollary 2 of Theorem 4, Chap. IV.

5. Show that if one adjoins to the real number system an imaginary root of *any* irreducible nonlinear real polynomial, one gets a field isomorphic with **C**.

6. Show that, over any ordered field, $ax^2 + bx + c$ is irreducible if $b^2 - 4ac < 0$.

7. Show that every automorphism of **C** in which the real numbers are all left fixed is either the identity automorphism $(z \to z)$ or the automorphism $z \to z^*$.

*5. Quadratic and Cubic Equations

In §3 we proved the existence of roots for any polynomial equation with complex coefficients, but did not show how to calculate roots effectively. We shall now show how to do this for polynomials of degrees two and three. The procedures will involve only the four rational operations (addition, multiplication, subtraction, and division) and the extraction of nth roots. We showed how to perform these operations on complex numbers in §§1–2; the procedure to be used now will also apply to any other field in which nth roots of arbitrary numbers can be constructed and in which $1 + 1 \neq 0$ and $1 + 1 + 1 \neq 0$.

Quadratic equations can be solved by "completing the square" as in high school algebra. Such an equation

$$(13) \qquad\qquad az^2 + bz + c = 0 \qquad (a \neq 0),$$

is equivalent to (has the same roots as) the simpler equation

$$(14) \qquad\qquad z^2 + Bz + C = 0, \qquad (B = b/a, \ C = c/a).$$

If one sets $w = z + B/2$ (that is, $z = w - B/2$), so as to complete the square, one sees that (14) is equivalent to

$$(15) \qquad\qquad w^2 = B^2/4 - C.$$

Substituting back z, a, b, c for w, B, C, this gives

$$(16) \qquad z = w - B/2 = (-b + \sqrt{b^2 - 4ac})/(2a)$$

and so yields two solutions, by §2.

Cubic equations can be solved similarly. First reduce the cubic, as in Chap. IV, (7), to the form

$$(17) \qquad z^3 + pz + q = 0.$$

Then make Vieta's substitution $z = w - p/(3w)$. The result (after cancellation) is

$$(18) \qquad w^3 - p^3/(27w^3) + q = 0.$$

Multiplying through by w^3, we get a quadratic in w^3, which can be solved by (16), giving

$$(19) \qquad w^3 = -q/2 + \sqrt{q^2/4 + p^3/27} \qquad \text{(two values)}.$$

This gives *six* solutions for w in the form of cube roots. Substituting these in the formula $z = w - p/(3w)$, we get three pairs of solutions for z, paired solutions being equal.

It is interesting to relate the preceding formulas to Theorem 6. Thus, in the quadratic case, writing $z^2 + Bz + C = (z - z_1)(z - z_2)$, we have

$$(20) \quad z_1 + z_2 = -B, \qquad z_1 z_2 = C, \qquad \text{whence} \qquad (z_1 - z_2)^2 = B^2 - 4C.$$

The quantity $B^2 - 4C = D$ is the discriminant of (14). In terms of the original coefficients of (13), $D = (b^2 - 4ac)/a^2$.

Similarly, if z_1, z_2, z_3 are the roots of the reduced cubic equation (17),

$$(21) \quad z_1 + z_2 + z_3 = 0, \qquad z_1 z_2 + z_2 z_3 + z_3 z_1 = p, \qquad z_1 z_2 z_3 = -q.$$

Combining the first two relations, we get the formulas

$$(22) \quad p = z_1 z_2 - z_3^2, \qquad (z_1 - z_2)^2 = -4p - 3z_3^2, \qquad z_1^2 + z_2^2 + z_3^2 = -2p.$$

We now define the *discriminant* of a cubic equation by

$$(23) \quad D = \prod_{i<j} (z_i - z_j)^2 = P^2, \qquad \text{where} \qquad P = (z_1 - z_2)(z_2 - z_3)(z_1 - z_3).$$

Squaring P, and using the second relation of (22), we get after some calculation

$$(24) \qquad D = -4p^3 - 27q^2,$$

which can be used to simplify (19).

Theorem 8. *A quadratic or cubic equation with real coefficients has real roots if its discriminant is nonnegative, and two imaginary roots if its discriminant is negative.*

Proof. By the Corollary of Theorem 7 either all roots are real or there are two conjugate imaginary roots $z_1 = x_1 + iy$, and $z_2 = x_1 - iy$. If all roots are real, $(z_i - z_j)^2 \geq 0$ for all $i \neq j$, and so $D \geq 0$. In the opposite case $(z_1 - z_2)^2 = -4y^2 < 0$ and, since $z_3 = x_3$ is real, $(z_1 - z_3)(z_2 - z_3) = (x_1 - x_3)^2 + y^2 > 0$, so that $D < 0$. Q.E.D.

By (23), the condition $D = 0$ gives a simple test for multiple roots.

EXERCISES

1. Prove that for any (complex) y, p there exists a z satisfying $y = z - p/3z$. How many exist?

2. Solve in radicals

(a) $z^2 + iz = 2$, (b) $z^3 + 3iz = 1 + i$, (c) $z^3 + 3iz^2 = 10i$.

3. Convert one root in Exs. 2(a)–2(c) into decimal form.

4. (a) Prove (22); (b) Prove (24).

★**5.** (a) Show that $\sinh 3\gamma = \sinh (3\gamma + 2\pi i)$.

(b) Using formula (9a) on p. 76, show that $4z^3 + 3z = C$ has, besides the real root $\sinh [1/3 \ \sinh^{-1} C] = \sinh \gamma$, also the complex roots $-1/3 \cosh \gamma \pm i \sqrt{3}/2 \sinh \gamma$.

6. Let $\omega = e^{2\pi i/5}$ be a primitive fifth root of unity, and let $\zeta = \omega + 1/\omega$.

(a) Show that $\zeta^2 + \zeta = 1$.

(b) Infer that in a regular pentagon with center at $(0, 0)$ and one vertex at $(1, 0)$, the x-coordinate of either adjacent vertex is $(\sqrt{5} - 1)/4$.

VI. Groups

1. Symmetries of the Square

The idea of "symmetry" is familiar to every educated person. But fewer people realize that there is a consequential algebra of symmetry. This algebra will now be introduced in the concrete case of the symmetries of the square.

Imagine a cardboard square laid on a plane with fixed axes, so that the center of the square falls on the origin of coordinates, and one side is horizontal. It is clear that the square has rotational symmetry: it is carried into itself by the following rigid motions.

R: a 90° rotation clockwise around its center O.
R', R'': similar rotations through 180° and 270°.

The square also has reflective symmetry; it can be carried into itself by the following rigid reflections.

H: a reflection in the horizontal axis through O.
V: a reflection in the vertical axis through O.
D: a reflection in the diagonal in quadrants I and III.
D': a reflection in the diagonal in quadrants II and IV.

Our list thus includes seven symmetries so far.

The algebra of symmetries has its genesis in the fact that we can *multiply* two motions by performing them in succession. Thus, the product HR is obtained by first reflecting the square in a horizontal axis, then rotating clockwise through 90°. By experimenting with a square piece of cardboard, one can verify that this has the same net effect as D', reflection about the diagonal from the upper left- to the lower right-hand corner. Alternatively, the equation $HR = D'$ can be checked by noting that both sides have the same effect on each vertex of the square. Thus, in Figure 1, HR sends 1 into 4 by H and then 4 into 3 by $R-$ hence 1 into 3, just as does D'.

Similarly, RH is defined as the result of a clockwise rotation through 90° followed by reflection in a horizontal axis. (*Caution:* The plane of Figure 1, which contains the axes of reflection, is not imagined as rotated with the square.)

A computation shows that $RH = D \neq HR$, from which we conclude incidentally that our "multiplication" is not in general commutative! It is, however, associative, as we shall see in §2.

The reader will find it instructive to compute other products of symmetries of the square (a complete list is given in the table in §4). If he does this, he will discover one exception to the principle that successive applications of any two symmetries yield a third symmetry. If, for example, he multiplies R with R'', he will see that their product is a motion which leaves every point fixed: it is the so-called "identity" motion I. This is not usually considered a symmetry by nonmathematicians; nevertheless, we shall consider it a (degenerate) symmetry, in order to be able to multiply all pairs of symmetries.

In general, a symmetry of a geometrical figure is, by definition, a one-one transformation of its points which preserves distance. It can be readily seen that any symmetry of the square must carry the vertex 1 into one of the four possible vertices, and that for each such choice there are exactly two symmetries. Thus all told there are only eight symmetries, which are those we have listed.

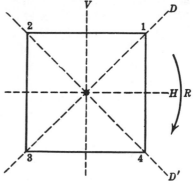

Figure 1

Not only the square, but every regular polygon and regular solid (e.g., the cube and regular icosahedron) has an interesting group of symmetries, which may be found by the elementary method sketched above.

Similarly, many ornaments have interesting symmetries. Thus consider the infinite ornamental pattern

in which the arrowheads are spaced uniformly one inch apart along a line. Three simple symmetries of this figure are T, a translation to the right by one inch, T', a translation to the left by one inch, and H, a reflection in the horizontal axis of the figure. Others (in fact, all others!) may be found by multiplying these together repeatedly.

EXERCISES

1. Compute HV, HD', $D'H$, $R'D'$, $D'R$, $R'R''$.
2. Describe TH and HT in the ornamental "arrowhead" pattern.
3. List the symmetries of an equilateral triangle, and compute five typical products.
4. List the symmetries of a general rectangle, and compute all their products.

★5. How many symmetries are possessed by the regular tetrahedron? by the regular octahedron? Draw figures.

★6. Show that any symmetry of the ornamental pattern of the text can be obtained by repeatedly multiplying H, T, and T'.

2. Groups of Transformations

The algebra of symmetry can be extended to one-one transformations of any set S of elements whatever. Although it is often suggestive to think of the set S as a "space" (e.g., a plane or a sphere) and of its elements as "points," the rules of calculation are the same no matter what S is.

Indeed, to understand clearly the algebra of symmetry, it is best to define first the general notion of a *function* or *transformation* $\phi\colon S \to T$ from a (nonempty) set S into a set T. By this is meant a rule ϕ which assigns to each element $p \in S$ a unique image element $p\phi$ in T. The notion of a transformation of S into T is thus the same as that of a function defined on the elements of the set S, with values in T, and as that of a many-one correspondence (Chap. I, §11) of the elements of S to those of T. The set S is called the *domain* of ϕ, and T its *codomain*. Note that the set $S\phi$ of all images under ϕ of elements in S, which is usually called the *range* of ϕ, may comprise only part of the codomain T.

Thus the function $f(x) = e^{2\pi i x}$ is a transformation of the set $\mathbf{R}$ of all real numbers into the set $\mathbf{C}$ of all complex numbers—although its range is the unit circle. Similarly, $g(z) = |z|$ is a transformation of $\mathbf{C}$ into $\mathbf{R}$ whose *range* or *image* consists of all nonnegative real numbers.

When the codomain of a transformation $\phi\colon S \to T$ equals its range, so that every $q \in T$ is the image $q = p\phi$ of at least one $p \in S$, ϕ is said to transform S *onto* T. Similarly, if ϕ carries distinct elements into distinct elements, so that $p\phi = p'\phi$ implies $p = p'$—or equivalently, so that each $q \in T$ is the image of at most one $p \in S$—ϕ is called *one-one* from S into T.

To illustrate these notions, consider the following transformations, ϕ_0 and ψ_0, of the set $\mathbf{Z}$ of integers into itself.

$$n\phi_0 = 2n, \quad \text{and} \quad m\psi_0 = \begin{cases} m/2 & \text{if } m \text{ is even,} \\ 0 & \text{if } m \text{ is odd.} \end{cases}$$

By the cancellation law of multiplication ϕ_0 is one-one; yet its range consists only of even integers, so that ϕ_0 does not transform $\mathbf{Z}$ onto $\mathbf{Z}$. On the other hand ψ_0 is not one-one, because all odd integers are mapped onto zero, but it does map $\mathbf{Z}$ onto $\mathbf{Z}$.

We turn now to the algebra of transformations. Two transformations $\phi\colon S \to T$ and $\phi'\colon S \to T$ with the same domain S and the same codomain T are called *equal* if they have the same effect upon every point of S; that is,

(1) $\phi = \phi'$ means that $p\phi = p\phi'$ for every $p \in S$.

The *product* or *composite* $\phi\psi$ of two transformations is again defined as the result of performing them in succession; first ϕ, then ψ, provided however that the codomain of ϕ is the domain of ψ. In other words, if

$$\phi\colon S \to T, \qquad \psi\colon T \to U,$$

then $\phi\psi$ is the transformation of S into U given by the equation

(2) $$p(\phi\psi) = (p\phi)\psi,$$

which defines the effect of $\phi\psi$ upon any point $p \in S$. In particular, the product of two transformations of S (into itself) is always defined. We shall now restrict our attention to this case, although almost all the identities proved below apply also to the general case, provided that the products involved are defined.

Multiplication of transformations conforms to the

Associative Law: $$(\phi\psi)\theta = \phi(\psi\theta),$$

whenever the products involved are defined. This is obvious intuitively: both $(\phi\psi)\theta$ and $\phi(\psi\theta)$ amount to performing first ϕ, then ψ, and finally θ, in that order. Formally, we have for each $p \in S$,

$$p[\phi(\psi\theta)] \underset{\phi(\psi\theta)}{=} (p\phi)(\psi\theta) \underset{\psi\theta}{=} [(p\phi)\psi]\theta \underset{\phi\psi}{=} [p(\phi\psi)]\theta \underset{(\phi\psi)(\theta)}{=} p[(\phi\psi)\theta],$$

where each step depends on applying the definition (2) of multiplication to the product indicated below the equality symbol for that step. By the definition (1) of equality for transformations this proves the associative law $\phi(\psi\theta) = (\phi\psi)\theta$.

The *identity* transformation $I = I_S$ on the set S is that transformation $I\colon S \to S$ which leaves every point of S fixed. This is stated algebraically in the identity

(3) $$pI = p \qquad \text{for every } p \in S.$$

From the above definitions there follows directly the

Identity Law: $$I\phi = \phi I = \phi \qquad \text{for all } \phi.$$

To see this, note that $p(I\phi) = (pI)\phi = p\phi$ for all p, and similarly, that $p(\phi I) = (p\phi)I = p\phi$.

In the choice of notation for transformations, many authors write the image of the point p under the transformation ϕ as $\phi(p)$, with the symbol for the transformation on the *left*. The product $\phi\psi$ is then defined by the analogue $(\phi\psi)(p) = \phi(\psi(p))$ of (2)—and it now means apply first ψ, then ϕ. We shall not use this notation; though either notation by itself is satisfactory, confusion between them must be avoided.

Return now to the special transformations ϕ_0 and ψ_0 defined above on the set $\mathbf{Z}$, and compute their products. Clearly $m\psi_0\phi_0 = m$ if m is even, and 0 if m is odd; hence $\psi_0\phi_0 \neq I$. On the other hand $m\phi_0\psi_0 = m$ for all $m \in \mathbf{Z}$, hence $\phi_0\psi_0 = I$. We may thus call ψ_0 a right-inverse (but not a left-inverse) of ϕ_0.

In general, if the transformations $\phi\colon S \to S$ and $\psi\colon S \to S$ have the product $\phi\psi = I\colon S \to S$, then ϕ is called a *left-inverse* of ψ, and ψ a *right-inverse* of ϕ. These definitions are closely related to the concepts of being "one-one" and "onto," as defined earlier.

Theorem 1.   *A transformation $\phi\colon S \to S$ is one-one if and only if it has a right-inverse; it is onto if and only if it has a left-inverse.*

Proof.   If ϕ has a right-inverse ψ, then $\phi\psi = I$. Hence $p\phi = p'\phi$ implies

$$p = p(\phi\psi) = (p\phi)\psi = (p'\phi)\psi = p'(\phi\psi) = p'.$$

Thus $p\phi = p'\phi$ implies $p = p'$, so that ϕ is one-one. Similarly, if ϕ has a left-inverse ψ', then $\psi'\phi = I$. Hence, any q in S can be written $q = qI = q(\psi'\phi) = (q\psi')\phi$, as the ϕ-image of a suitable point $p = q\psi'$. Therefore ϕ is onto.

Conversely, given *any* $\phi\colon S \to S$, we first construct a second transformation $\psi\colon S \to S$, as follows. For each q in S which is the image under ϕ of one or more points p of S, choose† as image $q\psi$ any one of these points p. Then $q(\psi\phi) = (q\psi)\phi = p\phi = q$, for any q of the form $p\phi$. Let ψ map the remaining points q of S in any way whatever, say on some fixed point of the (nonempty) set S.

Now if ϕ is onto, every q has the form $p\phi$, and hence $\psi\phi = I$, so that ϕ has ψ as left-inverse. On the other hand, if ϕ is one-one, then, for each p, $(p\phi)\psi$ must be the unique antecedent p of $q = p\phi$; hence $\phi\psi = I$ and ψ is a right-inverse of ϕ, as asserted.

Corollary 1.   *A transformation $\phi\colon S \to S$ is a one-one transformation of S onto S if and only if it has both a right-inverse and a left-inverse. When this is the case, any right-inverse of ϕ is equal to any left-inverse of ϕ.*

Indeed, if ϕ has a right-inverse θ and a left-inverse ψ, then

$$\theta = I\theta = (\psi\phi)\theta = \psi(\phi\theta) = \psi I = \psi.$$

Define a (two-sided) inverse of $\phi\colon S \to S$ as any transformation ϕ^{-1} which satisfies the

Inverse law: $\phi\phi^{-1} = \phi^{-1}\phi = I.$

These equations also state that ϕ^{-1} is a two-sided inverse of ϕ, hence the further corollary:

---

† In case the set of such points q is infinite, the "Axiom of Choice" asserts the possibility of making such an infinite number of choices of p, one for each q.

Corollary 2. *A transformation* $\phi\colon S \to S$ *is a one-one transformation of* S *onto itself if and only if* ϕ *has a (two-sided) inverse* ϕ^{-1}. *When this is the case, any two inverses of* ϕ *are equal, and*

$$(4) \qquad\qquad (\phi^{-1})^{-1} = \phi.$$

This corollary is what will be used below; it has an immediate direct proof. For ϕ^{-1} is simply that transformation of S which takes each point $q = p\phi$ back into its unique antecedent p. In the special case when S is finite, ϕ is one-one if and only if it is onto, so that the more elaborate discussion of left- and right-inverses is pointless in this case.

Theorem 1 and its corollaries also hold, together with their proofs, for functions $\phi\colon S \to T$ on a set into another set T. One need only observe that a left-inverse ψ or a right-inverse θ is a transformation of the second set T into S and that

$$\psi\phi = I_T\colon T \to T, \qquad \phi\theta = I_S\colon S \to S.$$

Here I_S and I_T are the identity transformations on S and T, respectively.

We are now ready to define the important concept of a group of transformations. By a *group of transformations* on a "space" S is meant any set G of one-one transformations ϕ of S onto S such that (i) the identity transformation of S is in G; (ii) if ϕ is in G, so is its inverse; (iii) if ϕ and ψ are in G, so is their product $\phi\psi$.

Theorem 2. *The set* G *of all one-one transformations of any space* S *onto itself is a group of transformations.*

Proof. Since $II = I$, the identity I on S is one-one onto, hence is in the set G, as required by condition (i) of the definition. If ϕ is in G, Corollary 2 above shows that ϕ^{-1} is also one-one onto, hence is likewise in G, as in (ii). Finally, the product of any two one-one transformations ϕ and ψ of S onto S has an inverse, for by hypothesis

$$(\phi\psi)(\psi^{-1}\phi^{-1}) = \phi(\psi\psi^{-1})\phi^{-1} = \phi I \phi^{-1} = \phi\phi^{-1} = I,$$
$$(\psi^{-1}\phi^{-1})(\phi\psi) = \psi^{-1}(\phi^{-1}\phi)\psi = \psi^{-1}I\psi = \psi^{-1}\psi = I,$$

so that $\phi\psi$ is also one-one onto, and has as inverse

$$(5) \qquad\qquad (\phi\psi)^{-1} = \psi^{-1}\phi^{-1}.$$

In words, the inverse of a product is the product of the inverses, taken in the opposite order. Q.E.D.

A one-one transformation on a finite set S is usually called a *permutation* of S. The group of all permutations of n elements is called the *symmetric group* of degree n; it evidently contains $n!$ permutations. For the image k_1 of the first element can be chosen in n ways, that of the second element can then be chosen in $n - 1$ ways from the elements not k_1, and so on.

EXERCISES

1. Compute VD, $(VD)R''$, DR'', $V(DR'')$ in the group of the square.
2. Compute similarly HR, $R'(HR)$, $R'H$, $(R'H)R$.
3. Let S consist of all real numbers (or, all points x on a line), while the transformations considered have the form $x\phi = ax + b$. In each of the following cases, find when the set of all possible ϕ's with coefficients a and b of the type indicated is a group of transformations. Give reasons.
   (a) a and b rational numbers,   (f) $a \neq 0$, a and b real numbers,
   (b) $a = 1$, b an odd integer,   (g) $a \neq 0$, a an integer, b a real number,
   (c) $a = 1$, b a positive integer or   (h) $a \neq 0$, a a real number, b an integer, zero,
   (d) $a = 1$, b an even integer,   (i) $a \neq 0$, a an integer, b an irrational number,
   (e) a an integer, $b = 0$,   (j) $a \neq 0$, a a rational, b a real number.
   In which of these groups is "multiplication" commutative?
4. Find all the transformations on a "space" S of exactly three "points." How many are there? How many of these are one-one?
5. Show that the transformation $n \to n^2$ on the set of positive integers has no left-inverse, and exhibit explicitly two right-inverses.
6. Exhibit two distinct left-inverses of the transformation $\psi_0 \colon \mathbf{Z} \to \mathbf{Z}$ defined in the text, and two right-inverses of ϕ_0.
7. Prove Corollary 2 directly in detail, without assuming Theorem 1 or Corollary 1.
8. Show that if ϕ and ψ both have right-inverses, then so does $\phi\psi$.
9. Compute $(R^{-1}(VR))^{-1}((R^{-1}D)R)$ for the group of the square.
10. Solve the equation $RXR' = D$ for the group of the square.
11. Check that, in the group of the square, $(RH)^{-1} = H^{-1}R^{-1} \neq R^{-1}H^{-1}$.
12. Find the inverse of every symmetry of the rectangle, and test the rule (5).
13. If $\phi_1, \cdots, \phi_n$ are one-one, prove that so is $\phi_1\phi_2 \cdots \phi_n$, with
$$(\phi_1\phi_2 \cdots \phi_n)^{-1} = \phi_n^{-1}\phi_{n-1}^{-1}, \cdots, \phi_1^{-1}.$$
14. Show that for any $\phi \colon S \to S$, the transformation ψ constructed in the second part of the proof of Theorem 1 satisfies $\phi\psi\phi = \phi$.
★15. Show that a transformation $\phi \colon S \to S$ which has a unique right-inverse or a unique left-inverse is necessarily a one-one transformation of S onto S.

3. Further Examples

The symmetries of a cube form another interesting group. Geometrically speaking, these symmetries are the one-one transformations which preserve distances on the cube. They are known as "isometries," and are 48 in number. To see this, note that any initial vertex can be carried into any one of the eight vertices. After the transform of any one vertex has been fixed, the three adjacent vertices can be permuted in any of six ways, giving $6 \cdot 8 = 48$ possibilities. When one vertex and the three adjacent vertices occupy known positions, every point of the cube is in fixed position, so the whole symmetry is known. Hence the cube has exactly 48 symmetries. Many of them have special geometrical properties, such as the one which reflects each point into the diametrically opposite point.

A familiar group containing an infinite number of transformations is the so-called Euclidean group. This consists of the "isometries" of the plane—or, in the language of elementary geometry, of the transformations under which the plane is congruent to itself. It is made up of products of translations, rigid rotations, and reflections; it will be discussed in greater detail in Chap. IX.

Another group consists of the "similarity" transformations of space—those one-one transformations which multiply all distances by a constant factor $k > 0$ (a factor of proportionality). The rigid motions of the surface of any sphere into itself again constitute a group.

The isometries of the plane leaving invariant a regular hexagonal net-work (Figure 2) form another interesting group.

Again, a rubber band held in a straight line between fixed endpoints P and Q may be deformed in many ways along this line. All such deformations form a group (the group of so-called "homeomorphisms" of the segment PQ).

Figure 2

Generally speaking, those one-one transformations of any set of elements which preserve any given property or properties of these elements form a group. Felix Klein (*Erlanger Programm*, 1872) has eloquently described how the different branches of geometry can be regarded as the study of those properties of suitable spaces which are preserved under appropriate groups of transformations. Thus Euclidean geometry deals with those properties of space preserved under all isometries, and topology with those which are preserved under all homeomorphisms. Similarly, "projective" and "affine" geometry deals with the properties which are preserved under the "projective" and "affine" groups to be defined in Chap. IX.

EXERCISES

1. Describe all the symmetries of a wheel with six equally spaced radial spokes.

2. Describe the six symmetries of a cube with one vertex held fixed.

3. Let S, T be reflections of a cube in planes parallel to distinct faces. Describe ST geometrically.

4. Describe some isometries of the plane which carry the hexagonal network of Figure 2 onto itself.

5. Do the same for a network of squares. Can you enumerate all such transformations (this is difficult)?

6. Do the same for the network of equilateral triangles, and relate this to the group of Ex. 1.

7. Do the same for an infinite cylinder, for a finite cylinder, for a helix wound around the cylinder making a constant angle with the axis of the cylinder.

★8. Show that the transformations $x \rightarrow x' = (ax + b)/(cx + d)$, with $ad - bc = 1$ and with coefficients in any field F, constitute a group acting on the set consisting of the elements of F and a symbolic element ∞.

4. Abstract Groups

Groups of transformations are by no means the only systems with a multiplication which satisfies the associative, identity, and inverse laws of §2. For instance, the non-zero numbers of any field (e.g., of the rational, real, or complex field) satisfy them. The product of any two non-zero numbers is a non-zero number; the associative law holds; the unit 1 of the field satisfies the identity law, and $1/x = x^{-1}$ satisfies the inverse law.

Similarly, the elements (including zero, this time) of any integral domain satisfy our laws when combined under addition. Thus, any two elements have a uniquely determinate sum; addition is associative; while zero satisfies the identity law, and $-x$ the inverse law, relative to addition. In other words, the elements of any integral domain form a group under addition.

It is convenient to introduce the abstract concept of a group to include these and other instances.

Definition. *A group G is a system of elements which is closed under a single-valued binary operation which is associative, and relative to which G contains an element satisfying the identity law, and with each element another element (called its inverse) satisfying the inverse law.*

Groups can be defined abstractly, without reference to transformations, in many ways; groups so defined are often called *abstract* groups.

In discussing abstract groups, elements will be denoted by small Latin letters $a, b, c, \cdots$. The product notation "ab" will ordinarily be used to denote the result of applying the group operation to two elements a and b of G—but other notations, such as "$a + b$" and "$a \circ b$," are equally valid. In the product notation, with "e" for the identity, the three laws defining groups become

Associative law:	$a(bc) = (ab)c$	for all	$a, b, c;$
Identity law:	$ae = ea = a$	for all	$a;$
Inverse law:	$aa^{-1} = a^{-1}a = e$	for each a and some $a^{-1}.$	

A group whose operation satisfies the commutative law is called a "commutative" or "Abelian" group. Using this concept, we can restate the definition of a field as follows.

Definition. *A field is a system F of elements closed under two uniquely defined binary operations, addition and multiplication, such that*
 (i) under addition, F is a commutative group with identity O;
 (ii) under multiplication, the nonzero elements form a commutative group;
 (iii) the distributive law holds: $a(b + c) = ab + ac$.

For the postulates just given include all those previously stated for a field, except for the associative law for products with a factor 0; this can be verified in detail.

Some of the results of the first sections of Chaps. I–II will now appear as corollaries of the following theorem on groups.

Theorem 3. *In any group, $xa = b$ and $ay = b$ have the unique solutions $x = ba^{-1}$ and $y = a^{-1}b$. Hence $ca = da$ implies $c = d$, and so does $ac = ad$ (cancellation law).*

Proof. Clearly, $(ba^{-1})a = b(a^{-1}a) = be = b$ and, similarly, $a(a^{-1}b) = b$. Conversely, $xa = b$ implies $x = xe = xaa^{-1} = ba^{-1}$ and, similarly, $ay = b$ implies $y = a^{-1}b$.

Note that in this proof a^{-1} is not assumed to be the only element satisfying $ax = e = xa$; we merely assume that $ax = e = xa$ has at least one solution $x = a^{-1}$.

Since in any group G the equations $ex = e$ and $ay = e$ have by Theorem 3 the unique solutions $x = e$ and $y = a^{-1}$, we get the

Corollary. *A group has only one identity element, and only one inverse a^{-1} for each element a.*

Theorem 4. *In the preceding definition of a group, the identity and inverse laws can be replaced by the weaker laws,*
Left-identity: *For some e, $ea = a$ for all a;*
Left-inverse: *Given a, $a^{-1}a = e$ for some a^{-1}.*

Proof. Given these weaker laws, cancellation on the left is possible; that is, $ca = cb$ implies $a = b$. For we need only premultiply each side of $ca = cb$ by c^{-1} and apply the associative law to get $(c^{-1}c)a = (c^{-1}c)b$, which is $ea = eb$, and gives $a = b$.

The given left-identity is also a right-identity. For

$$a^{-1}ae = ee = e = a^{-1}a,$$

whence, by left-cancellation, $ae = a$ for all a. Finally, left-inverses are also right-inverses. For

$$a^{-1}(aa^{-1}) = (a^{-1}a)a^{-1} = ea^{-1} = a^{-1} = a^{-1}e,$$

since the left-identity is a right-identity. Left-cancellation now gives
$aa^{-1} = e$. This completes our proof.

There are many other postulate systems for groups. A useful one may
be set up in terms of the possibility of division, as follows:

Theorem 5.   *If G is a nonvoid system closed under an associative multiplication for which all equations $xa = b$ and $ay = b$ have solutions x and y
in G, then G is a group.*

The proof is left as an exercise (Ex. 12).

	I	R	R'	R''	H	V	D	D'
I	I	R	R'	R''	H	V	D	D'
R	R	R'	R''	I	D	D'	V	H
R'	R'	R''	I	R	V	H	D'	D
R''	R''	I	R	R'	D'	D	H	V
H	H	D'	V	D	I	R'	R''	R
V	V	D	H	D'	R'	I	R	R''
D	D	H	D'	V	R	R''	I	R'
D'	D'	V	D	H	R''	R	R'	I

Figure 3

Besides systematizing the algebraic laws governing multiplication in
any group G, we may list in a "multiplication table" the special rules for
forming the product of any two elements of G, provided the number of
elements in G is finite. This is a square array of entries, headed both to the
left and above by a list of the elements of the group. The entry opposite a
on the left and headed above by b is the product ab (in that order).

In Figure 3 we have tabulated for illustration the multiplication table
for the group of symmetries of the square. The computations can be
modelled on those made in §1 in proving that $HR = D'$ and $RH = D$.
Another method is described in §6.

Most of the group properties can be read directly from the table. Thus,
the existence of an identity states that some row and the corresponding
column must be replicas of the top heading and of the left heading,
respectively. The possibility of solving the equation $ay = b$ means that

the row opposite a must contain the entry b; since the solution is unique, b can occur only once in this row. The group is commutative if and only if its table is symmetric about the principal diagonal (which extends from upper left to lower right). Unfortunately, the associative law cannot be easily visualized in the table.

EXERCISES

1. Let a, b, c be fixed elements of a group. Prove the equation $xaxba = xbc$ has one and only one solution.
2. In a group of $2n$ elements, prove there is an element besides the identity which is its own inverse.
3. Do the positive real numbers form a group under addition? under multiplication? Do the even integers form one under addition? Do the odd ones? Why?
4. In the field Z_{11} of integers modulo 11, which of the following sets are groups under multiplication?
   (a) $(1, 3, 4, 5, 9)$ (b) $(1, 3, 5, 7, 8)$ (c) $(1, 8)$,   (d) $(1, 10)$.
5. Prove that a group with 4 or fewer elements is necessarily Abelian. (*Hint:* ba is one of e, b, a, ab, except in trivial cases.)
6. Prove that if $xx = x$ in a group, then $x = e$.
7. Do the following multiplication tables describe groups?

	a	b	c	d
a	b	d	a	c
b	d	c	b	a
c	a	b	c	d
d	c	a	d	b

	a	b	c	d
a	a	b	c	d
b	b	a	d	c
c	c	d	a	a
d	d	c	b	b

8. Prove that Rules 2, 4 and 6 of Ch. I, §2, are valid in any commutative group.
9. Which of the following sets of numbers are groups. Why?
   (a) All rational numbers under addition; under multiplication;
   (b) All irrational numbers under multiplication;
   (c) All complex numbers of absolute value 1, under multiplication;
   (d) All complex numbers z with $|z| = 1$, under the operation $z \circ z' = |z| \cdot z'$;
   (e) All integers under the operation of subtraction;
   (f) The "units" (Chap. III, §6) of any integral domain under multiplication.
10. Prove that the following postulates describe an Abelian group; (i) $(ab)c = a(cb)$ for all a, b, c, (ii) the "left-identity" postulate of Theorem 4, (iii) the "left-inverse" postulate of Theorem 4.

★**11.** Prove that if $x^2 = e$ for all elements of a group G, then G is commutative.

★**12.** Prove Theorem 5. (*Hint:* If $ax = a$, then x is a right-identity, and any right-identity equals any left-identity.)

★**13.** Let S be a nonvoid set closed under a multiplication such that $ab = ba$, $a(bc) = (ab)c$, and $ax = ay$ implies $x = y$.
   (*a*) If S is finite, prove that S is a group.
   (*b*) If S is finite or infinite, prove that S can be embedded in a group.

5. Isomorphism

Consider the transformation $x \to \log x$ on the domain of real numbers. It is well known that as x increases in the interval $0 < x < +\infty$, $\log x$ increases continuously in the interval $-\infty < y < +\infty$; that is, the correspondence is one-one between the system of positive real numbers and the system of all real numbers (the inverse transformation being $y \to e^y$). Moreover $\log (xy) = \log x + \log y$ for all x, y: we can replace computations of products by parallel computations with sums. This is indeed the main practical use of logarithms!

Next, let $\mathbf{Z}_3$ be the field of the integers mod 3 (Chap. I, §10), and let G be the group of the rigid rotations of an equilateral triangle into itself. If I, R, and R' are the rotations through 0°, 120°, and 240°, respectively, the correspondence $0 \leftrightarrow I$, $1 \leftrightarrow R$, $2 \leftrightarrow R'$ associating integers with rotations is one which carries sums in $\mathbf{Z}_3$ into products of the corresponding rotations. For instance,

$$1 + 2 \equiv 0 \ (\text{mod } 3), \qquad RR' = I,$$
$$2 + 2 \equiv 1 \ (\text{mod } 3), \qquad R'R' = R \qquad (240° + 240° \to 120°).$$

These are instances of the general concept of "isomorphism" mentioned in Chap. I, §12. This concept is simpler and also more important for groups than for integral domains.

Definition. *By an* isomorphism *between two groups G and G' is meant a one-one correspondence $a \leftrightarrow a'$ between their elements which preserves group multiplication—i.e., which is such that if $a \leftrightarrow a'$ and $b \leftrightarrow b'$, then $ab \leftrightarrow a'b'$.*

Thus, in the first example, we have described an isomorphism between the group of positive real numbers under multiplication, and that of all real numbers under addition. In the second, we have pointed out the isomorphism of the additive group of the integers mod 3 with the group of rotational symmetries of the equilateral triangle.

Similarly, the group of the non-zero integers under multiplication mod 5 is isomorphic with the group of the integers under addition mod 4, the correspondence being $1 \leftrightarrow 0$, $2 \leftrightarrow 1$, $4 \leftrightarrow 2$, $3 \leftrightarrow 3$.

It is convenient to check this result by comparing the group table for the integers under addition mod 4 with that for the non-zero elements of $\mathbf{Z}_5$ under multiplication. These tables are exhibited in Figure 4.

In turn, the group of the integers under addition modulo four is isomorphic with the group of rotational symmetries of the square. That the correspondence $0 \leftrightarrow I$, $1 \leftrightarrow R$, $2 \leftrightarrow R'$, $3 \leftrightarrow R''$ is an isomorphism can be checked by comparing Figure 4 with part of Figure 3.

The notion of isomorphism is technically valuable because it gives form to the recognition that the same abstract group-theoretic situation can arise in entirely different contexts. The fact that isomorphic groups are abstractly the same (and differ only in the notation for their elements) can be seen in a number of ways.

Thus, by definition, two finite groups G and G' are isomorphic if and only if every group table for G yields a group table for G', by appropriate substitution. It follows from the next to the last sentence of §4 that G' is Abelian if and only if G is; that is, any isomorphic image of a finite Abelian group is Abelian.

+	0	1	2	3
0	0	1	2	3
1	1	2	3	0
2	2	3	0	1
3	3	0	1	2

×	1	2	4	3
1	1	2	4	3
2	2	4	3	1
4	4	3	1	2
3	3	1	2	4

Figure 4

Again, isomorphism behaves like equality in another respect.

Theorem 6.   *The relation "G is isomorphic to G'" is a reflexive, symmetric, and transitive relation between groups.*

Proof.   The reflexive property is trivial (every group is isomorphic to itself by the identity transformation). As for the symmetric property, let $a \leftrightarrow aT$ be any isomorphic correspondence between G and G'; since T is one-one, it has an inverse T^{-1}, which is an isomorphism of G' onto G. Finally, if T maps G isomorphically on G', while T' maps G' isomorphically on G'', then TT' is an isomorphism of G with G'', Q.E.D.

It is worth observing that Theorem 6 and its proof hold equally for isomorphisms between integral domains, and indeed for isomorphisms between algebraic systems of any kind whatever.

Theorem 7.   *Under an isomorphism between two groups, the identity elements correspond and the inverses of corresponding elements correspond.*

Proof.   The unique solution e of $ax = a$ goes into the unique solution e' of $a'x = a'$; hence the identities correspond. Consequently, the unique solution a^{-1} of the equation $ax = e$ in G goes into the unique solution a'^{-1} of $a'x = e'$ in G'; this complete the proof.

We shall finally prove a remarkable result of Cayley, which can be interpreted as demonstrating the completeness of our postulates on the multiplication of transformations.

Theorem 8.   *Any abstract group G is isomorphic with a group of transformations.*

Proof.   Associate with each element $a \in G$ the transformation ϕ_a: $x \to xa = x\phi_a$ on the "space" of all elements x of G. Since $e\phi_a = e\phi_b$ implies $a = ea = eb = b$, distinct elements of G correspond to distinct transformations. Since

$$(6) \qquad\qquad x(\phi_a\phi_b) = (x\phi_a)\phi_b = (xa)b = x(ab) = x\phi_{ab}$$

holds for all x, the product $\phi_a\phi_b$ is ϕ_{ab}, and the set G' of all ϕ_a contains with any two transformations their product. Again, since $x\phi_e = xe = x$ for all x, G' contains the identity. One can similarly show that $(\phi_a)^{-1}$ exists and is in G' for all a, being in fact $\phi_{a^{-1}}$. Hence G' is a group of transformations, which is by (6) isomorphic with G.

EXERCISES

1. Are any two of the following groups isomorphic: (a) the group of symmetries of an equilateral triangle; (b) the group of symmetries of a square; (c) the group of rotations of a regular hexagon; (d) the additive group of integers mod 6?

2. The same question for (a) group of rotations of a square; (b) group of symmetries of a rectangle; (c) group of symmetries of a rhombus (equilateral parallelogram); (d) multiplicative group of 1, 5, 8, 12, mod 13; (e) multiplicative group of 1, 5, 7, 11, mod 12.

3. (a) Prove that the additive group of "Gaussian" integers $m + n\sqrt{-1}$ $(m, n \in \mathbf{Z})$ is isomorphic to the multiplicative group of rational fractions of the form $2^n 3^m$ $(m, n \in \mathbf{Z})$.
   (b) Show that both are isomorphic to the group of all translations of a rectangular network.

★4. Is the multiplicative group of non-zero real numbers isomorphic with the additive group of all real numbers?

5. Determine all the isomorphisms between the additive group of $\mathbf{Z}_4$ and the group of rotations of the square.

6. (a) Exhibit an isomorphism between the group of the square and a group of transformations on the four vertices 1, 2, 3, 4 of the square.
   (b) Show explicitly how inverses correspond under this isomorphism, as in Theorem 7.

7. Do the same for the group of all rotations of a regular hexagon.

8. Illustrate Theorem 8 by exhibiting a group of transformations isomorphic with each of the following groups:
   (a) the additive group of all real numbers;
   (b) the multiplicative group of all non-zero real numbers;
   (c) the additive group of integers mod 8.

6. Cyclic Groups

In any group, the integral *powers* a^m of the group element a can be defined separately for positive, zero, and negative exponents. If $m > 0$, we define

(7) $a^m = a \cdot a \cdots a$ (to m factors), $a^0 = e$, $a^{-m} = (a^{-1})^m$.

Two of the usual laws of exponents hold,

(8) $a^r a^s = a^{r+s}$, $(a^r)^s = a^{rs}$.

On the other hand, $(ab)^r \neq a^r b^r$ in general (cf. Ex. 2 below).

If both exponents r and s are positive, the laws (8) follow directly† from the definition (7) (cf. Chap. I, §5). In the other cases for the first law of (8), one of r or s may be zero, in which case (8) is immediate, or both r and s may be negative, in which case the result comes directly from the last part of the definition (7). There remains the case when one exponent is negative and one positive, say $r = -m$ and $s = n$, with $m > 0$ and $n > 0$. Then

$$a^{-m}a^n = (a^{-1})^m a^n = (a^{-1} \cdots a^{-1})(a \cdots a).$$

By the associative law we can cancel successive a's against the inverses a^{-1}. In case $n \geq m$ we have left a^{n-m} while if $n < m$ we have some inverses left, $(a^{-1})^{m-n}$ or $a^{-(m-n)}$. In both cases we have the desired law $a^{-m}a^n = a^{n+(-m)}$.

The second half of (8) can be established even more simply. If s is positive, then by the first half of (8),

$$a^r a^r \cdots a^r \text{ (to } s \text{ factors)} = a^{r+r+\cdots+r} = a^{rs}.$$

If s is negative, we can make a similar expansion, noting that $(a^r)^{-1} = a^{-r}$ whether r is positive, zero, or negative. If s is zero, the result is immediate.

Definition.   *The* order *of an element a in a group is the least positive integer‡ m such that $a^m = e$; if no positive power of a equals the identity e, a has order infinity. The group G is* cyclic *if it contains some one element x whose powers exhaust G; this element is said to generate the group.*

For example, the group of all rotations of a square into itself consists of the four powers R, R^2, R^3, and $R^4 = I$ of the clockwise rotation R of $90°$. This group might equally well have been generated by R^3, which is a counterclockwise rotation of $90°$, since $R^2 = (R^3)^2$, $R = (R^3)^3$, and $I = (R^3)^4$ with R^3 exhaust the group.

---

† Thus r factors "a" followed by s factors "a" give all told $r + s$ factors. Again, s sets of r factors "a" each give all told sr factors.

‡ The well-ordering principle guarantees the existence of this m.

Theorem 9.   *If an element a generates the cyclic group G, then the order of a determines G to within isomorphism. In fact, if the order of a is infinite, G is isomorphic with the additive group of the integers; if the order of a is some finite integer n, G is isomorphic with the additive group of the integers modulo n.*

Proof.   First, $a^r = a^s$ if and only if

$$(9) \qquad\qquad e = a^r(a^s)^{-1} = a^r a^{-s} = a^{r-s}, \qquad\qquad \text{by (8)}.$$

Again, if $r \neq s$, either $r > s$, or $s > r$; hence if the order of a is infinite, so that $a^{r-s} = e$ for no $r > s$, no two powers of a are equal. Moreover, by (8) $a^s a^t = a^{s+t}$; therefore, the correspondence $a^s \to s$ makes G isomorphic with the additive group of the integers, proving our first assertion.

If the order of a is finite, then the set of those integers t with $a^t = e$ contains 0, and by (8) contains the sum and difference of any two of its members. Hence, by Theorem 6 of Chap. I, $a^t = e$ if and only if t is a multiple of the order n of a—and so by (9), $a^r = a^s$ if and only if $n \mid (r - s)$; that is, $a^r = a^s$ if and only if $r \equiv s \pmod{n}$. Finally, by (8) again, $a^r a^s = a^{r+s}$; consequently the correspondence $a^r \to r$ makes G isomorphic with the additive group of the integers modulo n, Q.E.D.

It is a corollary that the number of elements in any cyclic group G is equal to the order of any generator of G, and that any two cyclic groups of the same order are isomorphic.

The group of the square is not cyclic, but is generated by the two elements R and H; indeed the table in Figure 3 shows that

$$
\begin{aligned}
R^0 &= I, & R &= R, & R^2 &= R', & R^3 &= R''; \\
H &= H, & HR &= D', & HR^2 &= V, & HR^3 &= D.
\end{aligned}
$$

The elements of the group are thus represented uniquely as $H^i R^j$ with $i = 0, 1$ and $j = 0, 1, 2, 3$. Furthermore, H and R satisfy

$$R^4 = I, \qquad H^2 = I, \qquad RH = HR^3.$$

These are called "defining relations" because they suffice to put the product of any two elements $H^i R^j$ ($i = 0, 1$) into the same form. For example,

$$D'V = HRHR^2 = HHR^3R^2 = IR = R;$$

similar calculations will give the whole multiplication table for the group of the square.

EXERCISES

1. Using the definitions $a^1 = a$, $a^{m+1} = a^m a$, prove laws (8), for positive exponents, by induction.
2. Prove that if $(ab)^n = a^n b^n$ for all a and b in G and all positive integers n, then G is commutative, and conversely.
3. How many different generators has a cyclic group of order 6?

4. Show that if a commutative group with 6 elements contains an element of order 3, it is cyclic.

5. Is the multiplicative group of 1, 2, $\cdots$, 6 mod 7 cyclic? of 1, 3, 5, 7 mod 8? of 1, 2, 4, 5, 7, 8 mod 9?

6. If a cyclic group G is generated by a of order m, prove that a^k generates G if and only if g.c.d. $(k, m) = 1$.

7. Under the hypotheses of Ex. 6, find the order of any element a^k of G.

8. Find the order of every element in the group of the square.

9. Give the elements and the multiplication table of the group generated by two elements x and y subject to the defining relations $x^2 = y^3 = e$, $xy = yx$.

10. The dihedral group D_n is the group of all symmetries of a regular polygon of n sides (if $n = 4$, D_n is the group of the square). Show that D_n contains $2n$ elements and is generated by two elements R and H with $R^n = I$, $H^2 = I$, and $RH = HR^{n-1}$.

★11. Obtain generators and defining relations for the groups of symmetries of the three infinite patterns $\rightarrow \rightarrow \rightarrow$, $\nearrow \nearrow \nearrow$, $\vee \vee \vee$, imagined as extended to infinity in both directions. Are any two of these three groups isomorphic?

★12. Make similar studies for the groups described in Exs. 1, 2, 4, 5 of §3.

7. Subgroups

Many groups are contained in larger groups. Thus, the group of rotations of the square is a part of the group of all symmetries of the square. Again, the group of the eight permutations of the vertices of the square induced by symmetries is a part of the group of all 4! = 24 permutations of these vertices. The group of the even integers under addition is a part of the group of all integers under addition.

These examples suggest the concept of a subgroup. A subset S of a group G is called a *subgroup* of G if S is itself a group with respect to the binary operation (multiplication) of G.

In any group G, the set consisting of the identity e alone is a subgroup. The whole group G is also a subgroup of itself. Subgroups of G other than the trivial ("improper") subgroups e and G are called *proper* subgroups.

Theorem 10. *A nonvoid subset S of a group G is a subgroup if and only if (i) a and b in S imply ab in S, (ii) a in S implies a^{-1} in S.*

Proof. Under these hypotheses, clearly S is a subgroup: the associativity is trivial; the identity $e = aa^{-1}$ of G is in S, for there is at least one element a in S; the other group postulates are assumed. Conversely, we must prove that (i) and (ii) hold in any subgroup. The identity $x = e'$ of any subgroup of G satisfies $xx = x$, and so is the identity of G (Ex. 6, §4). Consequently, since G has but one inverse for any a, the inverse of any element a in the subgroup is the same as its inverse in G, so (ii) holds. Condition (i) is obvious.

For elements a of finite order m, clearly $a^{m-1}a = a^m = e$, and so $a^{-1} = a^{m-1}$. Hence one has the following simplified condition.

Theorem 11.   *A nonvoid subset S of a finite group G is a subgroup of G if and only if the product of any two elements in S is itself in S.*

Among the subgroups of a given non-Abelian group G, one of the most important is its *center*. This is defined as the set of all elements $a \in G$ such that $ax = xa$ for all $x \in G$. We leave to the reader the verification that the center is, in fact, always a subgroup of G.

The problem of determining all subgroups of a specified group G is in general very difficult. We shall now solve it in the case that G is a cyclic group.

Theorem 12.   *Any subgroup S of a cyclic group G is itself cyclic.*

Proof.   Let G consist of the powers of an element a. If a^s and a^t are in S, then $a^{s+t} = a^s a^t$ and $a^{s-t} = a^s(a^t)^{-1}$ are in S, by Theorem 10. The set of integers s for which a^s is in S is therefore closed under addition and subtraction, so† consists of the multiples of some least positive exponent r (Theorem 6, Chap. I). Therefore S itself consist of the powers $a^{kr} = (a^r)^k$, hence is cyclic with generator a^r, Q.E.D.

In case G is infinite, every $r > 0$ determines a different subgroup. If G has n elements, then since $a^n = e$ is surely in S, only those $r > 0$ which are divisors of n determine subgroups in this manner—but again these subgroups are all distinct.

To obtain material for further development, we now enumerate all the subgroups of the group of the square. By examining the definitions given in §1 for the operations of this group, one finds the (proper) subgroups leaving invariant each of the eight following configurations:

A diagonal	*An axis*	*A face*	*An axis and a diagonal*
$[I, D, D', R']$	$[I, H, V, R']$	$[I, R, R', R'']$	$[I, R']$

Vertex 1 (or 3)	*Vertex 2 (or 4)*	*A vertical side*	*A horizontal side*
$[I, D]$	$[I, D']$	$[I, H]$	$[I, V]$

By the transformations leaving a face invariant we understand those which do not turn the square over. All these subgroups may be displayed in their relation to each other in a table, where each group is joined to all of its subgroups by a descending line or sequence of lines.

† The conclusion, with $r = 0$, also holds if the set S consists of 0 alone.

Without using geometry we could still find all these subgroups. Indeed, the determination of all the subgroups of a specified finite group G is most efficiently handled by considering the group elements purely abstractly, as follows.

Observe first that if a subgroup S of G contains an element a, it also contains the "cyclic" subgroup $\{a\}$ (prove it is a subgroup!) consisting of all the powers of a. In the present case, this gives us all but the first two of the subgroups listed. Next, observe that any subgroup must contain not only two cyclic subgroups $\{a\}$ and $\{b\}$, but also the set $\{a, b\}$ of all products, such as $a^2b^{-3}a$, of powers of a and b. (Prove, using Theorem 11, that these form a subgroup!) In the present case, this procedure gives us the remaining subgroups. (We shall see in §8 why they all contain just 2 or 4 elements.) In general, we may have to test further for subgroups $\{a, b, c\}$ generated by three or more elements; but this can never happen unless the number of elements in the group is a product of at least four distinct primes.

The *intersection* $S \cap T$ of two subgroups (indeed, of any two sets!) S and T is the set of all elements which belong both to S and to T.

Theorem 13. *The intersection $S \cap T$ of two subgroups S and T of a group G is a subgroup of G.*

Proof. By Theorem 10, a in $S \cap T$ implies a in S, hence a^{-1} in S; likewise it implies a^{-1} in T, and so a^{-1} in $S \cap T$. Similarly, a and b in $S \cap T$ implies ab in S, ab in T, and so ab in $S \cap T$. Hence by Theorem 10, $S \cap T$ is a subgroup. Also, $S \cap T$ contains e, and so is nonvoid, Q.E.D.

Clearly, $S \cap T$ is the largest subgroup contained in both S and T; dually, there exists a least subgroup containing both S and T. It consists of all the products of positive and negative powers of elements of S and T—it is called the *join* of S and T, and denoted $S \cup T$. We shall recur to these concepts in Chap. XI.

EXERCISES

1. In the group of symmetries of the regular hexagon, what is the subgroup leaving a diagonal fixed?
2. If T is a subgroup of S, and S a subgroup of G, prove T is a subgroup of G.
3. In the group of all permutations ϕ of four digits 1, 2, 3, 4, find the following subgroups: (a) all ϕ carrying the set $\{1, 2\}$ into the set $\{1, 2\}$; (b) all ϕ such that $a \equiv b \pmod 2$ implies $a\phi \equiv b\phi \pmod 2$ for any digits a, b of the set 1, 2, 3, 4.
4. Prove that Theorem 11 still holds if G is infinite, but all elements of G have a finite order. Show that the additive group of $\mathbf{Z}_p[x]$ is such a group.
5. Tabulate all the subgroups of the following groups: (a) the additive group mod 12; (b) the group of a regular pentagon; (c) the group of a regular hexagon; (⋆d) the group of all permutations of four letters.

★**6.** Let $a \leftrightarrow a'$ be an isomorphism between two groups G and G' of permutations, and let S consist of those permutations of G leaving one letter fixed. Does the set S' of all elements of G' corresponding to a's in S necessarily form a subgroup of G'? Must the set S' leave a letter fixed? Illustrate.

7. Prove that the center of any group G is a subgroup of G.

8. Find the center of the group of the square—of the equilateral triangle.

★**9.** Do the same for the group of a regular polygon of n sides.

★**10.** Show that the elements of finite order in any commutative group G form a subgroup.

8. Lagrange's Theorem

We now come to a far-reaching concept of abstract group theory: the idea that any subgroup S of a group G decomposes G into cosets.

Definition. *By the* order *of a group or subgroup is meant the number of its elements. By a* right coset *(left coset) of a subgroup S of a group G is meant any set Sa (or aS) of all the right-multiples sa (left-multiples as) of the elements s of S by a fixed element a in G. The number of distinct right cosets is called the "index" of S in G.*

Since $Se = S$, S is a right coset of itself. Moreover, one has

Lemma 1. *If S is finite, each right coset Sa of S has exactly as many elements as S does.*

For the transformation $s \rightarrow sa$ is one-one: each element $t = sa$ of the coset Sa is the image of one and only one element $s = ta^{-1}$ of S. (Cf. also Theorem 8.)

Lemma 2. *Two right cosets Sa and Sb of S are either identical or without common elements.*

For suppose Sa and Sb have an element $c = s'a = s''b$ (s', s'' in S) in common. Then Sb contains every element $sa = ss'^{-1}s'a = (ss'^{-1}s'')b$ of Sa, and similarly Sa contains every element of Sb. Consequently, $Sa = Sb$.

It is easy to illustrate these results. Thus, if G is the group of symmetries of the square, the subgroup $S = [I, H]$ has the four right cosets

$$[I, H]I = [I, H], \qquad\qquad [I, H]R = [R, HR] = [R, D'],$$
$$[I, H]R' = [R', HR'] = [R', V], \qquad [I, H]R'' = [R'', HR''] = [R'', D].$$

Each coset has two elements, and every element of the group falls into one of the four right cosets.

Again, if G is the additive group of the integers, the subgroup of multiples $\pm 5n$ of 5 has for right cosets the different residue classes modulo five. Finally, let G be the symmetric group of all permutations of the symbols $1, \cdots, 6$, while S is the subgroup leaving the symbol 1 fixed. Then

$1\phi = k$ implies for all $\psi \in S$ that $1(\psi\phi) = (1\psi)\phi = 1\phi = k$. Hence the coset $S\phi$ contains only (and so by Lemma 1 all) the 5! permutations carrying $1 \to k$. Therefore the right cosets of S are the subsets carrying $1 \to 1, 1 \to 2, \cdots, 1 \to 6$, respectively.

From the preceding lemmas, we obtain a classic result which is of fundamental importance for the theory of finite groups. Since any right coset Sa always contains $a = ea$, any group G is exhausted by its right cosets. Therefore G is decomposed by S into nonoverlapping subsets, each of which has exactly as many elements as S. If G is finite,† the conclusion is:

Theorem 14 (Lagrange).   *The order of a finite group G is a multiple of the order of every one of its subgroups.*

Each element a of G generates a cyclic subgroup, whose order is (Theorem 9) simply the order of a. Therefore we have

Corollary 1.   *Every element of a finite group G has as order a divisor of the order of G.*

Corollary 2.   *Every group G of prime order p is cyclic.*

For the cyclic subgroup A generated by any element $a \neq e$ in such a group has an order $n > 1$ dividing p. But this implies $n = p$, and so $G = A$ is cyclic.

More generally, Lagrange's Theorem can be applied to the determination of all groups of any low order. As an example, define the *four group* as the group with four commuting elements: e (the identity) and a, b, $c = ab$, the latter each of order two. It will be shown in §9 that this group is isomorphic to the group of symmetries of a rectangle. We now prove

Corollary 3.   *The only abstract groups of order four are the cyclic group of that order and the four group.*

Proof.   If a group G of order 4 contains an element of order 4, it is cyclic. Otherwise, by Corollary 1, all elements of G except e must have order 2. Call them a, b, c. By the cancellation law, ab cannot be either $ae = a$, $eb = b$, or $aa = e$; hence $ab = c$. By symmetry, $ac = ca = b$, $bc = cb = a$, $ba = c$. But these, together with $a^2 = b^2 = c^2 = e$, and $ex = xe = x$ for all x, give the multiplication table of the four group.

Lagrange's Theorem can also be applied to number theory.

Corollary 4 (Fermat).   *If a is an integer, p a prime, then $a^p \equiv a$ (mod p).*

Proof.   The multiplication group mod p (excluding zero) has $p - 1$ elements. The order of any element a of this group is then a divisor of

---

† The extension to the infinite case follows immediately using the theory of transfinite numbers—but the importance of the result disappears.

$p - 1$, by Corollary 1, so that $a^{p-1} \equiv 1 \pmod{p}$ whenever $a \not\equiv 0 \pmod{p}$. If we multiply by a on both sides, we obtain the desired congruence, except for the case $a \equiv 0 \pmod{p}$, for which the conclusion is trivially true.

EXERCISES

1. Check Fermat's Theorem for $p = 7$ and $a = 2, 3, 6$.
2. (a) Enumerate the subgroups of the dihedral group (§6, Ex. 10) of order 26. How many are there?
   (b) Generalize your result.
3. Prove: the number of right cosets of any subgroup of a finite group equals the number of its left cosets. (*Hint:* Use the correspondence $x \rightarrow x^{-1}$.)
4. Determine the cosets of the subgroup $[I, D]$ of the group of the square.
5. If S is any subgroup of a group G, let SaS denote the set of all products sas' for s, s' in S. Prove that either $SaS \cap SbS$ is void, or $SaS = SbS$, for any $a, b \in G$.
6. For a subgroup S, let $x \equiv y \pmod{S}$ be defined to mean $xy^{-1} \in S$.
   (a) Prove that this relation is reflexive, symmetric, and transitive, and show that $x \equiv y \pmod{S}$ if and only if x and y lie in the same right coset of S.
   (b) Show that $x \equiv y \pmod{S}$ implies $xa \equiv ya \pmod{S}$ for all a.
7. Let G be the group of a regular hexagon, S the subgroup leaving one vertex fixed. Find the right and left cosets of S.
8. Prove that a group of order p^m, where p is a prime, must contain a subgroup of order p.
9. (a) If G is the group of all transformations $x \rightarrow ax + b$ of $\mathbf{R}$, where $a \neq 0$ and b are real, while S is the subgroup of all such transformations with $a = 1$, describe the right and left cosets of S in G.
   (b) Do the same for the subgroup T of all transformations with $b = 0$.
★10. (a) Show that, in any commutative ring R, the units (those elements with multiplicative inverses) form a group G.
   (b) Show that, if $R = \mathbf{Z}_n$, then G consists of the positive integers $k < n$ relatively prime to n.
   (c) The *order* of G, in case $R = \mathbf{Z}_n$, is denoted $\phi(n)$ and called Euler's ϕ-function. Show that $\phi(p) = p - 1$ if $n = p$ is a prime, and compute $\phi(12)$, $\phi(16)$, $\phi(30)$.
   (d) Using Lagrange's Theorem, infer that if $(k, n) = 1$, then $k^{\phi(n)} \equiv 1 \pmod{n}$.
★11. If S and T are subgroups of orders s and t of a group G, and if u and v are the orders of $S \cap T$ and $S \cup T$, prove that $st \leq uv$.
★12. Prove that the only abstract groups of order 6 are the cyclic group and the symmetric group on three letters.
★13. Let $2^h + 1$ be a prime p.
   (a) Prove that in the multiplicative group mod p, the order of 2 is $2h$.
   (b) Using Fermat's Theorem, infer that $2h$ divides $p - 1 = 2^h$.
   (c) Conclude that h is a power of 2.

9. Permutation Groups

A *permutation* is a one-one transformation of a finite set into itself.

For instance, the set might consist of the five digits 1, 2, 3, 4, 5. One permutation might be the transformation ϕ,

(10) $1\phi = 2$, $2\phi = 3$, $3\phi = 4$, $4\phi = 5$, $5\phi = 1$.

Another might be the transformation ϕ' with

(11) $1\phi' = 2$, $2\phi' = 3$, $3\phi' = 1$, $4\phi' = 5$, $5\phi' = 4$.

The reader will find it instructive to compute $\phi\phi'$, $\phi'\phi$, and to note that $\phi\phi' \neq \phi'\phi$.

Permutations which, like the permutation ϕ defined above give a circular rearrangement of the symbols permuted (Figure 5), are called *cyclic permutations* or *cycles*. There is a suggestive notation for cyclic permutations—simply write down inside parentheses first any letter involved, then its transform, $\cdots$, and finally the letter transformed into the original letter. Thus, the permutation ϕ of (10) might be written in any one of the equivalent forms (12345), (23451), (34512), (45123), or (51234).

Theorem 15. *A cyclic permutation of n symbols has order n.*

Figure 5

Proof. The cyclic permutation $\gamma = (a_1 a_2 \cdots a_n)$ carries a_i into a_{i+1}. Hence γ^2 has the doubled effect of carrying each a_i into a_{i+2}, and generally γ^k carries a_i into a_{i+k}, where all subscripts are to be reduced modulo n. We have in γ^k the identity I if and only if a_{i+k} equals a_i; that is, if and only if $k \equiv 0 \pmod{n}$. The smallest k with $\gamma^k = I$ is then n itself, so γ does have the order n (see the definition in §6). The cycle γ is said to have length n.

The notation for a cyclic permutation can be extended to any permutation. For example, the permutation ϕ' in (11) cyclically permutes the digits 1, 2, and 3 by themselves, and 4 and 5 by themselves. Thus, it is the product of these two cycles,

$$(123)(45) = (45)(123).$$

This product may be written in either order, since the symbols permuted by (123) are left unchanged by (45), which means that successive application of these permutations in either order gives the same result.

Theorem 16. *Any permutation ϕ can be written as a product of cycles, acting on disjoint sets of symbols (more briefly: a product of disjoint† cycles).*

† Two sets are called *disjoint* when they have no element in common.

Proof.   Select any symbol, denote it by a_1. Denote $a_1\phi$ by a_2, $a_2\phi$ by a_3, $\cdots$, $a_{n-1}\phi$ by a_n, until $a_n\phi = a_i$ is some element already named. Since the antecedent of any a_i $(i > 1)$ is a_{i-1}, $a_n\phi$ must be a_1. Thus the effect of ϕ on the letters a_1, $\cdots$, a_n is the cycle $(a_1 a_2 \cdots a_n)$. Moreover, $(a_1 \cdots a_n)$ contains, with any symbol a_i, its antecedent; hence ϕ permutes the remaining symbols among themselves. The result now follows by induction on the number of symbols. In particular, the identity permutation on m letters is represented by m "cycles," each of length one.

Conversely, evidently any product of disjoint cycles represents a permutation. Moreover, one may obtain

Theorem 17.   *The order of any permutation ϕ is the least common multiple of the lengths of its disjoint cycles.*

Proof.   Write the permutation ϕ as the product $\phi = \gamma_1 \cdots \gamma_r$ of disjoint cycles γ_i. If $i \neq j$, then γ_i and γ_j are disjoint; hence $\gamma_i\gamma_j = \gamma_j\gamma_i$, and the factors γ_i may be rearranged in ϕ and in its powers, to give $\phi^n = \gamma_1{}^n \cdots \gamma_r{}^n$ for all n. Therefore, $\phi^n = I$ if and only if every $\gamma_i{}^n$ is the identity. But by Theorem 15, this means $\phi^n = I$ if and only if n is a common multiple of the lengths of the γ_i, from which the conclusion of Theorem 17 follows immediately. Q.E.D.

Figure 6

Every finite group is isomorphic with one or more groups of permutations, by Theorem 8 of §5. In particular, this is true of finite groups of symmetries of geometrical figures, as we now illustrate by two examples.

Consider the group of symmetries of the rectangle (Figure 6). Under it, the vertices are transformed by the four permutations

$$I = (1)(2)(3)(4), \qquad R = (14)(23), \qquad H = (13)(24), \qquad V = (12)(34).$$

This group is known as the *four group*. According to Theorem 8 it is isomorphic with the group of permutations $\phi_I = (I)(R)(V)(H)$, $\phi_R = (IR)(HV)$, $\phi_H = (IH)(RV)$, $\phi_V = (IV)(RH)$.

The group of symmetries of the square (§1) can similarly be represented as a group of permutations of the four vertices. Using Theorem 8, we can also represent it as a group of permutations of the eight symbols which represent the elements of the group. Thus, R corresponds to the permutation effected on right-multiplication of these symbols by "R"; from the column headed "R" in the group table (Figure 3), one sees that this permutation is $(IRR'R'')(HD'VD)$. Similarly, H corresponds to $(IH)(RD)(R'V)(R''D')$.

Two cycles of the same length are closely related. For example, if $\gamma = (1234)$ and $\gamma' = (2143)$, then one may compute that $\gamma' = \phi^{-1}\gamma\phi$, where

$\phi = (12)(34)$ is the permutation taking each digit of the cycle γ into the corresponding digit in γ'. This is a special case of the following result.

Theorem 18. *Let ϕ and γ be permutations of n letters, where γ is a cyclic permutation $\gamma = (a_1, \cdots, a_m)$, and denote by $\gamma' = (a_1\phi, \cdots, a_m\phi)$ the cycle obtained by replacing each letter a_i in the representation of γ by its image under ϕ. Then $\phi^{-1}\gamma\phi = \gamma'$.*

Proof. The product $\phi^{-1}\gamma\phi$ carries each letter $a_i\phi$ in succession into $a_i\phi\phi^{-1} = a_i$; then to $a_i\gamma = a_{i+1}$, then to $a_i\gamma\phi = a_{i+1}\phi$, and hence has the same effect upon $a_i\phi$ as does γ' (call $a_{m+1} = a_1$). Similarly, one computes that $\phi^{-1}\gamma\phi$ and γ' both carry any letter b not of the form $a_i\phi$ into itself. Hence $\phi^{-1}\gamma\phi = \gamma'$, as asserted.

Corollary. *For any permutations ϕ and ψ, if $\psi = \gamma_1 \cdots \gamma_r$ is written as a product of cycles, we have $\phi^{-1}\psi\phi = \gamma_1' \cdots \gamma_r'$, where the γ_i' are obtained from the γ_i as in Theorem 18.*

EXERCISES

1. Express as products of disjoint cycles the permutations
   (a) $1\phi = 4$, $2\phi = 6$, $3\phi = 5$, $4\phi = 1$, $5\phi = 3$, $6\phi = 2$;
   (b) $1\phi = 5$, $2\phi = 3$, $3\phi = 2$, $4\phi = 6$, $5\phi = 4$, $6\phi = 1$;
   (c) $1\phi = 3$, $2\phi = 5$, $3\phi = 6$, $4\phi = 4$, $5\phi = 1$, $6\phi = 2$.
   Find the order of each of these permutations.
2. Represent the following products as products of disjoint cycles:
   $(1234)(567)(261)(47)$; $(12345)(67)(1357)(163)$; $(14)(123)(45)(14)$.
   Find the order of each product.
3. Find the order of $(abcdef)(ghij)(klm)$; of $(abcdef)(abcd)(abc)$.
4. Represent the group of the rhombus (equilateral parallelogram) as a group of permutations of its vertices.
5. Describe the right and left cosets of the subgroup of all those permutations of $x_1, \cdots, x_6$ which carry the set $\{x_1, x_2\}$ into itself.
6. Which symmetric groups are Abelian?
7. Let G be the group of all symmetries of the cube leaving one vertex fixed. Represent G as a group of permutations of the vertices (cf. §3).
8. (a) Prove that every permutation can be written as a product of (not in general disjoint) cycles of length two ("transpositions").
   (*b) How does this relate to the proof of the "generalized commutative law" from the law $ab = ba$ (Chap. I, §5)?
9. Represent the group of symmetries of the equilateral triangle as a group of permutations of (a) three and (b) six letters.
   (*c) Do (b) in two essentially different ways.
★10. Prove that the symmetric group of degree n is generated by the cycles $(1, 2, \cdots, n - 1)$ and $(n - 1, n)$.
★11. In what sense is the representation of Theorem 16 unique? Prove your answer.

10. Even and Odd Permutations

An important classification of permutations may be found by considering the homogeneous polynomial form

$$P = \prod_{i<j} (x_i - x_j),$$

where i and j run from 1 to n. If $n = 3$, P is

$$(x_1 - x_2)(x_1 - x_3)(x_2 - x_3)$$
$$= x_1^2 x_2 + x_2^2 x_3 + x_3^2 x_1 - x_1^2 x_3 - x_3^2 x_2 - x_2^2 x_1,$$

and P^2 is the discriminant discussed in Chap. V, §5. In general, P is a polynomial of degree $n(n-1)/2$. Clearly, any permutation of the subscripts in P leaves the set of factors of P, and hence P itself, unchanged except as to sign. Moreover, the transposition $(x_1 x_2)$ changes $(x_1 - x_2)$ into its negative $(x_2 - x_1)$, interchanges the $(x_1 - x_j)$ and the $(x_2 - x_j)$ $(j > 2)$, and leaves the other factors unchanged. Hence it does change P to $-P$.

The $n!$ permutations of the subscripts are therefore of two kinds: the *even* permutations leaving P (and $-P$) invariant, and the *odd* permutations interchanging P and $-P$. It follows that when we consider the effect of two permutations performed in succession, we have the rules

(12)   Even $\times$ Even $=$ Odd $\times$ Odd $=$ Even
        Even $\times$ Odd $=$ Odd $\times$ Even $=$ Odd.

It is a corollary of (12) and of Theorem 11 that the even permutations form a subgroup A_n of the symmetric group of degree n. This subgroup is usually called the "alternating group" of degree n.

Moreover, if β is a fixed, and ϕ a variable odd permutation, then $\phi\beta^{-1}$ is even, and so $\phi = (\phi\beta^{-1})\beta$ is in the right coset $A_n\beta$. In summary, the odd permutations form a single right coset of A_n. Hence by Lagrange's Theorem, the "alternating group" on n symbols contains just $(n!)/2$ elements.

A polynomial $g(x_1, \cdots, x_n)$ in n indeterminates x_i is called "symmetric" if it is invariant under the symmetric group of all permutations of its subscripts. Particular symmetric polynomials are (for $n = 3$)

(13) $\sigma_1 = x_1 + x_2 + x_3,$ $\sigma_2 = x_1 x_2 + x_1 x_3 + x_2 x_3,$ $\sigma_3 = x_1 x_2 x_3.$

They are the coefficients in the expansion

(14) $(t - x_1)(t - x_2)(t - x_3) = t^3 - \sigma_1 t^2 + \sigma_2 t - \sigma_3.$

In general, we call such polynomials *elementary symmetric polynomials* (in n variables); they are

$$(15) \quad \sigma_1 = \sum_i x_i, \quad \sigma_2 = \sum_{i<j} x_i x_j, \quad \sigma_3 = \sum_{i<j<k} x_i x_j x_k, \quad \cdots, \quad \sigma_n = x_1 \cdots x_n.$$

Since $(-1)^k \sigma_k$ is the coefficient of t^{n-k} in the expansion of $p(t) = \Pi_k(t - x_k)$ as a polynomial in t, the expressions σ_i give the coefficients of $p(t)$ as functions of its roots. They derive much of their importance from the so-called "fundamental theorem on symmetric polynomials," which we shall state without proof.†

Theorem 19. *Any symmetric polynomial $p(x_1, \cdots, x_n)$ can be expressed as a polynomial in the elementary symmetric polynomials.*

Thus, in the case of two variables x and y,

$$x^2 + y^2 = (x + y)^2 - 2xy = \sigma_1{}^2 - 2\sigma_2,$$
$$x^3 + y^3 = (x + y)^3 - 3xy(x + y) = \sigma_1(\sigma_1{}^2 - 3\sigma_2), \text{ and so on.}$$

Even if a polynomial $q(x_1, \cdots, x_n)$ is not symmetric, one can at least ask for the set of all those permutations of the indices which leave the polynomial unchanged. It is clear that this set is a group; it is called the group of the polynomial.

EXERCISES

1. List the odd permutations (a) of three letters; (b) of four letters.
2. For which positive integers n is a cycle of length n even? odd?
3. (a) Show that a product of not necessarily disjoint cycles is even if and only if it contains an even number of cycles of even length.
   (b) Are the permutations $(123)(246)(5432)$ and $(12)(345)(67)(891)$ odd or even?
4. (a) Construct sample even and odd permutations of order 14 on 11 letters.
   (b) Prove every permutation of order 10 on 8 letters is odd.
5. Show that a permutation is even if and only if it can be written as a product of an even number of transpositions (Ex. 8, §9).
★6. Show that every even permutation can be written as the product of cycles of length three.
7. Find the group of each of the following polynomials:

$$x_1 x_2 + x_3 x_4, \quad x_2 x_1 + x_3 x_2 + x_2 x_4, \quad x_1{}^2 x_2 + x_3 x_4{}^2 + x_1{}^2 x_3 + x_2 x_4{}^2.$$

8. Represent each of the following polynomials in terms of the elementary symmetric polynomials:

$$x^2 + y^2 + z^2, \quad x^2 y + y^2 z + z^2 x + x^2 z + y^2 x + z^2 y.$$

† See L. Weisner, *Introduction to the Theory of Equations* (New York: Macmillan, 1938), p. 108.

11. Homomorphisms

A single-valued transformation from a group G to a group G' may preserve multiplication without being one-one (that is, without being an isomorphism).

Thus, consider the correspondence between the symmetric group of degree n and the group of ± 1 under multiplication, which carries even permutations into $+1$ and odd ones into -1. By (12), it carries products into products.

Or consider the correspondence $n \to i^n$, where $i = \sqrt{-1}$, between the additive group of the integers and the multiplicative group of the fourth roots of unity. Again the group operation is preserved: $i^{m+n} = i^m i^n$, but the correspondence is many-one.

These and other examples lead to the following concept.

Definition. *A* homomorphism *of a group G to a group G' is a single-valued transformation $x \to x'$ mapping G into G', such that $(xy)' = x'y'$ for all x, y in G.*

Theorem 20. *Under any homomorphism $G \to G'$, the identity e of G goes into the identity of G', and inverses into inverses.*

Proof. Since $e^2 = e$, the image f of e satisfies $f^2 = f = fe'$, where e' is the identity of G'. Hence, by cancellation, $f = e'$, and the identity of G must go into the identity of G'. Likewise, if a goes into a' and a^{-1} into $(a^{-1})'$, then $aa^{-1} = e$ must go into $a'(a^{-1})' = e'$, and so $(a^{-1})'$ is the inverse of a'.

Corollary 1. *Any homomorphic image† of a cyclic group is cyclic.*

For by Theorem 20, $(a^m)' = (a')^m$ whether m is positive, zero, or negative. Hence if the powers a^m exhaust G, the powers $(a')^m = (a^m)'$ of a' exhaust G'.

Corollary 2. *The set N of all elements of G mapped on the identity e' of G', under a homomorphism of G to G', is a subgroup of G.*

This set N is called the *kernel* of the homomorphism.

Since $e \to e'$, N is nonvoid. Again, by Theorem 20 and hypothesis, $a \to e'$ and $b \to e'$ imply $a^{-1} \to (a')^{-1} = e'^{-1} = e'$ and $ab \to a'b' = e'e' = e'$; hence N is a subgroup.

Direct Products. Any two groups G and H have a *direct product* $G \times H$. The elements of $G \times H$ are the ordered pairs (g, h) with $g \in G$, $h \in H$; multiplication in $G \times H$ is defined by the formula

(15a) $$(g, h)(g', h') = (gg', hh').$$

---

† Homomorphisms onto are sometimes called epimorphisms, and correspondingly homomorphic images are called epimorphic images.

Evidently, (e, e) acts as an identity in $G \times H$; (g^{-1}, h^{-1}) is an inverse of (g, h), and multiplication is associative; hence $G \times H$ is a group. Moreover the function $\alpha(g, h) = g$ defines a homomorphism α from $G \times H$ onto G, and the function $\beta(g, h) = h$ is a homomorphism from $G \times H$ onto H.

It can be proved that *every* Abelian group of finite order is isomorphic to a direct product of cyclic groups of prime-power orders. We content ourselves here with the following, much weaker result.

Theorem 21. *If m and n are relatively prime, then the direct product of cyclic groups of orders m and n is itself a cyclic group, of order mn.*

Proof. Let a and b generate the cyclic groups A and B, of orders m and n, respectively. Then, in $C = A \times B$, $(a, b)^k = (a^k, b^k)$ is the identity (e, e) if and only if $k \equiv 0 \pmod{m}$ *and* $k \equiv 0 \pmod{n}$. By Theorem 17 of Chap. I, this implies $k \equiv 0 \pmod{mn}$. Hence $(a, b) = c$ is of order mn in C, which only contains mn elements, and is therefore cyclic, Q.E.D.

EXERCISES

1. In the homomorphism $n \to i^n$, where $i = \sqrt{-1}$ and $n \in \mathbf{Z}$, find the kernel.
2. Show that a cyclic group of order 8 has as homomorphic images (a) a cyclic group of order 4;   (b) a cyclic group of order 2.
3. Is the correspondence mapping x on the complex number $e^{2\pi i x}$ a homomorphism of the additive group of real numbers x? If so, what is its image G', and what is the kernel?
4. If G is a group of permutations of n letters $1, 2, \cdots, n$, in which each permutation ϕ of G carries the subset of letters $1, \cdots, k$ into itself, show that G is homomorphic onto the group G' of the permutations ϕ^* induced on $1, \cdots, k$.
5. In a square let the two diagonals be d and d', the axes h and v. Show that there is a homomorphism $\phi \to \phi^*$ in which each motion ϕ in the group of the square induces a permutation ϕ^* on d, d', h, and v. Exhibit the correspondence $\phi \to \phi^*$ in detail. What is the kernel?
6. If G is homomorphic to G' and G' to G'', prove that G is homomorphic to G''.
7. Which of the following correspondences map the multiplicative group of all non-zero real numbers homomorphically into itself? If the correspondence is a homomorphism, identify the homomorphic image G' and the kernel
   (a) $x \to |x|$;   (b) $x \to 2x$;   (c) $x \to x^2$;   (d) $x \to 1/x$;
   (e) $x \to -x$;   (f) $x \to x^3$;   (g) $x \to -1/x$;   (h) $x \to \sqrt{x}$.
8. Show that the four-group is the direct product of two cyclic groups of order 2.
★9. Show that the multiplicative group of all non-zero complex numbers is the direct product of the group of rotations of the unit circle and the group of all real numbers under addition. (*Hint:* Let $z = re^{i\theta}$.)
10. Prove that, for any groups G, H, K, $G \times H$ is isomorphic to $H \times G$ and $G \times (H \times K)$ is isomorphic to $(G \times H) \times K$.

12. Automorphisms; Conjugate Elements

Definition. *An isomorphism of a group G with itself is called an* automorphism *of G. Thus an automorphism α of G is a one-one transformation of G onto itself such that*

$$(16) \qquad\qquad (xy)\alpha = (x\alpha)(y\alpha) \qquad \text{for all } x,\ y \text{ in } G.$$

Theorem 22. *The automorphisms of any group G themselves form a group A.*

Proof. (Cf. Theorem 6.) It is obvious that the identity transformation is an automorphism, and that so is the product of any two automorphisms. Finally, if $x \to x\alpha$ is an automorphism, then by (16)

$$(xy)\alpha^{-1} = [(x\alpha^{-1}\alpha)(y\alpha^{-1}\alpha)]\alpha^{-1} = ([(x\alpha^{-1})(y\alpha^{-1})]\alpha)\alpha^{-1}$$
$$= (x\alpha^{-1})(y\alpha^{-1})$$

so that α^{-1} is an automorphism, Q.E.D.

A parallel definition and theorem apply to integral domains, and indeed to abstract algebras in general. One can fruitfully regard an "automorphism" of an abstract algebra A as just a symmetry of A.

Definition. *In any group G, $a^{-1}xa$ is called the* conjugate *of x under "conjugation" by a.*

In Theorem 18 we have already seen that the conjugate of any cycle in a permutation group is another cycle of the same length. A similar interpretation applies to any group of transformations. Thus if α and ϕ are one-one transformations of a space S onto itself, $\psi = \alpha^{-1}\phi\alpha$ is related to ϕ much as in Theorem 18. Specifically, any point q in S can be written as $q = p\alpha$ for some $p \in S$, and

$$(p\alpha)\psi = p\alpha(\alpha^{-1}\phi\alpha) = (p\alpha\alpha^{-1})\phi\alpha = (p\phi)\alpha.$$

Thus ψ is the transformation $p\alpha \to (p\phi)\alpha$; in other words, the conjugate $\psi = \alpha^{-1}\phi\alpha$ is obtained from ϕ by replacing each point p and its image $r = p\phi$ by $p\alpha$ and $r\alpha$, respectively. For example, in the group of the square, $V = R^{-1}HR$; reflection in the vertical axis is conjugate under R to reflection in the horizontal axis because R carries the horizontal axis into the vertical axis.

Theorem 23. *For any fixed element a of the group G, the conjugation $T_a\colon\ x \to a^{-1}xa$ is an automorphism of G.*

Proof. $(a^{-1}xa)(a^{-1}ya) = a^{-1}(xy)a$ for all $x,\ y$.

Automorphisms T_a of the form $x \to a^{-1}xa$ are called *inner* automorphisms; all other automorphisms are *outer*.

It may be checked that the group of symmetries of the square has four distinct inner automorphisms; it has four outer automorphisms. On the other hand, the cyclic group of order three has no inner automorphisms except the identity, but has the "outer" automorphism $x \leftrightarrow x^2$.

Theorem 24. *The inner automorphisms of any group G form a subgroup of the group of all automorphisms of G.*

Proof. Since $b^{-1}(a^{-1}xa)b = (ab)^{-1}x(ab)$, the product of the inner automorphisms T_a and T_b is the inner automorphism T_{ab}; similarly, since $(a^{-1})^{-1}(a^{-1}xa)(a^{-1}) = x$, the inverse of the conjugation T_a is $T_{(a^{-1})}$.

Definition (Galois). *A subgroup S of a group G is normal (in G) if and only if it is invariant under all inner automorphisms of G (i.e., contains with any element all its conjugates).*

A normal subgroup is sometimes called a "self-conjugate" or an "invariant" subgroup.

Thus, the group of rotations of the square is a normal subgroup of the group of all its symmetries; so is the subgroup $[I, R^2]$. Again, every subgroup of an Abelian group is normal, since $a^{-1}xa = a^{-1}ax = x$ for all a, x. The group of translations of the plane is also a normal subgroup of the Euclidean group of all rigid motions of the plane (cf. Chap. IX).

Theorem 25. *The kernel N of any homomorphism $\theta : G \to H$ is a normal subgroup of G.*

Proof. It is a subgroup, by Corollary 2 of Theorem 20. Again, if $a \in N$ and $b \in G$, then $\theta(b^{-1}ab) = b'^{-1}\theta(a)b' = b'^{-1}e'b' = e'$ for $b' = \theta(b)$ and $e' = \theta(e)$ since (by Theorem 20) $\theta(b^{-1}) = [\theta(b)]^{-1}$.

In general, let $a^{-1}Sa$ denote the set of all products $a^{-1}sa$, for s in S. The definition then states that S is normal if and only if the set $a^{-1}Sa$ equals S for every a in G.

Theorem 26. *A subgroup S is normal if and only if all its right cosets are left cosets.*

Proof. If S is normal, $aSa^{-1} = (a^{-1})^{-1}Sa^{-1} = S$ for all s; hence the set Sa of sa ($s \in S$) is the same as the set $(aSa^{-1})a$ of $(asa^{-1})a = as$ ($s \in S$). Thus, $Sa = aS$ for all a. Conversely, if the right coset Sa is a left coset bS, then $a^{-1}Sa = a^{-1}bS$ contains $e = a^{-1}ea$ and so (Lemma 2, §8) is $eS = S$.

It is a corollary that every subgroup S with only one other coset is normal; the elements not in S form the right and left coset of S. Hence the alternating group is a normal subgroup of the symmetric group of degree n.

Remark. Consider the correspondence between elements a of a group G and the inner automorphisms T_a which they induce. By the proof of Theorem 24, $T_a T_b = T_{ab}$: it preserves multiplication. Yet, as in the case of the group of symmetries of the square, it is usually not one-one (R^2 and I induce the same inner automorphism); it is a homomorphism. One easily verifies that the kernel of this homomorphism is precisely the center of G.

EXERCISES

1. How many automorphisms has a cyclic group of order p? one of order pq? (p, q distinct primes).
2. List all the automorphisms of the four group. Which are inner?
3. Find all the automorphisms of the cyclic group of order eight.
4. Show that the automorphisms of the cyclic group of order m are the correspondences $a^k \to a^{rk}$, where r is a unit of the ring $\mathbf{Z}_m$.
5. Prove that in any group, the relation "x is conjugate to y" is an equivalence relation.
6. Prove that an element a of a group induces the inner automorphism identity if and only if it is in the center.
★7. (a) Find an automorphism α of the group of the square such that $R\alpha = R$ and $H\alpha = D$.
   (b) Show that α is an outer automorphism. (*Hint:* Represent the group of the square by the generators R and H discussed in §6.)
8. Prove that if G and H are isomorphic groups, the number of different isomorphisms between G and H is the number of automorphisms of G.
9. Enumerate the inner automorphisms, sets of conjugate elements, and normal subgroups of the group of the square.
★10. Let G be any group, and A its group of automorphisms. Show that the couples (α, g) with $\alpha \in A$ and $g \in G$ form a group (the "holomorph" of G) under the multiplication $(\alpha, g)(\alpha', g') = (\alpha\alpha', (g\alpha')g')$.
★11. (a) Show that the holomorph of the cyclic group of order three is the symmetric group of degree three.
   (b) Show that the holomorph of the cyclic group of order four is the group of the square.
12. Prove that if M and N are normal subgroups of a group G, then so is their intersection.
13. Prove that, under the hypotheses of Ex. 12, the set MN of all products xy ($x \in M$, $y \in N$) is a normal subgroup of G.
14. Prove that the inner automorphisms of any group G are a normal subgroup of the group of all automorphisms of G.
★15. (a) Show that for every rational $c \neq 0$, the correspondence $x \to xc$ is an automorphism of the additive group of all rational numbers.
   (b) Show that this group has no other automorphisms.
★16. Let G be a group of order pq (p, q primes). Show that G either is cyclic or contains an element of order p (or q). In the second case, prove G contains either 1 normal or q conjugate subgroups of order p. In the latter case, show that the $pq - q(p - 1) = q$ elements not of order p form a normal subgroup. Infer that G always has a proper normal subgroup.
17. (a) Show that the defining relations $a^m = b^n = e$, $b^{-1}ab = a^k$ define a group of order mn with a normal subgroup of order m, if $k^n \equiv 1 \pmod{m}$.
   (b) Using Ex. 16, find all groups of order 6, and all groups of order 15.

⋆18. Using Ex. 16, find all possible groups of orders (a) six; (b) ten; (c) fourteen; (d) fifteen.

⋆19. Using the analysis of Ex. 16, show that there are only two nonisomorphic groups of any given prime-square order.

⋆13. Quotient-Groups

Now we shall show how to construct isomorphic replicas of all the homomorphic images* G' of a specified abstract group G.

Indeed, let $x \to x'$ be any homomorphism of G *onto* a group G', and let N be the kernel of this homomorphism. If a and b are any elements of G, we can write $b = at$, so that $b' = a't'$. But by the cancellation law, $a't' = a'$ if and only if $t' = e'$—that is, if and only if $t \in N$. In summary, $b' = a'$ if and only if $b = at$ $(t \in N)$.

Lemma 1. *Two elements of G have the same image in G' if and only if they are in the same coset $Nx = xN$ of the kernel N.*

This establishes a one-one correspondence between the elements of G' and the cosets of N in G. Hence the order of G' is the number of cosets (or "index") of N in G.

Lemma 2. *Let x' and y' be elements of G'. Then $x'y'$ may be found as follows. Let Nx and Ny correspond to x' and y', respectively; then $x'y'$ corresponds to the (unique) coset of N containing the set $NxNy$ of all products uv $(u \in Nx, v \in Ny)$.*

Proof.   If $u = ax, v = by$ $(a, b \in N)$, then

$$(uv)' = a'x'b'y' = e'x'e'y' = x'y'.$$

Thus G' is determined to within isomorphism by G and N: it is isomorphic with the system of cosets of N in G, multiplied by the rule that the "product" $Nx \circ Ny$ of two cosets is the (unique) coset containing all products uv $(u \in Nx, v \in Ny)$.

We can illustrate the preceding discussion by considering the homomorphism between the group G of the symmetries of the square and the "four group" G': $[e, a, b, c]$ (§8), under which $[I, R^2] \to e$, $[R, R^3] \to a$, $[H, V] \to b$, $[D, D'] \to c$. (Check from the group table that this is a homomorphism!) The antecedents of e form the normal subgroup $[I, R^2]$, and those of the other elements are the cosets of $[I, R^2]$. Finally, we can derive the sample rule $ab = c$ by computing the products $[RH, RV, R^3H, R^3V]$—which lie in (in fact, form) the coset $[D, D']$ of antecedents of c.

Conversely, let there be given any normal subgroup N of G, not associated *a priori* with any homomorphism. One can construct from N a homomorphic image G' of G as follows.

* Homomorphic images are also called *epimorphic* images.

The elements of G' are defined as the different cosets Nx of N. The product $[Nx] \circ [Ny]$ of any two cosets Nx and Ny of N is defined as the coset (if any) containing the set $NxNy$ of all products uv ($u \in Nx, v \in Ny$). If $u = ax$ and $v = by$, for a, b in N, then $uv = axby = ab'xy$, where $b' = xbx^{-1}$ is also in N because N is normal. Therefore $N(xy)$ is a coset containing $NxNy$; moreover, since distinct cosets are nonoverlapping, and the set $NxNy$ is nonvoid, there cannot be two different cosets each containing $NxNy$.

We have thus defined a single-valued binary operation on the elements of G' (*alias* cosets of G), which may be written as

(17) $$[Nx] \circ [Ny] = N(xy).$$

In words: the product of any two cosets is found by multiplying in G any pair of "representatives" x and y, and forming the coset containing the product xy. The product $[Ne] \circ [Ny] = N(ey) = Ny$, by (17), so the coset $N = Ne$ is a left identity for the system of cosets. Both $([Nx] \circ [Ny]) \circ [Nz]$ and $[Nx] \circ ([Ny] \circ [Nz])$ contain $(xy)z = x(yz)$, so the multiplication of cosets is associative. Finally, the coset $[Nx^{-1}] \circ [Nx]$ contains $x^{-1}x = e$, so must be $Ne = N$; therefore, left-inverses of cosets exist. These results, with Theorem 4, prove the following

Lemma 3.   *The cosets of any normal subgroup N of G form a group under multiplication.*

Definition.   *The group of cosets of N is called the* quotient-group *(or factor group) of G by N and is denoted by*† G/N.

The correspondence $x \to Nx$ is by (17) a homomorphism of G onto G/N, and the kernel of this homomorphism is N.

Conversely, we have already seen (following Lemma 2) that for any homomorphism of G onto a group G' in which the kernel is N, the image G' is isomorphic with the quotient-group G/N. We conclude

Theorem 27.   *The homomorphic images of a given abstract group G are the quotient-groups G/N by its different normal subgroups, multiplication of cosets of N being defined by (17).*

Remark.   The preceding "construction" of quotient-groups from groups and normal subgroups is analogous to the construction of the ring of integers "mod n" from the integral domain of all integers (Chap. I, §§9–10). The cosets of N are the analogues of the residue classes mod n, and the relation $x \equiv y$ (mod n) can be paralleled by defining $x \equiv y$ (mod N) as the relation $xy^{-1} \in N$—which is equivalent to the assertion that x and y are in the same coset of N (see Ex. 6 of §8).

---

† If G is an Abelian group in which the binary operation is denoted by " $+$," then every subgroup N is normal in G; and the quotient-group is often called the difference group, written $G - N$.

EXERCISES

1. List all abstract groups which are homomorphic images of the group of symmetries of a square.
2. Do the same for the group of a regular hexagon.
3. Prove that the center Z of any group G is a normal subgroup of G, and that G/Z is isomorphic with the group of inner automorphisms of G.
4. Prove that in §8, Ex. 6, $x \equiv y \pmod{S}$ implies $ax \equiv ay \pmod{S}$ for all a if and only if S is a normal subgroup.
5. If G is the group of all rational numbers of the form $2^k 3^m 5^n$, with integral exponents k, m, and n, while S is the multiplicative subgroup of all numbers 2^k, describe (a) the cosets of S; (b) G/S.
6. Let $G \to G'$ be a homomorphism. Show that the set of all antecedents of any subgroup S' of G' is a subgroup S of G—and that if S' is normal, then so is S.
★7. If S is a subgroup and N a normal subgroup of a group G, if $S \cap N = e$ and $S \cup N = G$, prove that G/N is isomorphic to S.
★8. If G is a group, elements of the form $x^{-1}y^{-1}xy$ are called *commutators*. Prove that the set C of all products of such commutators forms a normal subgroup of G.
★9. In Ex. 8, prove that G/C is Abelian. Finally, if N is a normal subgroup of G and G/N is Abelian, prove that N contains C.
★10. Two subgroups S and T of a group G are called *conjugate* if $a^{-1}Sa = T$ for some $a \in G$. Prove that the intersection of any subgroup S of G with its conjugates is a normal subgroup of G.
11. (a) Show that, if M and N are normal subgroups of G with $M \cap N = 1$, then $ab = ba$ for all $a \in M$, $b \in N$. (*Hint:* Show that $aba^{-1}b^{-1} \in M \cap N$.)
    (★b) Show that, in (a), if $M \cup N = G$, then $G = M \times N$.
★12. Let G be any group, S any subgroup of G. For any $a \in G$, let T_a be the permutation $(Sx) \to (Sxa)$ on the right cosets Sx of S. Prove
    (a) the correspondence $a \to T_a$ is a homomorphism;
    (b) the kernel is the normal subgroup of Ex. 10.
13. Prove that the cosets of a nonnormal subgroup do not form a group under the multiplication (17).

VII. Vectors and Vector Spaces

1. Vectors in a Plane

In physics there arise quantities called *vectors* which are not merely numbers, but which have *direction* as well as magnitude. Thus a parallel displacement in the plane depends for its effect not only on the distance but also on the direction of displacement. It may conveniently be repre-

Figure 1

sented by an arrow α of the proper length and direction (Figure 1). The combined effect of two such displacements α and β, executed one after another, is a third "total" displacement γ. If β is applied after α by placing the origin of the arrow β at the terminus of α, then the combined displacement $\gamma = \alpha + \beta$ is the arrow leading from the origin of α to the terminus of β. This is the diagonal of the parallelogram with sides α and β. This rule for finding $\alpha + \beta$ is the so-called *parallelogram law* for the addition of vectors.

A displacement α may be tripled to give a new displacement $3 \cdot \alpha$, or halved to give a displacement $(1/2)\alpha$. One may even form a negative multiple such as -2α, representing a displacement twice as large as α in the direction opposite to α. In general, α may be multiplied by any real number c to form a new displacement $c \cdot \alpha$. If c is positive, $c\alpha$ has the direction of α and a magnitude c times as large, while if c is negative, the direction must be reversed. The numbers c are called *scalars* and the product $c\alpha$ a "scalar" product.

Forces acting on a point in a plane, and velocities and accelerations have similar representations by means of vectors—and in all cases the parallelogram law of vector addition, and multiplication by (real) scalars have much the same significance as with displacements. This illustrates the principle that various physical situations may have the same mathematical representation.

Analytical geometry suggests representing vectors in a plane by pairs of real numbers. We may represent any such vector by an arrow α with origin at $(0, 0)$ and terminus at a suitable point (a_1, a_2), where the coordinates a_1, a_2 are *real* numbers. Then vector sums and scalar products may be computed coordinate by coordinate, using the rules

(1) $$(a_1, a_2) + (b_1, b_2) = (a_1 + b_1, a_2 + b_2),$$

(2) $$c(a_1, a_2) = (ca_1, ca_2).$$

From these rules we easily get the various laws of vector algebra,† such as

(3) $\alpha + \beta = \beta + \alpha,$ $\alpha + (\beta + \gamma) = (\alpha + \beta) + \gamma,$

(4) $c(\alpha + \beta) = c\alpha + c\beta,$ $1 \cdot \alpha = \alpha,$

and so on. Many of these (notably the commutative law of vector addition) also correspond to geometrical principles.

Vector operations may be used to express many familiar geometric ideas. For example, the midpoint of the line joining the terminus of the vector $\alpha = (a_1, a_2)$ to that of $\beta = (b_1, b_2)$ is given by the formulas $((a_1 + b_1)/2, (a_2 + b_2)/2)$, hence by the vector sum $(1/2)(\alpha + \beta)$. The resulting vector is also known as the center of gravity of α and β. A complete list of postulates for vector algebra will be given in §3; we shall first describe other examples of vectors.

EXERCISES

1. Prove the laws (3) and (4) of vector algebra, using the rules (1) and (2).

2. Illustrate the distributive law (4) by a diagram.

3. Show that the vectors in the plane form a group under addition.

4. Show that every vector α in the plane can be represented uniquely as a sum $\alpha = \beta + \gamma$, where β is a vector along the x-axis, γ a vector along the y-axis.

2. Generalizations

The example just described can be generalized in two ways. First, the number of *dimensions* (which was two in §1) can be arbitrary. The first hint of this is seen in the possibility of treating forces and displacements in space in the same way that plane displacements and forces were treated in §1. The only difference is that, in the case of space, vectors have *three* components (x_1, x_2, x_3) instead of two.

Again, it is shown in the theory of statics that the forces acting on a rigid solid can be resolved into *six* components: three pulling the center of gravity in perpendicular directions and three of torque causing rotation about perpendicular axes. The sum of two forces may again be computed component by component, while multiplication by scalars (real numbers) has the same significance as before.

More generally, for any positive whole number n, the n-tuples $\alpha = (a_1, \cdots, a_n)$ of real numbers form an *n-dimensional* vector space which may be regarded as an *n-dimensional* geometry. Thus, straight lines are the sets of elements of the form $\alpha + x\beta$ (α, β fixed, $\beta \neq 0$; x variable); the center of gravity of $\alpha_1, \cdots, \alpha_m$ is $(1/m)(\alpha_1 + \cdots + \alpha_m)$, and so on

---

† We shall systematically use small Greek letters such as α, β, γ, $\cdots$, ξ, η, ζ, $\cdots$ to denote vectors, and small Latin letters to denote scalars.

(this will be developed in Chap. IX). To get a complete geometrical theory, one need only introduce *distance* as in §9 below.

In fact, "phase-spaces" of arbitrarily high dimension (each coordinate corresponds to a degree of freedom) have long been used in dynamics. To the sophisticated mathematician, it seems quite modest to use only four (three of space, one of time), as in relativity. To illustrate this point further, we shall now construct an *infinite*-dimensional vector space commonly used in mathematical analysis.

Let S denote the set of all functions $f(x)$ of a real variable x, which are single-valued and continuous on the interval $0 \leq x \leq 1$. Two such functions $f(x)$ and $g(x)$ have as sum a function $h(x) = f(x) + g(x)$ in S, and the "scalar" product of $f(x)$ by a real constant c is also such a function $cf(x)$. These functions cannot be represented by arrows, but their operations of addition and scalar multiplication have the same formal algebraic properties as our other examples. Vectors in this set S may even be regarded as having one "component" (the value of the function!) at each point x on the line $0 \leq x \leq 1$.

A second line of generalization begins with the observation that, so far as algebraic properties are concerned, the components of vectors and the scalars need not be real numbers, but can be elements of any *field*. Indeed, vectors with *complex* components are constantly used in the theory of electric circuits and in electromagnetism, while one can base the theory of algebraic numbers on the study of vectors with *rational* scalars.

To be specific, we shall define, for any positive integer n and any field F, the system $V_n(F)$ as the set of all n-tuples $\alpha = (a_1, \cdots, a_n)$, $\beta = (b_1, \cdots, b_n)$, $\cdots$ with components a_i and b_i in F. Two operations of (vector) "addition" and "scalar multiplication" (by elements c of F) will be defined as follows:

$$(5) \qquad (a_1, \cdots, a_n) + (b_1, \cdots, b_n) = (a_1 + b_1, \cdots, a_n + b_n),$$

$$(6) \qquad\qquad c(a_1, \cdots, a_n) = (ca_1, \cdots, ca_n).$$

We shall see in §3 that not only all the laws (3), (4) mentioned in §1, but some others as well, are satisfied by $V_n(F)$.

EXERCISES

1. Let $\alpha = (1, 1, 0)$, $\beta = (-1/2, 0, 2/3)$, $\gamma = (0, 1/4, 2)$. Compute
   (a) $\alpha + 2\beta + 3\gamma$,
   (b) $3(\alpha + \beta) - 2(\beta + \gamma)$.
   (c) What is the center of gravity of α, β, γ?
   (d) Solve $6\beta + 5\xi = \alpha$.
2. Let $\alpha = (1, i, 0)$, $\beta = (0, 1 - i, 2i)$, $\gamma = (1, 2 - i, 1)$. Compute
   (a) $2\alpha - i\beta$,
   (b) $i\alpha + (1 + i)\beta - (i + 3)\gamma$,
   (c) Solve $\alpha - i\xi = \beta$.

3. Divide the line segment $\overrightarrow{\alpha\beta}$ in the ratio $2:1$ in Ex. 1 and Ex. 2.

★4. In Ex. 2, can you "divide the line segment $\overrightarrow{\alpha\beta}$ in the ratio $1:2i$"? Explain.

5. Let $V_n(\mathbf{Z}_3)$ consist of vectors with n components in the field of integers mod 3. (a) How many vectors are there in $V_n(\mathbf{Z}_3)$? (b) What can you say about $\alpha + \alpha + \alpha$ in $V_n(\mathbf{Z}_3)$?

★6. Can you define a "midpoint" between two arbitrary points in $V_n(\mathbf{Z}_3)$? A center of gravity for three—for four—arbitrary points? (*Hint:* Try numerical examples.)

3. Vector Spaces and Subspaces

By collecting the basic algebraic properties of vectors, one is led to the concept of a vector space (also often called a "linear space"). This is defined as follows.

Definition. *A vector space V over a field F is a set of elements, called vectors, such that any two vectors α and β of V determine a (unique) vector $\alpha + \beta$ as sum, and that any vector $\alpha \in V$ and any scalar $c \in F$ determine a scalar product $c \cdot \alpha$ in V, with the properties*

(7)   *V is an Abelian group under addition,*

(8) $c \cdot (\alpha + \beta) = c \cdot \alpha + c \cdot \beta, \qquad (c + c') \cdot \alpha = c \cdot \alpha + c' \cdot \alpha,$
$$\text{(Distributive laws)}$$

(9) $(cc') \cdot \alpha = c \cdot (c' \cdot \alpha), \qquad 1 \cdot \alpha = \alpha.$

(Rules (8) and (9) are to hold for all vectors α and β and all scalars c and c'.)

EXAMPLES. The addition and scalar multiplication of n-tuples as defined by (5) and (6) satisfy all these formal laws; for example, the definitions (5) and (6) reduce each side of the distributive laws (8) to a corresponding distributive law which holds component by component. Therefore the set $V_n(F)$ of n-tuples is a vector space over F, in the sense of our definition.

Again, consider the functions f whose domain is any set S whatever (say, any plane region), with the field F as range, so that f assigns to each $x \in S$ a value $f(x) \in F$. The set of all such functions f forms a vector space over F, if the sum $h = f + g$ and the scalar product $h' = c \cdot f$ are the functions defined for each $x \in S$ by the equations $h(x) = f(x) + g(x)$ and $h'(x) = c \cdot f(x)$.

Conforming with our use of the additive notation for the group operation, we shall denote by O the identity element of the group; it is the unique "null" or "zero" vector satisfying

(10) $\alpha + O = O + \alpha = \alpha$ for all α.

The null vector O is not to be confused with the zero scalar 0. However, the two are connected by an identity.

Indeed, the two distributive laws give, for all c and α,

$$c\alpha + 0\alpha = (c + 0)\alpha = c\alpha = c\alpha + O,$$
$$c\alpha + cO = c(\alpha + O) = c \cdot \alpha = c\alpha + O.$$

Now, canceling $c\alpha$ on both sides, we get the two laws

(11) $0\alpha = O$ for all α, $cO = O$ for all c.

Again, the scalar multiple $(-1)\alpha$ acts as the inverse of any given vector α in the group, for

$$\alpha + (-1)\alpha = 1 \cdot \alpha + (-1)\alpha = (1 + (-1))\alpha = 0\alpha = O;$$

hence

(12)   the (additive) group *inverse* of any vector α is $(-1)\alpha$.

It follows from (11)–(12) that the cyclic subgroup of the "powers" of any vector α consists of the *multiples* of α by the different integers n.

In ordinary three-dimensional vector space, $V_3(\mathbf{R})$, the vectors which lie in a fixed plane through the origin form by themselves a "two-dimensional" vector space which is part of the whole space. Similarly, the set S of all vectors lying on a fixed line through the origin is closed under the operations of addition and multiplication by scalars, hence this set is also a "subspace" of $V_3(\mathbf{R})$.

Definition. *A subspace S of a vector space V is a subset of V which is itself a vector space with respect to the operations of addition and scalar multiplication in V.*

A nonvoid subset S is a subspace if and only if the sum of any two vectors of S lies in S and any product of any vector of S by a scalar lies in S. This statement may be easily checked from the definition. The analogy with earlier definitions of a subfield and subgroup is obvious. Geometrically, a "subspace" is simply a linear subspace (line, plane, etc.) through the origin O.

For example, the vectors of the form $(0, x_2, 0, x_4)$ constitute a subspace of $V_4(F)$, for any field F. Also, the null vector O alone is a subspace of any vector space.

Again, the set of polynomials of degree at most seven is a subspace of the vector space of all polynomials—whether the base field is real or not. Similarly, the set of all continuous functions $f(x)$ defined for $0 \leq x \leq 1$ is a subspace of the linear space of all functions defined on the same domain.

For given vectors $\alpha_1, \cdots, \alpha_m$ in a vector space V, the set of all *linear combinations*

$$c_1\alpha_1 + c_2\alpha_2 + \cdots + c_m\alpha_m \qquad \text{(each } c_i \text{ a scalar)}$$

of the α_i is a subspace. This is because of the identities

$$(13) \quad (c_1\alpha_1 + \cdots + c_m\alpha_m) + (c_1'\alpha_1 + \cdots + c_m'\alpha_m)$$
$$= (c_1 + c_1')\alpha_1 + \cdots + (c_m + c_m')\alpha_m,$$
$$(14) \quad c'(c_1\alpha_1 + \cdots + c_m\alpha_m) = (c'c_1)\alpha_1 + \cdots + (c'c_m)\alpha_m,$$

valid for all vectors α_i and for all scalars c_i, c_i', and c'. This proves

Theorem 1. *The set of all linear combinations of any set of vectors in a space V is a subspace of V.*

This subspace is evidently the smallest subspace containing all the given vectors; hence it is called the subspace *generated* or *spanned* by them. The subspace spanned by a single vector $\alpha_1 \neq O$ is the set S_1 of all scalar multiples $c\alpha_1$; geometrically, this is simply the line through the origin and α_1. Similarly, the subspace spanned by two noncollinear vectors α_1 and α_2 turns out to be the plane passing through the origin, α_1, and α_2.

Theorem 2. *The intersection $S \cap T$ of any two subspaces of a vector space V is itself a subspace of V.*

Proof. The *intersection* of two given subspaces S and T is defined to be the set $S \cap T$ of all those vectors belonging both to S and to T (cf. Theorem 17 of Chap. VI, on the intersection of two subgroups). If α and β are two such vectors, their sum $\alpha + \beta$ must be in S (since S is a subspace containing α and β) and likewise in T, hence is also in the intersection $S \cap T$. Similarly, any scalar multiple $c \cdot \alpha$ of α is in $S \cap T$. Q.E.D.

Again, any two subspaces S and T of a vector space V determine a set $S + T$ consisting of all sums $\alpha + \beta$, for α in S and β in T. By the commutative, associative, and distributive laws (3) and (4) this set is itself a subspace, called the *linear sum* of S and T. It clearly contains S and T, and is contained in any other subspace R containing both S and T; hence the concept of linear sum is analogous to that of the join (cf. Chap. VI, §8) of two subgroups. These properties of $S + T$ may be stated as

$$(15) \quad \begin{array}{l} S \subset S + T, \quad T \subset S + T; \\ S \subset R \ \text{ and } \ T \subset R \ \text{ imply } \ S + T \subset R, \end{array}$$

where $S \subset R$ means that the subspace S is contained in the subspace R.

EXERCISES

1. Prove that, in any vector space, $c\alpha = O$ implies $c = 0$ or $\alpha = O$.

2. In Ex. 1, §2, compute $7(2(\alpha - 3\beta) + (1/3)(3\beta - 6\gamma)) - 2(\alpha - \gamma) + 5\beta + 2\alpha$.

3. In Ex. 2, §2, compute $(1 + 2i)[(2 - i)(2\alpha - 3\beta)] - 8\alpha - 9i\beta$.

4. Which of the following subsets of $V_n(Q)$ $(n \geqq 2)$ constitute subspaces (here ξ denotes $(x_1, \cdots, x_n)$):

(a) all ξ with x_1 an integer; (b) all ξ with $x_2 = 0$;

(c) all ξ with either x_1 or x_2 zero; (d) all ξ such that $3x_1 + 4x_2 = 1$;

(e) all ξ such that $7x_1 - x_2 = 0$?

5. Which of the following sets of real functions $f(x)$ defined on $0 \leqq x \leqq 1$ are subspaces of the vector space of all such functions:

   (a) all polynomials of degree four;
   (b) all polynomials of degree $\leqq$ four (including $f(x) = 0$);
   (c) all functions f such that $2f(0) = f(1)$;
   (d) all functions such that $0 + f(1) = f(0) + 1$;
   (e) all positive functions;
   (f) all functions satisfying $f(x) = f(1 - x)$ for all x?

6. Which of the sets of functions described in Ex. 3, §3, Chap. III, form vector spaces when D is taken to be a field F?

7. Let S be the subspace of $V_3(\mathbf{Q})$ consisting of all vectors of the form $(0, x_2, x_3)$, and T the subspace spanned by $(1, 2, 0)$ and $(3, 1, 2)$. Which vectors are in $S \cap T$? Which in $S + T$?

8. In $V_3(\mathbf{Z}_3)$, how many vectors are spanned by $(1, 2, 1)$ and $(2, 1, 1)$? By $(1, 2, 1)$ and $(2, 1, 2)$?

9. In $V_3(\mathbf{Q})$ show that the plane $x_3 = 0$ may be spanned by each of the following pairs of vectors: $(1, 0, 0)$ and $(1, 1, 0)$; $(2, 2, 0)$ and $(4, 1, 0)$; $(3, 2, 0)$ and $(-3, 2, 0)$.

10. If S is spanned by ξ_1 and ξ_2, T by η_1, η_2, and η_3, show that $S + T$ is spanned by ξ_1, ξ_2, η_1, η_2, η_3. Generalize this result.

11. Construct an addition table for $V_2(\mathbf{Z}_2)$ and list its subspaces.

12. Construct $V_3(\mathbf{Z}_2)$ and tabulate its subspaces.

13. Prove that the set of all solutions $(x_1, \cdots, x_n)$ of a pair of homogeneous linear equations $a_1x_1 + \cdots + a_nx_n = 0$, $b_1x_1 + \cdots + b_nx_n = 0$ is a subspace of $V_n(F)$, where a_i, b_i, x_i all lie in F.

★14. Prove that the vector space postulate $1 \cdot \alpha = \alpha$ cannot be proved from the other postulates. (*Hint:* Construct in the plane a pseudo-scalar product $c \otimes \alpha$, the projection of $c \cdot \alpha$ on a fixed line.)

★15. Show that the postulate of commutativity for vector addition is redundant. (*Hint:* Expand $(1 + 1)(\alpha + \beta)$ in two ways.)

4. Linear Independence and Dimension

The important geometric notion of the dimension of a vector space or subspace remains to be defined abstractly. It will be described as the minimum number of vectors spanning the space (or subspace).

Thus, ordinary space $V_3(\mathbf{R})$ can be spanned by the three vectors $(1, 0, 0)$, $(0, 1, 0)$, and $(0, 0, 1)$ of unit length lying along the three coordinate axes, but by no set of two vectors (a set of two noncollinear vectors spans a plane through the origin).

More generally, any $V_n(F)$ is spanned by n *unit vectors*

$$(16) \quad \varepsilon_1 = (1, 0, \cdots, 0), \varepsilon_2 = (0, 1, \cdots, 0), \cdots,$$
$$\varepsilon_n = (0, 0, \cdots, 1).$$

Indeed, any vector of $V_n(F)$ is a linear combination of these, because

(17) $(x_1, x_2, \cdots, x_n) = x_1\varepsilon_1 + x_2\varepsilon_2 + \cdots + x_n\varepsilon_n.$

We shall prove in Corollary 2 of Theorem 4 that $V_n(F)$ cannot be spanned by fewer than n vectors. This justifies calling $V_n(F)$ an n-dimensional vector space over the field F.

Not only do $\varepsilon_1, \cdots, \varepsilon_n$ generate the whole of $V_n(F)$; in addition, $x_1\varepsilon_1 + \cdots + x_n\varepsilon_n = O$ if and only if $(x_1, \cdots, x_n) = (0, \cdots, 0)$—that is, if and only if $x_1 = \cdots = x_n = 0$. This means that the unit vectors are "linearly independent" in the following sense.

Definition. *The vectors $\alpha_1, \cdots, \alpha_m$ are linearly independent (over F) if and only if, for all scalars c_i in F,*

(18) $c_1\alpha_1 + c_2\alpha_2 + \cdots + c_m\alpha_m = O$
          implies $c_1 = c_2 = \cdots = c_m = 0.$

Vectors which are not linearly independent are called linearly dependent.

It is a trivial consequence of the definition that any subset of a linearly independent set is linearly independent. However, the following relation of dependence to linear combinations is more important:

Theorem 3. *The non-zero vectors $\alpha_1, \cdots, \alpha_m$ in a space V are linearly dependent if and only if some one of the vectors α_k is a linear combination of the preceding ones.*

Proof. In case the vector α_k is a linear combination $\alpha_k = c_1\alpha_1 + \cdots + c_{k-1}\alpha_{k-1}$ of the preceding ones, we have at once a linear relation

$$c_1\alpha_1 + c_2\alpha_2 + \cdots + c_{k-1}\alpha_{k-1} + (-1)\alpha_k = O,$$

with at least one coefficient, (-1), not zero. Hence the vectors are dependent, by (18).

Conversely, suppose that the vectors are dependent, so that $d_1\alpha_1 + d_2\alpha_2 + \cdots + d_m\alpha_m = O$, and choose the last subscript k for which $d_k \neq 0$. One can then solve for α_k as the linear combination

$$\alpha_k = (-d_k^{-1}d_1)\alpha_1 + \cdots + (-d_k^{-1}d_{k-1})\alpha_{k-1}.$$

This gives α_k as a combination of preceding vectors, except in the case $k = 1$. In this case $d_1\alpha_1 = O$, with $d_1 \neq 0$, so $\alpha_1 = O$, contrary to the hypothesis that none of the given vectors equals zero. Q.E.D.

For instance, the three vectors $\beta_1 = (2, 0, 0)$, $\beta_2 = (1, 3, 0)$, and $\beta_3 = (0, -2, 0)$ do not span the whole of ordinary space $V_3(\mathbf{R})$ because they all lie in one plane. We can express this linear dependence either by the relation $\beta_1 - 2\beta_2 - 3\beta_3 = O$, or (solving for β_1) by $\beta_1 = 2\beta_2 + 3\beta_3$. Thus, the set $(\beta_1, \beta_2, \beta_3)$ spans the same subspace as does its proper subset (β_2, β_3). This illustrates

Corollary 1. *A set of vectors is linearly dependent if and only if it contains a proper (i.e., smaller) subset generating the same subspace.*

Namely, we can delete from the set any one vector which is O or which is a linear combination of the preceding ones, and show that the remaining vectors generate the same subspace. Now using induction, we obtain

Corollary 2. *Any finite set of vectors contains a linearly independent subset which spans (generates) the same subspace.*

We can now state the fundamental theorem on linear dependence.

Theorem 4. *Let n vectors span a vector space V containing r linearly independent vectors. Then $n \geqq r$.*

Proof. Let $A_0 = [\alpha_1, \cdots, \alpha_n]$ be a sequence of n vectors spanning V, and let $X = [\xi_1, \cdots, \xi_r]$ be a sequence of r linearly independent vectors of V. Since A_0 spans V, ξ_1 is a linear combination of the α_i, so that the sequence $B_1 = [\xi_1, \alpha_1, \cdots, \alpha_n]$ both spans V and is linearly dependent. By Theorem 3, some vector of B_1 must be dependent on its predecessors. This cannot be ξ_1, since ξ_1 belongs to a set X of independent vectors. Hence some vector α_i is dependent on its predecessors $\xi_1, \alpha_1, \cdots, \alpha_{i-1}$ in B_1. Deleting this term, we obtain, as in Corollary 1, a subsequence $A_1 = [\xi_1, \alpha_1, \cdots, \alpha_{i-1}, \alpha_{i+1}, \cdots, \alpha_n]$ which still spans V.

Now repeat the argument. Construct the sequence $B_2 = [\xi_2, A_1] = [\xi_2, \xi_1, \alpha_1, \cdots, \alpha_{i-1}, \alpha_{i+1}, \cdots, \alpha_n]$. Like B_1, B_2 spans V and is linearly dependent. Hence as before, some vector of B_2 is a linear combination of its predecessors. Because the ξ_i are linearly independent, this vector cannot be ξ_2 or ξ_1, so must be some α_j, with a subscript $j \neq i$ (say, with $j > i$). Deletion of this α_j leaves a new sequence

$$A_2 = [\xi_2, \xi_1, \alpha_1, \cdots, \alpha_{i-1}, \alpha_{i+1}, \cdots, \alpha_{j-1}, \alpha_{j+1}, \cdots, \alpha_n]$$

of n vectors spanning V. This argument can be repeated r times, until the elements of X are exhausted. Each time, an element of A_0 is thrown out. Hence A_0 must have originally contained at least r elements, proving $n \geqq r$, Q.E.D.

Theorem 4 has several important consequences. We shall prove these now for convenience, even though the full significance of the concepts of "basis" and "dimension" which they involve, will not become apparent until §8.

Definition. *A basis of a vector space is a linearly independent subset which generates (spans) the whole space. A vector space is* finite-dimensional *if and only if it has a finite basis.*

For example, the unit vectors $\varepsilon_1, \cdots, \varepsilon_n$ of (16) are a basis of $V_n(F)$.

Corollary 1. *All bases of any finite-dimensional vector space V have the same finite number of elements.*

Proof. Since V is finite-dimensional, it has a finite basis $A = [\alpha_1, \cdots, \alpha_n]$; let B be any other basis of V. Since A spans V and B is linearly independent, Theorem 4 shows that B is finite, say with r elements, and that $n \geq r$. On the other hand, B spans V and A is linearly independent, so $r \geq n$. Hence $n = r$.

The number of elements in any basis of a finite-dimensional vector space V is called the *dimension* of V, and is denoted by $d[V]$. By Theorem 4, we have

Corollary 2. *If a vector space V has dimension n, then (i) any n + 1 elements of V are linearly dependent, and (ii) no set of n − 1 elements can span V.*

Theorem 5. *Any independent set of elements of a finite-dimensional vector space V is part of a basis.*

Proof. Let the independent set be $\xi_1, \cdots, \xi_r$, and let $\alpha_1, \cdots, \alpha_n$ be a basis for V. Form the sequence $C = [\xi_1, \cdots, \xi_r, \alpha_1, \cdots, \alpha_n]$. We can extract (Theorem 3, Corollary 2) an independent subsequence of C which also spans V (hence is a basis for V), by deleting every term which is a linear combination of its predecessors. Since the ξ_i are independent, no ξ_i will be deleted, and so the resulting basis will include every ξ_i.

Corollary. *For n vectors $\alpha_1, \cdots, \alpha_n$ of an n-dimensional vector space to be a basis, it is sufficient that they span V or that they be linearly independent.*

Proof. If $A = \{\alpha_1, \cdots, \alpha_n\}$ spans V, it contains a subset A' which is a basis of V (Theorem 3, Corollary 2); since the dimension of V is n, this subset A' must have n elements (Theorem 4, Corollary 1). Hence $A' = A$, and A is a basis of V. Again, if A is independent, then it is a part of a basis by Theorem 5, and this basis has n elements by Corollary 1 of Theorem 4, and so will be A itself.

EXERCISES

1. Show that the vectors (a_1, a_2) and (b_1, b_2) in $V_2(F)$ are linearly dependent if and only if $a_1 b_2 - a_2 b_1 = 0$.
2. Do the vectors $(1, 1, 0)$ and $(0, 1, 1)$ form a basis of $V_3(Q)$? Why?
3. Prove that if β is not in the subspace S, but is in the subspace spanned by S and α, then α is in the subspace spanned by S and β.
4. Prove that if ξ_1, ξ_2, ξ_3 are independent in $V_n(\mathbf{R})$, then so are $\xi_1 + \xi_2$, $\xi_1 + \xi_3$, $\xi_2 + \xi_3$. Is this true in every $V_n(F)$?

5. How many elements are in each subspace spanned by four linearly independent elements of $V_7(\mathbf{Z}_3)$? Generalize your result.

6. Define a "vector space" over an integral domain D. Which of the postulates and theorems discussed so far fail to hold in this more general case?

★7. Prove: Three vectors with rational coordinates are linearly independent in $V_3(\mathbf{Q})$ if and only if they are linearly independent in $V_3(\mathbf{R})$. Generalize this result in two ways.

8. If the vectors $\alpha_1, \cdots, \alpha_m$ are linearly independent, show that the vector β is a linear combination of $\alpha_1, \cdots, \alpha_m$ if and only if the vectors $\alpha_1, \cdots, \alpha_m, \beta$ are linearly dependent.

★9. Show that the real numbers 1, $\sqrt{2}$, and $\sqrt{5}$ are linearly independent over the field of rational numbers.

10. Find four vectors of $V_3(\mathbf{C})$ which together span a subspace of two dimensions, any two vectors being linearly independent.

11. If $c_1\alpha + c_2\beta + c_3\gamma = 0$, where $c_1 c_3 \neq 0$, show that α and β generate the same subspace as do β and γ.

12. If two subspaces S and T of a vector space V have the same dimension, prove that $S \subset T$ implies $S = T$.

★13. (a) How many linearly independent sets of two elements has $V_3(\mathbf{Z}_2)$? How many of three elements? Of four elements?

   (b) Generalize your formula to $V_n(\mathbf{Z}_2)$ and to $V_3(\mathbf{Z}_p)$.

★14. How many different k-dimensional subspaces has $V_n(\mathbf{Z}_p)$?

5. Matrices and Row-equivalence

Problems concerning specific vectors in $V_n(F)$ with given numerical coordinates can almost always be formulated as problems in simultaneous linear equations. As such, they usually can be solved by the process of *elimination* described in Chap. II, §3. We will now begin a systematic study of this process, which centers around the fundamental concept of *matrices* and their *row-equivalence*. We first define the former concept.

Definition. *A rectangular array of elements of a field F, having m rows and n columns, is called an $m \times n$ matrix over F.*

An important application of the concept of a matrix is to the subspace spanned by a given set of vectors $\alpha_1, \cdots, \alpha_m$ in $V_n(F)$. These vectors define the $m \times n$ matrix

$$(19) \qquad A = \begin{pmatrix} a_{11} & a_{12} & \cdots & a_{1n} \\ a_{21} & a_{22} & \cdots & a_{2n} \\ \vdots & \vdots & & \vdots \\ a_{m1} & a_{m2} & \cdots & a_{mn} \end{pmatrix},$$

whose ith row consists of the components $a_{i1}, \cdots, a_{in}$ of the vector α_i. The matrix (19) may be written compactly as $\| a_{ij} \|$. The *row space* of the matrix A is that subspace of $V_n = V_n(F)$ which is spanned by the rows of A, regarded as vectors in V_n. We now ask: when do two $m \times n$ matrices have the same row space? That is, when do their rows span the same sub-space of V_n? A partial answer to this question is provided by the concept of *row-equivalence*, which we now define.

We now consider the effect on the matrix A in (19) of the following three types of steps, called *elementary row operations:*

(i) The interchange of any two rows,
(ii) Multiplication of a row by any non-zero constant c in F,
(iii) The addition of any multiple of one row to any other row.

The $m \times n$ matrix B is called *row-equivalent* to the $m \times n$ matrix A if B can be obtained from A by a finite succession of elementary row operations. Since the effect of each such operation can be undone by another operation of the same type, we have the following

Lemma. *The inverse of any elementary row operation is itself an elementary row operation.*

Hence, if B is row-equivalent to A, then A is row-equivalent to B; that is, the relation of row-equivalence is symmetric. It is clearly also reflexive and transitive, hence it is an equivalence relation.

Theorem 6. *Row-equivalent matrices have the same row space.*

Proof. Denote the successive row vectors of the $m \times n$ matrix A by $\alpha_1, \cdots, \alpha_m$. The row space of A is then the set of all vectors of the form $c_1\alpha_1 + \cdots + c_m\alpha_m$, and the elementary row operations become:

(i) Interchanging any α_i with any α_j $(i \neq j)$,
(ii) Replacing α_i by $c\alpha_i$ for any scalar $c \neq 0$,
(iii) Replacing α_i by $\alpha_i + d\alpha_j$, for any $j \neq i$ and any scalar d.

It suffices to consider the effect upon the row space of a single elementary row operation of each type. Since operations of types (i) and (ii) clearly do not alter the row space, we shall confine our attention to the case of a single elementary operation of type (iii). Take the typical case of the addition of a multiple of the second row to the first row, which replaces the rows $\alpha_1, \cdots, \alpha_m$ of A by the new rows

$$(20) \qquad \beta_1 = \alpha_1 + d\alpha_2, \qquad \beta_2 = \alpha_2, \cdots, \beta_m = \alpha_m$$

of the row-equivalent matrix B. Any vector γ in the row space of B has the form $\gamma = \sum c_i\beta_i$, hence on substitution from (20) we have

$$\gamma = c_1(\alpha_1 + d\alpha_2) + c_2\alpha_2 + \cdots + c_m\alpha_m,$$

which shows that γ is in the row space of A. Conversely, by the Lemma, the rows of A can be expressed in terms of the rows of B as

$$\alpha_1 = \beta_1 - d\beta_2, \qquad \alpha_2 = \beta_2, \cdots, \alpha_m = \beta_m,$$

so that the same argument shows that the row space of A is contained in the row space of B; thus these row spaces are equal.

This proof gives at once

Corollary 1. *Any sequence of elementary row operations reducing a matrix A to a row-equivalent matrix B yields explicit expressions for the rows of B as linear combinations of the rows of A.*

Simultaneous linear equations. A second application of the concept of row-equivalent matrices is to the solution of systems of simultaneous linear equations, by the method of *elimination*. This method has been described in Chap. II, §3; we now treat it systematically.

Consider the system of simultaneous linear equations

$$(21) \quad \begin{pmatrix} a_{11}x_1 + a_{12}x_2 + \cdots + a_{1n}x_n = a_{1,n+1} \\ a_{21}x_1 + a_{22}x_2 + \cdots + a_{2n}x_n = a_{2,n+1} \\ \vdots \\ a_{m1}x_1 + a_{m2}x_2 + \cdots + a_{mn}x_n = a_{m,n+1} \end{pmatrix}$$

where the coefficients a_{ij} are given constants in the field F. We wish to know which *solution vectors* $\xi = (x_1, \cdots, x_n)$, if any, satisfy the given system of equations (21).

It is easy to verify that the set of solution vectors ξ satisfying (21) is invariant under each of the following operations: (i) The interchange of any two equations, (ii) Multiplication of an equation by any non-zero constant c in F, (iii) Addition of any multiple of one equation to any other equation. But as applied to the $m \times (n + 1)$ matrix of constants a_{ij} in (21), these are just the three elementary row operations defined earlier. This proves

Corollary 2. *If A and B are row-equivalent $m \times (n + 1)$ matrices over the same field F, then the system of simultaneous linear equations (21) has the same set of solution vectors $\xi = (x_1, \cdots, x_n)$ as the system*

$$(21') \quad \begin{pmatrix} b_{11}x_1 + b_{12}x_2 + \cdots + b_{1n}x_n = b_{1,n+1} \\ b_{21}x_1 + b_{22}x_2 + \cdots + b_{2n}x_n = b_{2,n+1} \\ \vdots \\ b_{m1}x_1 + b_{m2}x_2 + \cdots + b_{mn}x_n = b_{m,n+1} \end{pmatrix}.$$

EXERCISES

1. If A and B are row-equivalent matrices, prove that the rows of A are linearly independent if and only if those of B are.
2. Show that the meaning of row-equivalence is unchanged if one replaces the operation (iii) by:
   (iii') The addition of any row to any other row.
★3. Show that any elementary row operation of type (i) can be effected by a succession of four operations of types (ii) and (iii). (*Hint:* Try 2×2 matrices.)

6. Tests for Linear Dependence

We now aim to use elementary row operations to simplify a given $m \times n$ matrix A as much as possible. In any non-zero row of A, the first non-zero entry may be called the "leading" entry of that row. We say that a matrix A is *row-reduced* if:

(a) Every leading entry (of a non-zero *row*) is 1,
(b) Every *column* containing such a leading entry 1 has all its other entries zero.

Sample 4×6 row-reduced matrices are

$$(22) \quad \begin{pmatrix} 0 & 0 & 1 & r_{14} & r_{15} & r_{16} \\ 1 & 0 & 0 & r_{24} & r_{25} & r_{26} \\ 0 & 1 & 0 & r_{34} & r_{35} & r_{36} \\ 0 & 0 & 0 & 0 & 0 & 0 \end{pmatrix}, \quad \begin{pmatrix} 1 & d_{12} & 0 & d_{14} & 0 & d_{16} \\ 0 & 0 & 1 & d_{24} & 0 & d_{26} \\ 0 & 0 & 0 & 0 & 1 & d_{36} \\ 0 & 0 & 0 & 0 & 0 & 0 \end{pmatrix}.$$

Theorem 7. *Any matrix A is row-equivalent to a row-reduced matrix, by elementary row operations of types (ii) and (iii).*

Proof. Suppose that the given matrix A with entries a_{ij} has a non-zero first row with leading entry a_{1t}, located in the tth column. Multiply the first row by a_{1t}^{-1}; this leading entry becomes one. Now subtract a_{it} times the first row from the ith row, for every $i \neq 1$. This reduces every other entry in column t to zero, so that conditions (a) and (b) are satisfied as regards the first row.

Now let the same construction be applied to the other rows in succession. The application involving row k does not alter the columns containing the leading entries of rows $1, \cdots, k-1$, because row k already had entry zero in each such column. Hence, after the application involving row k, we have a matrix satisfying conditions (a) and (b) at its first k rows. Theorem 7 now follows by induction on k.

By permutations of rows (i.e., a succession of elementary row operations of type (i)), we can evidently rearrange the rows of a row-reduced matrix R so that

(c) Each zero row of R comes below all non-zero rows of R.

Suppose that there are r non-zero rows, and that the leading entry of row i appears in column t_i, for $i = 1, \cdots, r$. Since any such column has all its other entries zero, we have $t_i \neq t_j$ whenever $i \neq j$. By a further permutation of rows, we can then arrange R so that

(d) $t_1 < t_2 < \cdots < t_r$ (leading entry of row i in column t_i).

A row-reduced matrix which also satisfies (c) and (d) is called a (row) *reduced echelon matrix* (the leading entries appear "in echelon"). We have proved the

Corollary. *Any matrix is row-equivalent to a reduced echelon matrix.*

For example, the second matrix of (22) is already a reduced echelon matrix; the first matrix of (22) is not, but can be brought to this form by placing the first row after the third row.

Theorem 8. *Let E be a row-reduced matrix with non-zero rows $\gamma_1, \cdots,$ γ_r, and leading entries 1 in columns $t_1, \cdots, t_r$. Then, for any vector*

$$\beta = y_1\gamma_1 + \cdots + y_r\gamma_r$$

in the row space of E, the coefficient y_i of γ_i is the entry of β in the column t_i; i.e., the t_i-th entry of β.

Proof. Since all entries of E in column t_i are zero, except that of γ_i, which is one, the t_i-th component of β must be $y_i \cdot 1$.

Corollary 1. *The non-zero rows of a row-reduced matrix are linearly independent.*

For if $\beta = O$, then every $y_i = 0$ in the preceding theorem.

Corollary 2. *Let the $m \times n$ matrix A be row-equivalent, as in Theorem 7, to a row-reduced matrix R. Then the non-zero rows of R form a basis of the row space of A.*

Proof. These rows of R are linearly independent, by Corollary 1, and span the row space of R. They are thus a basis of this row space, which by Theorem 6 is identical to the row space of A.

The *rank* r of a matrix A is defined as the dimension of the row space of A. Since this space is spanned by the rows of A, which must contain a linearly independent set of rows spanning the row space, we see that the rank of A can also be described as the maximum number of linearly independent rows of A. By Theorem 6, row-equivalent matrices have the same rank.

In particular, an $n \times n$ (square!) matrix A has rank n if and only if all its rows are linearly independent. One such matrix is the $n \times n$ *identity matrix* I_n, which has entries 1 along the main diagonal (upper left to lower right) and zeros elsewhere.

Corollary 3. *An $n \times n$ matrix A has rank n if and only if it is row-equivalent to the $n \times n$ identity matrix I_n.*

Proof. A is row-equivalent to a reduced echelon matrix E which also has rank n. This matrix E then has n non-zero rows, hence n leading entries 1 in n different columns and no other non-zero entries in these columns (which include all the columns). Because of the ordering of the rows (condition (d) above), E is then just the identity matrix. Q.E.D.

In testing vectors for linear independence, or more generally in computing the dimension of a subspace (= rank of a matrix), it is needless to use the *reduced* echelon form. It is sufficient to bring the matrix to any echelon form, such as the form of the following 4×7 matrix:

$$E = \begin{pmatrix} 0 & 1 & d_{13} & d_{14} & d_{15} & d_{16} & d_{17} \\ 0 & 0 & 0 & 1 & d_{25} & d_{26} & d_{27} \\ 0 & 0 & 0 & 0 & 1 & d_{36} & d_{37} \\ 0 & 0 & 0 & 0 & 0 & 0 & 0 \end{pmatrix}.$$

Such an echelon matrix may be defined by the condition that the leading entry in each non-zero row is 1, and that, in each row after the first, the number of zeros preceding this entry 1 is larger than the corresponding number in the preceding row.

Thus, after reduction to echelon form, the rank of a matrix can be found immediately by applying the following theorem.

Theorem 9.   *The rank of any matrix A is the number of non-zero rows in any echelon matrix row-equivalent to A.*

The proof will be left as an exercise.

Example.   Test $\alpha_1 = (1, -1, 1, 3)$, $\alpha_2 = (2, -5, 3, 10)$,   and $\alpha_3 = (3, 3, 1, 1)$ for independence. By transformations of type (iii), obtain the new rows $\beta_1 = \alpha_1$, $\beta_2 = \alpha_2 - 2\alpha_1 = (0, -3, 1, 4)$, $\beta_3 = \alpha_3 - 3\alpha_1 = (0, 6, -2, -8)$. Finally, set $\gamma_1 = \beta_1$, $\gamma_2 = -(1/3)\beta_2$, $\gamma_3 = \beta_3 - 6\gamma_2 = \beta_3 + 2\beta_2 = O$. There results the echelon matrix C with rows γ_1, γ_2, γ_3, sketched below; since C has a row of zeros, the original α_i are linearly

$$C = \begin{pmatrix} 1 & -1 & 1 & 3 \\ 0 & 1 & -1/3 & -4/3 \\ 0 & 0 & 0 & 0 \end{pmatrix}$$

dependent. By substitution in the definition of $\gamma_3 = O$, we have the explicit dependence relation

$$O = \gamma_3 = \beta_3 + 2\beta_2 = (\alpha_3 - 3\alpha_1) + 2(\alpha_2 - 2\alpha_1) = -7\alpha_1 + 2\alpha_2 + \alpha_3$$

between the α's.

Appendix on Row-equivalence.   Reduced echelon matrices provide a convenient test for row-equivalence.

Theorem 10.   *There is only one $m \times n$ reduced echelon matrix E with a given row space $S \subset V_n$.*

Proof.   Let the reduced echelon matrix E with row space S have the non-zero rows $\gamma_1, \cdots, \gamma_r$, where γ_i has leading entry 1 in column t_i. By condition (d), $t_1 < t_2 < \cdots < t_r$. Let $\beta = y_1\gamma_1 + \cdots + y_r\gamma_r$ be any non-zero vector in the row space of E; by Thm. 8, β has entry y_i in column t_i. If y_s is the first non-zero y_i, then $\beta = y_s\gamma_s + \cdots + y_r\gamma_r$. Because $t_s < \cdots < t_r$, the leading entries of the remaining $\gamma_{s+1}, \cdots, \gamma_r$

lie beyond t_r, so that β has y_s as its leading entry in column t_s. In other words, every vector β of S has leading entry in one of the columns $t_1, \cdots, t_s$. Each of these columns occurs (as the leading entry of a γ_i); hence the row space S determines the indices $t_1, \cdots, t_r$.

The rows $\gamma_1, \cdots, \gamma_r$ of E have leading entry 1, and entries zero in all but one of the columns $t_1, \cdots, t_r$. If β is any vector of S with leading entry 1 in some column t_i and entries zero in the other columns t_j, then, by Theorem 8, β must be γ_i. Thus the row space and the column indices uniquely determine the rows $\gamma_1, \cdots, \gamma_r$ of E as required. Q.E.D.

Corollary 1. *Every $m \times n$ matrix A is row-equivalent to one and only one reduced echelon matrix.*

This result, which is immediate, may be summarized by saying that the reduced echelon matrices provide a *canonical form* for matrices under row-equivalence: every matrix is row-equivalent to one and only one matrix in the canonical form.

Corollary 2. *Two $m \times n$ matrices A and B are row-equivalent if and only if they have the same row space.*

Proof. If A is row-equivalent to B, then A and B have the same row space, by Theorem 6. Conversely, if A and B have the same row space, they are row-equivalent to reduced echelon matrices E and E', respectively. Since E and E' have the same row space, they are identical, by Theorem 10. Hence A is indeed row-equivalent (through $E = E'$) to B.

These results emphasize again the fact that the row-equivalence of matrices is just another language for the study of subspaces of $V_n(F)$.

EXERCISES

1. Show the row-equivalence of $\begin{pmatrix} 5 & 2 & 7 \\ -3 & 4 & 1 \\ -1 & -2 & -3 \end{pmatrix}$ and $\begin{pmatrix} 1 & 0 & 1 \\ 0 & 1 & 1 \\ 0 & 0 & 0 \end{pmatrix}$.

2. Reduce each of the following matrices to row-equivalent echelon form:

(a) $\begin{pmatrix} 1 & -1 & 3 \\ 2 & -4 & 1 \\ 0 & 3 & 2 \end{pmatrix}$, (b) $\begin{pmatrix} -5 & 6 & -3 \\ 3 & 1 & 11 \\ 4 & -2 & 8 \end{pmatrix}$, (c) $\begin{pmatrix} 1 & 6 & -2 & 5 \\ 4 & 0 & 4 & -2 \\ 7 & 2 & 0 & 2 \\ -6 & 3 & -3 & 3 \end{pmatrix}$,

(d) $\begin{pmatrix} 2 & -1 & 3 & 2 \\ 0 & 2 & 1 & 4 \\ 4 & -2 & 3 & 9 \\ 2 & -3 & 4 & 5 \end{pmatrix}$, (e) $\begin{pmatrix} i & 1 & -i & 1+i \\ 1 & -i & i & 2-i \\ -1 & 0 & 1 & 0 \\ 2 & i & 2i & 3i \end{pmatrix}$.

3. In Ex. 2, express the rows of each associated echelon matrix as linear combinations of the rows of the original matrix.

4. Test the following sets of vectors for linear dependence:
  (a) $(1, 0, 1)$, $(0, 2, 2)$, $(3, 7, 1)$ in $V_3(\mathbf{Q})$ and $V_3(\mathbf{C})$;
  (b) $(0, 0, 0)$, $(1, 0, 0)$, $(0, 1, 1)$ in $V_3(\mathbf{R})$;
  (c) $(1, i, 1 + i)$, $(i, -1, 2 - i)$, $(0, 0, 3)$ in $V_3(\mathbf{C})$;
  (d) $(1, 1, 0)$, $(1, 0, 1)$, $(0, 1, 1)$ in $V_3(\mathbf{Z}_2)$ and $V_3(\mathbf{Z}_3)$.
In every case of linear dependence, extract a linearly independent subset which generates the same subspace.

5. In $V_6(\mathbf{Q})$, test each of the following sets of vectors for independence, and find a basis for the subspace spanned:
  (a) $(2, 4, 3, -1, -2, 1)$, $(1, 1, 2, 1, 3, 1)$, $(0, -1, 0, 3, 6, 2)$;
  (b) $(2, 1, 3, -1, 4, -1)$, $(-1, 1, -2, 2, -3, 3)$, $(1, 5, 0, 4, -1, 7)$.

6. In Ex. 5, find a basis for the subspace spanned by the two sets of vectors, taken together.

7. Find the ranks and bases for the row spaces of the following matrices:

$$
\text{(a)} \begin{pmatrix} 1 & 2 & 3 \\ 2 & 3 & 4 \\ 3 & 4 & 5 \end{pmatrix}, \quad
\text{(b)} \begin{pmatrix} 1 & 2 & 1 & 2 \\ 3 & 2 & 3 & 2 \\ -1 & -3 & 0 & 4 \\ 0 & 4 & -1 & -3 \end{pmatrix}, \quad
\text{(c)} \begin{pmatrix} 1 & 2 & 4 & 5 & 7 \\ 1 & 2 & 3 & 4 & 5 \\ -1 & -2 & 0 & 2 & 1 \end{pmatrix}.
$$

8. List all possible forms for a 2×4 reduced echelon matrix with two non-zero rows. (These yield a cell decomposition of the "Grassmann manifold" whose points are the planes through the origin in 4-space.)

9. Prove: The rank of an $m \times n$ matrix exceeds neither m nor n.

10. If the $m \times (n + k)$ matrix B is formed by adding k new columns to the $m \times n$ matrix A, then rank $(A) \leqq$ rank (B).

11. Prove directly (without appeal to Theorem 7) that any matrix A is row-equivalent to a (not necessarily reduced) echelon matrix.

7. Vector Equations; Homogeneous Equations

It is especially advantageous to use elementary row operations on a matrix in place of linear equations (21) when one wishes to solve several vector equations of the form

$$
(23) \qquad\qquad \lambda = x_1 \alpha_1 + \cdots + x_m \alpha_m
$$

for fixed vectors $\alpha_1, \cdots, \alpha_m$ of $V_n(F)$ and various vectors λ.

For instance, let $\alpha_1, \alpha_2, \alpha_3$ be as in the Example of §6, and let $\lambda = (2, 7, -1, -6)$. Having reduced the matrix A to echelon form, we first solve the equation

$$
\lambda = y_1 \gamma_1 + y_2 \gamma_2 + y_3 \gamma_3 = y_1 \gamma_1 + y_2 \gamma_2.
$$

Equating first components, we get $2 = y_1$; equating second components, we then get $7 = -y_1 + y_2$ or $y_2 = 9$. Hence

$$
\lambda = 2\gamma_1 + 9\gamma_2 = 2\alpha_1 - 3\beta_2 = 2\alpha_1 - 3(\alpha_2 - 2\alpha_1) = 8\alpha_1 - 3\alpha_2,
$$

if λ is a linear combination of the α's at all. Computing the third and fourth components of $8\alpha_1 - 3\alpha_2$, we see that λ is indeed such a linear combination.

Since $\gamma_3 = -7\alpha_1 + 2\alpha_2 + \alpha_3 = O$, other solutions of (23) in this case are

$$\lambda = (8 - 7y)\alpha_1 + (-3 + 2y)\alpha_2 + y\alpha_3,$$

for arbitrary y. This is actually the most general solution of (23). Had the vector λ been $\lambda' = (2, 7, 1, -6)$, the above procedure would have shown that λ' cannot be expressed as a linear combination of the α's at all.

In fact, when several vectors λ are involved, it is usually best to first transform the $m \times n$ matrix whose rows are $\alpha_1, \cdots, \alpha_m$ to *reduced echelon form* C with non-zero rows $\gamma_1, \cdots, \gamma_r$. Since each elementary row operation on a matrix involves only a finite number of rational operations, and since a given matrix can be transformed to reduced echelon form after a finite number of elementary row operations, this can be done after a finite number of rational operations (i.e., additions, subtractions, multiplications, and divisions).

One can then apply Theorem 8 to get the only possible coefficients which will make $\lambda = y_1\gamma_1 + \cdots + y_r\gamma_r$. If this equation is not satisfied by *all* components of γ, then λ is not in the row space of A, and (23) has no solution. If it is satisfied, then since the rows of C will be known linear combinations $\gamma_i = \sum_{j=1}^{m} e_{ij}\alpha_j$ of the α's, then we obtain a solution for (23) in the form $\lambda = \Sigma y_i e_{ij}\alpha_j$, whence we have $x_j = y_1 e_{1j} + \cdots + y_r e_{rj}$. This proves the following result.

Theorem 11. *For given vectors λ, $\alpha_1, \cdots, \alpha_m$ in $V_n(F)$, the vector equation $\lambda = x_1\alpha_1 + \cdots + x_m\alpha_m$ can be solved (if a solution exists) by a finite number of rational operations in F.*

Corollary. *Let S and T be subspaces of $V_n(F)$ spanned by vectors $\alpha_1, \cdots, \alpha_m$ and $\beta_1, \cdots, \beta_k$ respectively. Then the relations $S \supset T$, $T \supset S$, and $S = T$ can be tested by a finite number of rational operations.*

Indeed, one can form from the α's, by elementary operations, a sequence of non-zero vectors $\gamma_1, \cdots, \gamma_r$ forming the rows of a reduced echelon matrix and also spanning S. One then tests as above whether all the β's are linear combinations of the γ's, which is clearly necessary and sufficient for $S \supset T$. By reversing the preceding process, one determines whether or not $T \supset S$. These two procedures combined test for $S = T$; alternatively, $S = T$ may be tested by transforming the matrix with rows α and the matrix with rows β to reduced echelon form, for $S = T$ holds only if these two reduced forms have the *same* non-zero vectors.

Reduced echelon matrices are also useful for determining the solutions of systems of *homogeneous* linear equations, of the form

$$a_{11}x_1 + a_{12}x_2 + \cdots + a_{1n}x_n = 0,$$
(24)
$$a_{m1}x_1 + a_{m2}x_2 + \cdots + a_{mn}x_n = 0.$$

Thus let S be the set of all vectors $\xi = (x_1, \cdots, x_n)$ of $V_n(F)$ satisfying (24). It is easy to show that S is a subspace. We shall now show how to determine a basis for this subspace.

First observe, as in Chap. II, §3, that elementary row operations on the system (24) transform it into an equivalent system of equations. Specifically, as applied to the $m \times n$ matrix A which has as ith row the coefficients $(a_{i1}, \cdots, a_{in})$ in the ith equation of (24), these operations carry A into another matrix having the same set S of "solution vectors" $\xi = (x_1, \cdots, x_n)$. Now bring A to a reduced echelon form, with leading entries 1 in the columns $t_1, \cdots, t_r$. The corresponding system of equations has r non-zero equations, and the ith equation is the only one containing the unknown x_{t_i}.

To simplify the notation, assume that the leading entries appear in the first r columns (this actually can always be brought about by a suitable permutation, applied to the unknowns x_i and thus to the columns of A). The reduced equations then have the form

$$x_1 \qquad + c_{1,r+1}x_{r+1} + \cdots + c_{1n}x_n = 0,$$
(25)
$$x_2 \qquad + c_{2,r+1}x_{r+1} + \cdots + c_{2n}x_n = 0,$$
$$x_r + c_{r,r+1}x_{r+1} + \cdots + c_{rn}x_n = 0.$$

In this simplified form, we can clearly obtain all solutions by choosing arbitrary values for $x_{r+1}, \cdots, x_n$, and solving (25) for $x_1, \cdots, x_r$, to give the solution vector

$$(26) \quad \xi = \left(- \sum_{j=r+1}^{n} c_{1j}x_j, \cdots, - \sum_{j=r+1}^{n} c_{rj}x_j, x_{r+1}, \cdots, x_n\right)$$

In particular, we obtain $n - r$ solutions by setting one of the parameters $x_{r+1}, \cdots, x_n$ equal to 1 and the remaining parameters equal to zero, giving the solutions

$$\xi_{r+1} = (-c_{1,r+1}, \cdots, -c_{r,r+1}, 1, 0, \cdots, 0)$$
$$\xi_n = (-c_{1n}, \cdots, -c_{rn}, 0, 0, \cdots, 1).$$

These $n - r$ solution vectors are linearly independent (since they are independent even if one neglects entirely the first r coordinates!). Equation (26) states that the general solution ξ is just the linear combination $\xi = x_{r+1}\xi_{r+1} + \cdots + x_n\xi_n$ of these $n - r$ basic solutions. We have thus found a basis for the space S of solution vectors of the given system of equations (24), thereby proving

Theorem 12. *The "solution space" of all solutions* $(x_1, \cdots, x_n)$ *of a system of* r *linearly independent homogeneous linear equations in* n *unknowns has dimension* $n - r$.

Corollary. *The only solution of a system of* n *linearly independent homogeneous linear equations in* n *unknowns* $x_1, \cdots, x_n$ *is*

$$x_1 = x_2 = \cdots = x_n = 0.$$

EXAMPLE. Let S be defined by the equations $x_1 + x_2 = x_3 + x_4$ and $x_1 + x_3 = 2(x_2 + x_4)$. Thus, geometrically, S is the intersection of two three-dimensional "hyperplanes" in four-space. The matrix of these equations reduces as follows:

$$\begin{pmatrix} 1 & 1 & -1 & -1 \\ 1 & -2 & 1 & -2 \end{pmatrix} \rightarrow \begin{pmatrix} 1 & 1 & -1 & -1 \\ 0 & -3 & 2 & -1 \end{pmatrix} \rightarrow \begin{pmatrix} 1 & 4 & -3 & 0 \\ 0 & -3 & 2 & -1 \end{pmatrix}.$$

The final matrix (except for sign and column order) is in reduced echelon form. It yields the equivalent system of equations $x_1 + 4x_2 - 3x_3 = 0$, $-3x_2 + 2x_3 - x_4 = 0$, with the general solution $\xi = (3x_3 - 4x_2, x_2, x_3, -3x_2 + 2x_3)$; a basis for the space of solutions is provided by the cases $x_2 = 0, x_3 = 1$, and $x_2 = 1, x_3 = 0$.

By duality, one can obtain a basis for the linear equations satisfied by all the vectors of any subspace. Thus, let T be the subspace of $V_4(F)$ spanned by the vectors $(1, 1, -1, -1)$ and $(1, -2, 1, -2)$. Then the homogeneous linear equation $\sum a_i x_i = 0$ is satisfied identically for (x_1, x_2, x_3, x_4) in T if and only if $a_1 + a_2 = a_3 + a_4$ and $a_1 + a_3 = 2(a_2 + a_4)$. A basis for the set of coefficient vectors (a_1, a_2, a_3, a_4) satisfying these equations has been found above, with x's in place of a's.

The linear equations of our example, $x_1 + x_2 - x_3 - x_4 = 0$ and $x_1 - 2x_2 + x_3 - 2x_4 = 0$, are equivalent to the vector equation

$$x_1(1, 1) + x_2(1, -2) + x_3(-1, 1) + x_4(-1, -2) = (0, 0).$$

The solutions are thus all relations of linear dependence between the four vectors $(1, 1)$, $(1, -2)$, $(-1, 1)$, and $(-1, -2)$ of the two-dimensional space $V_2(F)$. This could also be solved as in §5 by reducing to echelon form the 4×2 matrix having these vectors as rows, this matrix being obtained from that displayed above by transposing rows and columns.

EXERCISES

1. Let $\xi_1 = (1, 1, 1)$, $\xi_2 = (2, 1, 2)$, $\xi_3 = (3, 4, -1)$, $\xi_4 = (4, 6, 7)$. Find numbers c_i not all zero such that $c_1\xi_1 + c_2\xi_2 + c_3\xi_3 + c_4\xi_4 = O$.

2. Let $\eta_1 = (1 + i, 2i)$, $\eta_2 = (2, -3i)$, $\eta_3 = (2i, 3 + 4i)$. Find *all* complex numbers c_i such that $c_1\eta_1 + c_2\eta_2 + c_3\eta_3 = O$.

3. Find two vectors which span the subspace of all vectors (x_1, x_2, x_3, x_4) satisfying $x_1 + x_2 = x_3 - x_4 = 0$.

4. Do Ex. 3 for the vectors satisfying

$$3x_1 - 2x_2 + 4x_3 + x_4 = x_1 + x_2 - 3x_3 - 2x_4 = 0.$$

5. Find a basis of the proper number of linearly independent solutions for each of the following four systems of equations:

(a) $x + y + 3z = 0,$
   $2x + 2y + 6z = 0;$

(b) $x + y + z = 0,$
   $y + z + t = 0;$

(c) $x + 2y - 4z = 0,$
   $3x + y - 2z = 0;$

(d) $x + y + z + t = 0,$
   $2x + 3y - z + t = 0,$
   $3x + 4y + 2t = 0.$

6. Do Ex. 5 if the equations are taken to be congruences modulo 5.

7. Determine whether each of the following vector equations (over the rational numbers) has a solution, and when this is the case, find one solution.

(a) $(1, -2) = x_1(1, 1) + x_2(2, 3),$

(b) $(1, 1, 1) = x_1(1, -1, 2) + x_2(2, 1, 3) + x_3(1, -1, 0),$

(c) $(2, -1, 1) = x_1(2, 0, 3) + x_2(3, 1, 2) + x_3(1, 2, -1).$

8. In $V_4(\mathbf{Q})$ let $\alpha_1 = (1, 1, 2, 2),$ $\alpha_2 = (1, 2, 3, 4),$ $\alpha_3 = (0, 1, 3, 2),$ and $\alpha_4 = (-1, 1, -1, 1)$. Express each of the following four vectors in the form $x_1\alpha_1 + x_2\alpha_2 + x_3\alpha_3 + x_4\alpha_4$:

(a) $(1, 0, 1, 0),$ (b) $(3, -2, 1, -1),$ (c) $(0, 1, 0, 0),$ (d) $(2, -2, 2, -2).$

9. Show that an $m \times n$ matrix can be put in row-reduced form by at most m^2 elementary operations on its rows.

10. Show that a 4×6 matrix can be put in row-reduced form after at most 56 multiplications, 42 additions and subtractions, and 4 formations of reciprocals. (Do not count computations like $aa^{-1} = 1$, $a - a = 0$, or $0a = 0$.)

★11. State and prove an analogue of Ex. 10 for $n \times n$ matrices.

8. Bases and Coordinate Systems

A basis of a space V was defined to be an independent set of vectors spanning V. The real significance of a basis lies in the fact that the vectors of any basis of $V_n(F)$ may be regarded as the unit vectors of the space, under a suitably chosen coordinate system, in virtue of the following theorem.

Theorem 13. *If $\alpha_1, \cdots, \alpha_n$ form a basis for V, then every vector $\xi \in V$ has a unique expression*

$$(27) \qquad \qquad \xi = x_1\alpha_1 + x_2\alpha_2 + \cdots + x_n\alpha_n$$

as a linear combination of the α_i.

Proof. Since the α_i form a basis, they span V, hence every vector ξ in V has at least one expression of the form (27). If some $\xi \in V$ has a second such expression $\xi = x_1'\alpha_1 + \cdots + x_n'\alpha_n$, then subtraction from (27) and recombination gives

$$O = \xi - \xi = (x_1 - x_1')\alpha_1 + \cdots + (x_n - x_n')\alpha_n.$$

Since the α_i are a basis, they are independent, and the preceding equation implies that $(x_1 - x_1') = \cdots = (x_n - x_n') = 0$, so that each $x_i = x_i'$, whence the expression (27) is unique.

We shall call the scalars x_i in (27) the *coordinates* of the vector ξ *relative to the basis* $\alpha_1, \cdots, \alpha_n$. If

$$\eta = y_1\alpha_1 + y_2\alpha_2 + \cdots + y_n\alpha_n$$

is a second vector of V, with coordinates $y_1, \cdots, y_n$, then by the identities of vector algebra

$$(28) \quad \xi + \eta = (x_1 + y_1)\alpha_1 + (x_2 + y_2)\alpha_2 + \cdots + (x_n + y_n)\alpha_n.$$

In words, the coordinates of a vector sum are found by adding corresponding coordinates of the summands. Similarly, the product of the vector ξ of (27) by a scalar c is

$$(29) \quad c\xi = c(x_1\alpha_1 + \cdots + x_n\alpha_n) = (cx_1)\alpha_1 + \cdots + (cx_n)\alpha_n,$$

so that each coordinate of $c\xi$ is the product of c and the corresponding coordinate of ξ.

By analogy with the corresponding definitions for integral domains and groups, let us now define an *isomorphism* $C: V \to W$ between two vector spaces V and W, over the same field F, to be a one-one correspondence $\xi \to \xi C$ of V onto W such that

$$(30) \qquad (\xi + \eta)C = \xi C + \eta C \qquad \text{and} \qquad (c\xi)C = c(\xi C)$$

for all vectors ξ, η in V and all scalars c in F. Equations (28) and (29) then show that each basis $\alpha_1, \cdots, \alpha_n$ in a vector space V over F provides an isomorphism of V onto $V_n(F)$. This isomorphism is the correspondence C_α which assigns to each vector ξ of V the n-tuple of its coordinates relative to α, as in

$$(31) \qquad (x_1\alpha_1 + \cdots + x_n\alpha_n)C_\alpha = (x_1, \cdots, x_n) \in V_n(F).$$

Since the number n of vectors in a basis is determined by the dimension n, which is an invariant (Theorem 4, Corollary 1), we have proved

Theorem 14.   *Any finite-dimensional vector space over a field F is isomorphic to one and only one space $V_n(F)$.*

We have thus solved the problem of determining (up to isomorphism) all finite-dimensional vector spaces. What is more, we have shown that all bases of the same vector space V are equivalent, in the sense that there is an automorphism of V carrying any basis into any other basis.

A vector space can have many different bases. Thus by Theorem 6, any sequence of vectors of $V_n(F)$ obtained from $\varepsilon_1, \cdots, \varepsilon_n$ by a succession of elementary row operations, is a basis for $V_n(F)$. In particular $\alpha_1 = (1, 1, 0)$, $\alpha_2 = (0, 1, 1)$, and $\alpha_3 = (1, 0, 1)$ are a basis for $V_3(F)$, for any field F in which $1 + 1 \neq 0$. More generally, any three noncoplanar vectors in ordinary 3-space define a basis of vectors for "oblique coordinates" in $V_3(\mathbf{R})$. Theorem 5 gives a general way of constructing bases.

Again, the field $\mathbf{C}$ of all complex numbers may be considered as a vector space over the field $\mathbf{R}$ of real numbers, if one ignores all the algebraic operations in $\mathbf{C}$ except the addition of complex numbers and the ("scalar") multiplication of complex numbers by reals. This space has the dimension 2, for 1 and i form a basis, generating respectively the "subspaces" of real and pure imaginary numbers. The two numbers $1 + i$ and $1 - i$ form another, but less convenient, basis for $\mathbf{C}$ over $\mathbf{R}$.

Or, consider the homogeneous linear differential equation $d^2x/dt^2 - 3dx/dt + 2x = 0$. One verifies readily that the sum $x_1(t) + x_2(t)$ of two solutions is itself a solution, and that the product of a solution by any (real) constant is a solution. Therefore the set V of all solutions of this differential equation is a vector space, sometimes called the "solution-space" of the differential equation. The easiest way to describe this space is to say that e^t and e^{2t} form a *basis* of solutions, which means precisely that the most general solution can be expressed in the form $x = c_1e^t + c_2e^{2t}$, in one and only one way.

Finally, the domain $F[x]$ of all polynomial forms in an indeterminate x over a field F is a linear space over F, for all the postulates for a vector space are satisfied in $F[x]$. The definition of equality applied to the equation $p(x) = 0$ implies that the powers $1, x, x^2, x^3, \cdots$ are linearly independent over F. Hence $F[x]$ has an infinite *basis* consisting of these powers, for any vector (polynomial form) can be expressed as a linear combination of a finite subset of this basis.

In $V_3(\mathbf{R})$, a plane S and a line T not in S, both through the origin, span the whole space, and any vector in the space can be expressed uniquely as a sum of a vector in the plane and a vector in the line. More generally, we say that a vector space V is the *direct sum* of two subspaces S and T if every vector ξ of V has one and only one expression

$$(32) \qquad \xi = \eta + \zeta, \qquad \eta \in S, \qquad \zeta \in T$$

as a sum of a vector of S and a vector of T.

Since $(\eta + \zeta) + (\eta' + \zeta') = (\eta + \eta') + (\zeta + \zeta')$, it follows that the additive group of the vector space V is isomorphic to the *direct product* (Chap. VI, §11) of the additive groups of S and T, the isomorphism being given by the correspondence $(\eta, \zeta) \to (\eta + \zeta)$. Conversely, if S and T are any two given vector spaces over the same field F, one can define a new vector space $V = S \oplus T$ whose additive group is the direct product of those of S and T, scalar multiplication being defined by the formula $c(\eta, \zeta) = (c\eta, c\zeta)$, for any $c \in F$. In this V, the subsets of $(\eta, 0)$ and $(0, \zeta)$ constitute *subspaces* isomorphic to S and T, respectively; moreover V is their direct sum in the sense of the preceding paragraph. One also speaks of $S \oplus T$ as the direct sum of the given vector spaces S and T.

Theorem 15. *If the finite-dimensional vector space V is the direct sum of its subspaces S and T, then the union of any basis of S with any basis of T is a basis of V.*

Proof. Let S and T have the bases $\beta_1, \cdots, \beta_k$ and $\gamma_1, \cdots, \gamma_m$, respectively; we wish to prove that $\beta_1, \cdots, \beta_k, \gamma_1, \cdots, \gamma_m$ is a basis of V. First, these vectors span V, for any ξ in V can be written as $\xi = \eta + \zeta$, where η is a linear combination of the β's and ζ of the γ's. Secondly, these vectors are linearly independent, for if

$$(33) \qquad O = b_1\beta_1 + \cdots + b_k\beta_k + c_1\gamma_1 + \cdots + c_m\gamma_m,$$

then O is represented as a sum of the vector $\eta_0 = \sum b_i\beta_i$ in S and $\zeta_0 = \sum c_j\gamma_j$ in T. But $O = O + O$ is another representation of O as a sum of a vector in S and one in T. By assumption, the representation is unique, so that $O = \eta_0 = \sum b_i\beta_i$ and $O = \sum c_j\gamma_j$. But the β's and the γ's are separately linearly independent, so that $b_1 = \cdots = b_k = 0$ and $c_1 = \cdots = c_m = 0$. The relation (33) thus holds only when all the scalar coefficients are zero, so that the $\beta_1, \cdots, \beta_k, \gamma_1, \cdots, \gamma_m$ are indeed linearly independent.

This theorem and its proof can readily be extended to the case of a direct sum of a finite number of subspaces.

Corollary. *If the finite-dimensional space V is the direct sum of its subspaces S and T, then*

$$(34) \qquad d[V] = d[S] + d[T].$$

Proof. Since the dimension of a space is the number of vectors in (any) basis, the above proof shows that when $d[S] = k$ and $d[T] = m$, then $d[V] = k + m$. Q.E.D.

When V is the direct sum of S and T, we call S and T *complementary* subspaces of V. We then have

$$(35) \qquad S + T = V, \qquad S \cap T = 0.$$

Indeed, (32) states that V is the linear sum of the subspaces S and T. Secondly, if ξ_1 is any vector common to S and T, then ξ_1 has two representations $\xi_1 = \xi_1 + O$ and $\xi_1 = O + \xi_1$ of the form (32); since these two representations must be the same, $\xi_1 = O$, so that the intersection $S \cap T$ is zero, as asserted. Conversely, we can prove that under the conditions (35), V is the direct sum of S and T. Thus in this case we can write the equation (34) as $d[V] = d[S + T] + d[S \cap T] = d[S] + d[T]$. This latter result holds for any two subspaces.

Theorem 16. *Let S and T be any two finite-dimensional subspaces of a vector space V. Then*

(36) $$d[S] + d[T] = d[S \cap T] + d[S + T].$$

Proof. Let $\xi_1, \cdots, \xi_n$ be a basis for $S \cap T$; by Theorem 5, S and T have bases $\xi_1, \cdots, \xi_n, \eta_1, \cdots, \eta_r$ and $\xi_1, \cdots, \xi_n, \zeta_1, \cdots, \zeta_s$ respectively. Clearly, the ξ_i, η_j, and ζ_k together span $S + T$. They are even a basis, since

$$a_1\xi_1 + \cdots + a_n\xi_n + b_1\eta_1 + \cdots + b_r\eta_r + c_1\zeta_1 + \cdots + c_s\zeta_s = 0$$

implies that $\sum b_j\eta_j = -\sum a_i\xi_i - \sum c_k\zeta_k$ is in T, whence $\sum b_j\eta_j$ is in $S \cap T$ and so $\sum b_j\eta_j = \sum d_i\xi_i$, for some scalars d_i. Hence (the ξ_i and η_j being independent) every b_j is 0. Similarly, every $c_k = 0$; substituting, $\sum a_i\xi_i = 0$, and every $a_i = 0$. This shows that the ξ_i, η_j, and ζ_k are a basis for $S + T$.

But having proved this, the conclusion of the theorem reduces to the arithmetic rule $(n + r) + (n + s) = n + (n + r + s)$.

EXERCISES

1. In Ex. 4 of §6, which of the indicated sets of vectors are bases for the spaces involved there?
2. In $V_4(\mathbf{Q})$, find the coordinates of the unit vectors $\varepsilon_1, \varepsilon_2, \varepsilon_3, \varepsilon_4$ relative to the basis
   $$\alpha_1 = (1, 1, 0, 0), \quad \alpha_2 = (0, 0, 1, 1), \quad \alpha_3 = (1, 0, 0, 4), \quad \alpha_4 = (0, 0, 0, 2).$$
3. Find the coordinates of $(1, 0, 1)$ relative to the following basis in $V_3(\mathbf{C})$:
   $(2i, 1, 0), (2, -i, 1), (0, 1 + i, 1 - i)$.
4. In $V_4(\mathbf{Q})$, find (a) a basis which contains the vector $(1, 2, 1, 1)$,
   (b) a basis containing the vectors $(1, 1, 0, 2)$ and $(1, -1, 2, 0)$,
   (c) a basis containing the vectors $(1, 1, 0, 0), (0, 0, 2, 2), (0, 2, 3, 0)$.
5. Show that the numbers $a + b\sqrt{2} + c\sqrt{3} + d\sqrt{6} + e\sqrt{12}$ with rational $a, \cdots, e$ form a commutative ring, and that this ring is a vector space over the rational field $\mathbf{Q}$. Find a basis for this space.
6. In $V_4(\mathbf{Q})$, two subspaces S and T are spanned respectively by the vectors:
   S: $(1, -1, 2, -3), \quad (1, 1, 2, 0), \quad (3, -1, 6, -6)$,
   T: $(0, -2, 0, -3), \quad (1, 0, 1, 0)$.
   Find the dimensions of S, of T, or $S \cap T$, and of $S + T$.
★7. Solve Ex. 6 for the most general $V_4(\mathbf{Z}_p)$.
8. Find the greatest possible dimension of $S + T$ and the least possible dimension of $S \cap T$, where S and T are variable subspaces of fixed dimensions s and t in $V_n(F)$. Prove your result.
★9. Prove that, for subspaces, $S \cap T = S \cap T'$, $S + T = S + T'$, and $T \subset T'$ imply $T = T'$.

10. If S is a subspace of the finite-dimensional vector space V, show that there exists a subspace T of V such that V is the direct sum of S and T.

★11. V is called the direct sum of its subspaces $S_1, \cdots, S_p$ if each vector ξ of V has a unique expression $\xi = \eta_1 + \cdots + \eta_p$, with $\eta_i \in S_i$. State and prove the analogue of Theorem 15 for such direct sums.

12. Prove that V is the direct sum of S and T if and only if (35) holds.

★13. State and prove the analogue of Ex. 12 for the direct sum of p subspaces.

14. By an "automorphism" of a vector space V is meant an isomorphism of V with itself.
    (a) Show that the correspondence $(x_1, x_2, x_3) \rightarrow (x_2, -x_1, x_3)$ is an automorphism of $V_3(F)$.
    (b) Show that the set of all automorphisms of V is a group of transformations on V.

15. An automorphism of $V_2(F)$ carries $(1, 0)$ into $(0, 1)$ and $(0, 1)$ into $(-1, -1)$. What is its order? Does your answer depend on the base field?

★16. Establish a one-one correspondence between the automorphisms (cf. Ex. 14) of a finite-dimensional vector space and its ordered bases. How many automorphisms does $V_2(\mathbf{Z}_2)$ have? What about $V_n(\mathbf{Z}_p)$?

9. Inner Products

Ordinary space is a three-dimensional vector space over the real field: it is $V_3(\mathbf{R})$. In *real* n-dimensional vector spaces, one can define *lengths* of vectors and *angles* between vectors. To do this, one needs an additional operation. The most convenient such operation for this purpose is that of forming *inner products*. By the "inner product" of two vectors $\xi = (x_1, \cdots, x_n)$ and $\eta = (y_1, \cdots, y_n)$, with real components, is meant the quantity

$$(37) \qquad (\xi, \eta) = x_1 y_1 + x_2 y_2 + \cdots + x_n y_n.$$

(Since this is a scalar, physicists often speak of our inner product as a "scalar product" of two vectors.) Inner products have four important properties, which are immediate consequences of the definition (37):

$$(38) \qquad (\xi + \eta, \zeta) = (\xi, \zeta) + (\eta, \zeta), \qquad (c\xi, \eta) = c(\xi, \eta);$$
$$(39) \qquad (\xi, \eta) = (\eta, \xi), \qquad (\xi, \xi) > 0 \text{ unless } \xi = O.$$

The first two laws assert that inner products are *linear* in the left-hand factor; the third is the *symmetric* law, and gives with the first two the linearity of inner products in both factors (*bilinearity*); the fourth is that of *positiveness*.

Thus, the Cartesian formula for the *length* (also called the "absolute value" or the "norm") $|\xi|$ of a vector ξ in the plane $V_2(\mathbf{R})$ gives the length as the square root of an inner product,

$$(40) \qquad |\xi| = (x_1^2 + x_2^2)^{1/2} = (\xi, \xi)^{1/2}.$$

A similar formula is used for length in 3-dimensional space. Again, if α and β are any two vectors, then for the triangle with sides $\alpha, \beta, \gamma = \beta - \alpha$ (Figure 2), the trigonometric law of cosines gives

$$| \beta - \alpha |^2 = | \alpha |^2 + | \beta |^2 - 2 | \alpha | \cdot | \beta | \cdot \cos C,$$

$(C = \angle(\alpha, \beta))$. But by (38) and (40),

$$| \beta - \alpha |^2 = (\beta - \alpha, \beta - \alpha) = (\beta, \beta) - 2(\alpha, \beta) + (\alpha, \alpha).$$

Combining and canceling, we get

(41) $$\cos \angle(\alpha, \beta) = (\alpha, \beta)/| \alpha | \cdot | \beta |.$$

In words, the cosine of the angle $\angle(\alpha, \beta)$ between two vectors α and β is the quotient of their inner product by the product of their lengths. It follows that α and β are geometrically *orthogonal* (or "perpendicular") if and only if the inner product (α, β) vanishes.

In view of the ease with which the concepts of vector addition and scalar multiplication extend to spaces of an arbitrary dimension over an arbitrary field, it is natural to try to generalize the concepts of length and angle similarly. When we do this, however, we find

Figure 2

that although the *dimension* number can be arbitrary, trouble arises with most fields. Inner products can be defined by (37); but lengths

(42) $$| \xi | = (\xi, \xi)^{1/2} = (x_1{}^2 + x_2{}^2 + \cdots + x_n{}^2)^{1/2}$$

are not definable unless every sum of n squares has a square root. The same applies to distances, while angles cause even more trouble.

For these reasons we shall at present confine our discussion of lengths, angles, and related topics to vector spaces over the *real* field.

EXERCISES

1. In the plane, show by analytic geometry that the square of the distance between $\xi = (x_1, x_2)$ and $\eta = (y_1, y_2)$ is given by $| \xi |^2 + | \eta |^2 - 2(\xi, \eta)$.
2. Use direction cosines in three-dimensional space to show that two vectors ξ and η are orthogonal if and only if $(\xi, \eta) = 0$.
3. If length is defined by the formula (42) for vectors ξ with complex numbers as components, show that there will exist non-zero vectors with zero length.
4. Show that there is a sum of two squares which has no square root in the fields Z_3 and Q.
5. Prove formulas (38) and (39) from the definition (37).
6. Prove formulas analogous to (38) asserting that the inner product is linear in the right-hand factor.

★**7.** In $V_3(\mathbf{R})$, define outer products by

$$\xi \times \eta = (x_2 y_3 - x_3 y_2, \ x_3 y_1 - x_1 y_3, \ x_1 y_2 - x_2 y_1).$$

(a) Prove that $(\xi \times \eta, \ \zeta \times \tau) = (\xi, \zeta)(\eta, \tau) - (\xi, \tau)(\eta, \zeta)$.

(b) Setting $\xi = \zeta$, $\eta = \tau$, infer the Schwarz inequality in $V_3(\mathbf{R})$ as a corollary. (Cf. Theorem 17.)

(c) Prove that $\xi \times (\eta \times \zeta) = (\xi, \zeta)\eta - (\xi, \eta)\zeta$.

10. Euclidean Vector Spaces

Our discussion of geometry without restriction on dimension will be based on the following definition, suggested by the considerations of §9.

Definition. *A* Euclidean vector space *is a vector space E with real scalars, such that to any vectors ξ and η in E corresponds a (real) "inner product" (ξ, η) which is symmetric, bilinear, and positive in the sense of (38) and (39).*

Example 1. Any $V_n(\mathbf{R})$ is an n-dimensional Euclidean vector space, if (ξ, η) is defined by equation (37).

Example 2. The continuous real functions $\phi(x)$ on the domain $0 \leq x \leq 1$ form an *infinite*-dimensional Euclidean vector space, if we make the definition $(\phi, \psi) = \int_0^1 \phi(x)\psi(x)dx$.

The "length" $|\xi|$ of a vector ξ of a Euclidean vector space E may be defined in terms of the inner product as the positive square root $(\xi, \xi)^{1/2}$—the existence of the root being guaranteed by the positiveness condition of (39).

Theorem 17. *In any Euclidean vector space, length has the following properties:*

(i) $|c\xi| = |c| \cdot |\xi|$,

(ii) $|\xi| > 0 \ unless \ \xi = O$,

(iii) $|(\xi, \eta)| \leq |\xi| \cdot |\eta|$ (*The Schwarz inequality*),

(iv) $|\xi + \eta| \leq |\xi| + |\eta|$ (*The triangle inequality*).

Proof. Since $(c\xi, c\xi) = c^2(\xi, \xi)$, we have (i). Property (ii) is a corollary of the condition of positiveness required in the definition of a Euclidean vector space.

The proof of (iii) is less immediate. If $\xi = O$ or $\eta = O$, then (iii) reduces to the trivial inequality $0 \leq 0$. Otherwise,

$$0 \leq (a\xi \pm b\eta, \ a\xi \pm b\eta) = a^2(\xi, \xi) \pm 2ab(\xi, \eta) + b^2(\eta, \eta).$$

Set $a = |\eta|$ and $b = |\xi|$, so that $a^2 = (\eta, \eta)$ and $b^2 = (\xi, \xi)$. Transposing, we then have

(43) $\mp 2 \mid \xi \mid \cdot \mid \eta \mid \cdot (\xi, \eta) \leqq 2(\xi, \xi)(\eta, \eta) = 2 \mid \xi \mid^2 \cdot \mid \eta \mid^2.$

Dividing through by $2 \mid \xi \mid \cdot \mid \eta \mid > 0$, we get (iii).
 From (iii) we now get (iv) easily, for

$$\mid \xi + \eta \mid^2 = (\xi + \eta, \xi + \eta) = (\xi, \xi) + 2(\xi, \eta) + (\eta, \eta)$$
$$\leqq \mid \xi \mid^2 + 2 \mid \xi \mid \cdot \mid \eta \mid + \mid \eta \mid^2 = (\mid \xi \mid + \mid \eta \mid)^2.$$

Now, if we define the *distance* between any two vectors ξ and η of E
as $\mid \xi - \eta \mid$, we can show that it has the so-called "metric" properties of
ordinary distance, first considered abstractly by Fréchet (1906).

Theorem 18. *Distance has the properties:*

(M1) $\mid \xi - \xi \mid = 0$, *while* $\mid \xi - \eta \mid > 0$ *if* $\xi \neq \eta$,
(M2) *distance is symmetric,* $\mid \xi - \eta \mid = \mid \eta - \xi \mid$;
(M3) $\mid \xi - \eta \mid + \mid \eta - \zeta \mid \geqq \mid \xi - \zeta \mid.$

Proof. First, $\mid \xi - \xi \mid = \mid O \mid = \mid 0 \cdot \xi \mid = 0 \cdot \mid \xi \mid = 0$ by (i), while
$\mid \xi - \eta \mid > 0$ if $\xi - \eta \neq O$ (or $\xi \neq \eta$) by (ii), proving $M1$. Secondly,
$\mid \xi - \eta \mid = \mid (-1)(\eta - \xi) \mid = \mid -1 \mid \cdot \mid \eta - \xi \mid = \mid \eta - \xi \mid$ by (i), proving $M2$. Finally, $M3$ follows from (iv) because

$$\mid \xi - \eta \mid + \mid \eta - \zeta \mid \geqq \mid (\xi - \eta) + (\eta - \zeta) \mid = \mid \xi - \zeta \mid.$$

From Schwarz's inequality, we deduce in particular that for any ξ, η not O,
we have $-1 \leqq (\xi, \eta)/\mid \xi \mid \cdot \mid \eta \mid \leqq 1$. Hence $(\xi, \eta)/\mid \xi \mid \cdot \mid \eta \mid$ is the cosine
of one and only one angle between $0°$ and $180°$, which we can *define* as the
angle between the vectors ξ and η (compare the special case (41)). We
shall not prove except in the case of *right* angles that the angles so defined
have any properties (could you prove that $\angle(\xi, \eta) + \angle(\eta, \zeta) \geqq \angle(\xi, \zeta)$?).
 Two vectors ξ and η will be called *orthogonal* (in symbols, $\xi \perp \eta$) whenever $(\xi, \eta) = 0$. This definition, applied to Example 2 above, yields an
instance of the important analytical concept of orthogonal functions. It is
easy to prove that if $\xi \perp \eta$, then $\eta \perp \xi$ (the orthogonality relation is
"symmetric"), and $c\xi \perp c'\eta$ for all c, c'. Also, O is the only vector orthogonal to itself. Furthermore, whenever $(\eta, \xi_1) = \cdots = (\eta, \xi_m) = 0$, then
for any scalars c_i,

$$(\eta, c_1\xi_1 + \cdots + c_m\xi_m) = c_1(\eta, \xi_1) + \cdots + c_m(\eta, \xi_m)$$
$$= c_1 \cdot 0 + \cdots + c_m \cdot 0 = 0,$$

so that η is also orthogonal to every linear combination of the ξ_i. This
proves

Theorem 19. *If a vector is orthogonal to* $\xi_1, \cdots, \xi_m$, *then it is orthogonal to every vector in the subspace spanned by* $\xi_1, \cdots, \xi_m$.

EXERCISES

1. Set $\xi = (1, 2, 3, 4)$, $\eta = (0, 3, -2, 1)$. Compute (ξ, η), $|\xi|$, $|\eta|$, $\angle(\xi, \eta)$.
2. If ξ and η are as in Ex. 1, find a vector of the form $(1, 1, 0, 0) + c_1\xi + c_2\eta$ orthogonal to both ξ and η.
3. (a) Are $\sin 2\pi x$ and $\cos 2\pi x$ "orthogonal" in Example 2 of the text?
   (b) Are $\sin 2m\pi x$ and $\sin 2n\pi x$ orthogonal?
   (c) Find a polynomial of degree two orthogonal to 1 and x.
4. Prove that $|\xi - \eta|^2 + |\xi + \eta|^2 = 2(|\xi|^2 + |\eta|^2)$.
5. Prove that in $V_3(\mathbf{R})$, there are precisely two vectors of length one perpendicular to two given linearly independent vectors.
6. Prove that there is a vector with rational coordinates in $V_3(\mathbf{R})$ perpendicular to any two given vectors with rational coordinates.
7. If α and $\beta \neq O$ are fixed vectors of a Euclidean vector space, find the shortest vector of the form $\gamma = \alpha + t\beta$. Is this orthogonal to β? Draw a figure.
★8. If α is equidistant from β and γ, prove that the midpoint of the segment $\overline{\beta\gamma}$ is the foot of the perpendicular from α to $\overline{\beta\gamma}$.
9. Prove that if $|\xi| = |\alpha|$ in a Euclidean vector space, then $\xi - \alpha \perp \xi + \alpha$. Interpret this geometrically.
★10. (a) Show that the discriminant $B^2 - 4AC$ of the quadratic equation

$$(\xi, \xi)t^2 + 2(\xi, \eta)t + (\eta, \eta) = |t\xi + \eta|^2 = 0$$

   is four times $(\xi, \eta)^2 - (\xi, \xi)(\eta, \eta)$.
   (b) Using this fact, prove the Schwarz inequality. *Hint:* $|t\xi + \eta| = 0$ cannot have two distinct real solutions t, unless $\xi = O$.
11. Prove $\big||\xi| - |\eta|\big| \leq |\xi - \eta|$, in any Euclidean vector space.
12. Show that $V_3(\mathbf{R})$ becomes a Euclidean vector space if inner products are defined by

$$(\xi, \eta) = (x_1 + x_2)(y_1 + y_2) + x_2y_2 + (x_2 + 2x_3)(y_2 + 2y_3).$$

11. Normal Orthogonal Bases

In Example 1 of §10, the "unit vectors" $\varepsilon_1 = (1, 0, \cdots, 0)$, $\cdots$, $\varepsilon_n = (0, 0, \cdots, 1)$ have unit length and are mutually orthogonal. This is an instance of what is called a "normal orthogonal basis."

Definition. *Vectors* $\alpha_1, \cdots, \alpha_m$ *are called* normal orthogonal *when* (i) $|\alpha_i| = 1$ *for all* i, (ii) $\alpha_i \perp \alpha_j$ *if* $i \neq j$.

Lemma 1. *Non-zero orthogonal vectors* $\alpha_1, \cdots, \alpha_m$ *of a Euclidean vector space* E *are linearly independent.*

Proof. If $x_1\alpha_1 + \cdots + x_m\alpha_m = O$, then for $k = 1, \cdots, m$

$$0 = (O, \alpha_k) = x_1(\alpha_1, \alpha_k) + \cdots + x_m(\alpha_m, \alpha_k) = x_k(\alpha_k, \alpha_k),$$

where the last equality comes from the orthogonality assumption. But $\alpha_k \neq O$ by assumption; hence $(\alpha_k, \alpha_k) > 0$ and $x_k = 0$.

Corollary. *Normal orthogonal vectors spanning E are a basis for E (a so-called "normal orthogonal basis").*

We shall now show how to orthogonalize any basis of a Euclidean vector space, using only rational operations. This is called the *Gram-Schmidt orthogonalization process.*

Lemma 2. *From any finite sequence of independent vectors $\gamma_1, \cdots, \gamma_m$ of a finite-dimensional Euclidean vector space E, an orthogonal sequence of non-zero vectors*

$$(44) \qquad \alpha_i = \gamma_i - \sum_{k<i} d_{ik}\gamma_k \qquad [i = 1, \cdots, m]$$

can be constructed, which spans the same subspace of E as the sequence $\gamma_1, \cdots, \gamma_m$.

Proof. By induction on m, we can assume that orthogonal non-zero vectors $\alpha_1, \cdots, \alpha_{m-1}$ have been constructed which span the same subspace S as $\gamma_1, \cdots, \gamma_{m-1}$. We now split γ_m into a part β_m "parallel" to S, and a part α_m perpendicular to S. To do this, set

$$(44') \qquad \alpha_m = \gamma_m - \sum_{k<m} c_{mk}\alpha_k, \qquad \text{where } c_{mk} = (\gamma_m, \alpha_k)/(\alpha_k, \alpha_k).$$

Then for $j = 1, \cdots, m - 1$, we have

$$(\alpha_m, \alpha_j) = (\gamma_m, \alpha_j) - \sum_{k=1}^{m-1} c_{mk}(\alpha_k, \alpha_j) = 0,$$

since $(\alpha_k, \alpha_j) = 0$ if $k \neq j$ by orthogonality, while $c_{mj}(\alpha_j, \alpha_j) = (\gamma_m, \alpha_j)$ by (44'). Substituting in (44), we have by induction on m,

$$\alpha_m = \gamma_m - \sum_{k<m} c_{mk}\alpha_k = \gamma_m - \sum_{k<m} c_{mk}\gamma_k + \sum_{j<k<m} c_{mk}d_{kj}\gamma_j.$$

This proves (44), with

$$d_{mk} = c_{mk} - \sum_{k<j<m} c_{mj}d_{jk}.$$

Since γ_m is not dependent on $\gamma_1, \cdots, \gamma_{m-1}$, it cannot be in S; hence $\alpha_m \neq 0$. Finally, $\gamma_1, \cdots, \gamma_m$ and $\alpha_1, \cdots, \alpha_m$ both span the subspace spanned by S and γ_m. This completes the proof of Lemma 2.

Theorem 20. *Every set $\gamma_1, \cdots, \gamma_m$ of normal orthogonal vectors of a finite-dimensional Euclidean vector space E is part of a normal orthogonal basis.*

Proof. By Theorem 5, the γ_i are part of a basis $\gamma_1, \cdots, \gamma_n$ of E. This basis may be orthogonalized by Lemma 2, and then normalized by setting $\beta_i = \alpha_i/|\alpha_i|$; the process will not change the original vectors $\gamma_1, \cdots, \gamma_m$.

Corollary. *Any finite-dimensional Euclidean vector space E has a normal orthogonal basis.*

The Gram-Schmidt orthogonalization process has other implications. Thus let S be any m-dimensional subspace of a Euclidean vector space E; as above, S has a normal orthogonal basis $\alpha_1, \cdots, \alpha_m$. If γ is any vector not in S, the process represents γ as the sum $\gamma = \alpha + \beta$ of a component β in S and a component α perpendicular to every vector of S. The vector β is called the *orthogonal projection* of γ on S.

We shall conclude by determining all inner products on a given (real) finite-dimensional vector space V. Clearly, if $\alpha_1, \cdots, \alpha_n$ is any basis for V, then for any vectors $\xi = x_1\alpha_1 + \cdots + x_n\alpha_n$ and $\eta = y_1\alpha_1 + \cdots + y_n\alpha_n$, we have by bilinearity

$$(45) \qquad (\xi, \eta) = \left(\sum x_i\alpha_i, \sum y_k\alpha_k\right) = \sum_{i,k} x_iy_k(\alpha_i, \alpha_k).$$

Thus, the inner product of any two vectors is determined by the n^2 real constants $(\alpha_i, \alpha_k) = a_{ik}$ as a certain "bilinear" form $\sum_{i,k} a_{ik}x_iy_k$ in the coordinates x_i and y_k. Because $(\alpha_i, \alpha_k) = (\alpha_k, \alpha_i)$, this form is called "symmetric."

Conversely, any symmetric bilinear form $\sum_{i,k} a_{ik}x_iy_k$ $(a_{ik} = a_{ki})$ in $V_n(F)$ satisfies the first three conditions of (38) and (39). The fourth condition is that the *quadratic* form $\sum a_{ik}x_ix_k$ be "positive definite"—i.e., be positive unless every $x_i = 0$. It is difficult to interpret this as a condition on the coefficients a_{ik} (cf. Ch. IX, §9).

Relative to a normal orthogonal basis, we have $(\alpha_i, \alpha_k) = 0$ if $i \neq k$, and $(\alpha_i, \alpha_i) = 1$; hence (45) reduces to

$$(46) \qquad (\xi, \eta) = \sum_{i=1}^{n} x_iy_i = x_1y_1 + \cdots + x_ny_n.$$

This formula enables us to conclude with

Theorem 21. *Relative to any normal orthogonal basis, an "abstract" inner product assumes the "concrete" form (46).*

Thus we have determined all finite-dimensional Euclidean vector spaces up to isomorphism.

EXERCISES

1. Find normal orthogonal bases for the subspaces of Euclidean four-space spanned by:
   (a) $(1, 1, 0, 0)$, $(0, 1, 2, 0)$, and $(0, 0, 3, 4)$;
   (b) $(2, 0, 0, 0)$, $(1, 3, 3, 0)$, and $(0, 4, 6, 1)$.
   (*Hint: First* find orthogonal bases, *then* normalize.)

2. Draw a figure to illustrate the orthogonal projection of a vector on a one-dimensional subspace.
3. Find the orthogonal projection of $\beta = (2, 1, 3)$ on the subspace spanned by $\alpha = (1, 0, 1)$.
4. Find the orthogonal projection of $\beta = (0, 0, 0, 3)$ on each of the subspaces of Ex. 1.
5. Let S be any subspace of a Euclidean vector space E. Show that the set $S^\perp$ of all vectors orthogonal to every ξ in S is a subspace satisfying

$$S \cap S^\perp = O, \qquad S + S^\perp = E, \qquad \text{and} \qquad d[S] + d[S^\perp] = d[E].$$

(The subspace $S^\perp$ is called the *orthogonal complement* of S.)
6. Find a basis for the orthogonal complement of the subspace spanned by $(2, -1, -2)$ in Euclidean three-space.
7. Find bases for the orthogonal complements of each of the subspaces of Ex. 1.
★8. (a) Exhibit a nontrivial subspace of $V_2(\mathbf{Q})$ which does not contain any vector of unit length.
   (b) State and prove an analogue of Lemma 2, valid for vector spaces with scalars in any ordered field.

VIII. The Algebra of Matrices

1. Linear Transformations and Matrices

There are many ways of mapping a plane into itself *linearly:* that is, so that any linear combination of vectors is carried into the same linear combination of transformed vectors. Symbolically this means that

$$(1) \qquad (c\xi + d\eta)T = c(\xi T) + d(\eta T).$$

Equivalently, it means that T preserves sums and scalar products, in the sense that

$$(2) \qquad (\xi + \eta)T = \xi T + \eta T, \qquad (c\xi)T = c(\xi T).$$

For example, consider the (counterclockwise) rigid rotation R_θ of the plane about the origin through an angle θ. It is clear geometrically that

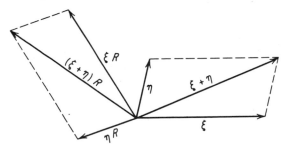

Figure 1

R_θ transforms the diagonal $\xi + \eta$ of the parallelogram with sides ξ and η into the diagonal $\xi R_\theta + \eta R_\theta$ of the rotated parallelogram with sides ξR_θ and ηR_θ. This is illustrated in Figure 1, where $\theta = 135°$; it shows that $(\xi + \eta)R_\theta = \xi R_\theta + \eta R_\theta$. Also, if c is any real scalar, the multiple $c\xi$ of ξ is rotated into $c(\xi R_\theta)$, so that $(c\xi)R_\theta = c(\xi R_\theta)$. Hence any rigid rotation of the plane is linear; moreover the same considerations apply to rotations of space about any axis.

Again, consider a simple expansion D_k of the plane away from the origin, under which each point is moved radially to a position k times its original distance from the origin. Thus, symbolically,

$$(3) \qquad \xi D_k = k\xi, \qquad \text{for all } \xi.$$

This transformation again carries parallelograms into parallelograms, hence vector sums into sums, so that $(\xi + \eta)D_k = \xi D_k + \eta D_k$. Moreover, $(c\xi)D_k = kc\xi = ck\xi = c(\xi D_k)$; hence D_k is linear. Note that if $0 < k < 1$, equation (3) defines a simple contraction toward the origin; if $k = -1$, it defines reflection in the origin (rotation through 180°), so that these transformations are also linear.

More generally, let T be any transformation of the plane which carries each vector $\xi = (x, y)$ into a vector $\xi' = (x', y')$ whose coordinates x', y' are given by homogeneous linear functions

(4) $$x' = xa + ya^*, \qquad y' = xb + yb^*$$

of x and y. Clearly, if x and y are both multiplied by the scalar c, then in (4) x' and y' are multiplied by c, so that $(c\xi)T = c\xi' = c(\xi T)$. Similarly, the transform of a sum $(x_1 + x_2, y_1 + y_2)$ of two vectors $\xi_1 = (x_1, y_1)$ and $\xi_2 = (x_2, y_2)$ may be computed by (4) to have the coordinates

$$x' = (x_1 + x_2)a + (y_1 + y_2)a^*$$
$$= (x_1a + y_1a^*) + (x_2a + y_2a^*) = x_1' + x_2'$$

and $y' = y_1' + y_2'$, where $\xi_1 T = (x_1', y_1')$ and $\xi_2 T = (x_2', y_2')$. Hence T is always linear—that is, T satisfies (2).

Conversely, any linear transformation T of the plane into itself is of the form (4). To see this, denote the transforms of the unit vectors $\varepsilon_1 = (1, 0)$ and $\varepsilon_2 = (0, 1)$ by $\varepsilon_1 T = (a, b)$ and $\varepsilon_2 T = (a^*, b^*)$. Since $(x, y) = x\varepsilon_1 + y\varepsilon_2$, the conditions (1) for linearity imply

$$(x, y)T = (x\varepsilon_1 + y\varepsilon_2)T \qquad = (x\varepsilon_1)T + (y\varepsilon_2)T$$
$$= x(a, b) + y(a^*, b^*) = (xa + ya^*, xb + yb^*).$$

Hence, if T is linear, it is defined by equations of the form (4).

This construction gives the coefficients of (4) explicitly. Thus consider the counterclockwise rotation R_θ about the origin through an angle θ. The very definition of the sine and cosine functions shows that the unit vector $\varepsilon_1 = (1, 0)$ is rotated into $(\cos \theta, \sin \theta)$, while the unit vector $\varepsilon_2 = (0, 1)$ is rotated into

$$(\cos (\theta + \pi/2), \sin (\theta + \pi/2)) = (- \sin \theta, \cos \theta).$$

Thus in (4) we have $a = \cos \theta$, $b = \sin \theta$, $a^* = - \sin \theta$, $b^* = \cos \theta$, so that the equations for R_θ are

(5) $$R_\theta: x' = x \cos \theta - y \sin \theta, \qquad y' = x \sin \theta + y \cos \theta.$$

Likewise, reflection F_α in a line through the origin making an angle α with the x-axis carries the point whose polar coordinates are (r, θ) into one with polar coordinates $(r, 2\alpha - \theta)$. Hence the effect of F_α is expressed by

(5') $F_\alpha: x' = x \cos 2\alpha + y \sin 2\alpha, \quad y' = x \sin 2\alpha - y \cos 2\alpha.$

The concept of linearity also applies more generally to transformations between any two vector spaces over the same field.

Definition.   *A linear transformation $T: V \to W$, of a vector space V to a vector space W over the same field F, is a transformation T of V into W which satisfies $(c\xi + d\eta)T = c(\xi T) + d(\eta T)$, for all vectors ξ and η in V and all scalars c and d in F.*

For example, consider the transformation

(6) $T_1: (x, y) \to (x + y, x - y, 2x) = (x', y', z'),$

defined by the equations $x' = x + y$, $y' = x - y$, $z' = 2x$. This carries the plane vectors $(1, 0)$ and $(0, 1)$ into the orthogonal space vectors $(1, 1, 2)$ and $(1, -1, 0)$, respectively, and transforms the plane linearly into a subset of space.

The finite-dimensional case is most conveniently treated by means of the following principle.

Theorem 1.   *If $\beta_1, \cdots, \beta_m$ is any basis of the vector space V, and $\alpha_1, \cdots, \alpha_m$ are any m vectors in W, then there is one and only one linear transformation $T: V \to W$ with $\beta_1 T = \alpha_1, \cdots, \beta_m T = \alpha_m$. This transformation is defined by*

(7) $(x_1\beta_1 + \cdots + x_m\beta_m)T = x_1\alpha_1 + \cdots + x_m\alpha_m.$

For example, let $\beta_1 = (1, 0)$, $\beta_2 = (0, 1)$, $\alpha_1 = (1, 0)$ and $\alpha_2 = (a, 1)$ in the plane. Then Theorem 1 asserts that the horizontal *shear* transformation

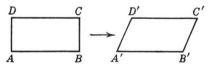

Figure 2

(8) $S_a: (x, y) \to (x + ay, y)$

is linear, and is the only linear transformation satisfying $\beta_1 S_a = \alpha_1$, $\beta_2 S_a = \alpha_2$. Geometrically, each point is moved parallel to the x-axis through a distance proportional to its altitude above the x-axis, and rectangles with sides parallel to the axes go into parallelograms (see Figure 2, and picture this with a deck of cards!).

Proof.   If T is linear and $\beta_i T = \alpha_i$ $[i = 1, \cdots, m]$, then the definition (1) and induction give the explicit formula (7). Since every vector in V can be expressed uniquely as $x_1\beta_1 + \cdots + x_m\beta_m$, formula (7) defines a single-valued transformation T of V into W; hence there can be no other linear transformation of V into W with $\beta_i T = \alpha_i$. To show that

T is linear, let $\eta = \sum y_i \beta_i$ be a second vector of V. Then,

$$(c\xi + d\eta)T = \left[\sum_{i=1}^{m} cx_i\beta_i + \sum_{i=1}^{m} dy_i\beta_i \right] T = \left[\sum_{i=1}^{m} (cx_i + dy_i)\beta_i \right] T$$

$$= \sum_{i=1}^{m} (cx_i + dy_i)\alpha_i = c \sum_{i=1}^{m} x_i\alpha_i + d \sum_{i=1}^{m} y_i\alpha_i$$

$$= c(\xi T) + d(\eta T).$$

Hence T is linear, Q.E.D.

If $V = V_m(F)$ and $W = V_n(F)$, and we let the β_i be the unit vectors $\varepsilon_1 = (1, 0, \cdots, 0), \cdots, \varepsilon_m = (0, 0, \cdots, 1)$ of V_m, we obtain a very important application of Theorem 1. In this case, we can give each α_i its coordinate representation

(9)
$$\begin{aligned}
\varepsilon_1 T &= \alpha_1 = (a_{11}, a_{12}, \cdots, a_{1n}) \\
\varepsilon_2 T &= \alpha_2 = (a_{21}, a_{22}, \cdots, a_{2n}) \\
&\cdot \quad \cdot \quad \cdot \quad \cdot \quad \cdot \quad \cdot \quad \cdot \quad \cdot \quad \cdot \\
\varepsilon_m T &= \alpha_m = (a_{m1}, a_{m2}, \cdots, a_{mn}).
\end{aligned}$$

Theorem 1 states that there is just one linear transformation associated with the formula (9). This transformation is thus determined by the $m \times n$ matrix $A = \| a_{ij} \|$, which has the coordinates $(a_{i1}, \cdots, a_{in})$ as its ith row, and a_{ij} as the entry in its ith row and jth column. We have proved

Theorem 2.   *There is a one-one correspondence between the linear transformations $T: V_m(F) \to V_n(F)$ and the $m \times n$ matrices A with entries in the field F. Given T, the corresponding matrix A is the matrix with ith row the row of coordinates of $\varepsilon_i T$; given $A = \| a_{ij} \|$, T is the (unique) linear transformation carrying each unit vector ε_i of $V_m(F)$ into the ith row $(a_{i1}, \cdots, a_{in})$ of A.*

We denote by T_A the linear transformation of V_m into V_n corresponding to A in this fashion. For example, in the plane, the rotation, similitude, and shear of (5), (3), and (8) correspond respectively to the matrices

$$R_\theta \to \begin{pmatrix} \cos\theta & \sin\theta \\ -\sin\theta & \cos\theta \end{pmatrix}, \quad D_k \to \begin{pmatrix} k & 0 \\ 0 & k \end{pmatrix}, \quad S_a \to \begin{pmatrix} 1 & 0 \\ a & 1 \end{pmatrix}.$$

The general transformation $T = T_A$ of (9) carries any given vector $\xi = (x_1, \cdots, x_m) = x_1\varepsilon_1 + \cdots + x_m\varepsilon_m$ of $V_m(F)$ into the vector

$$\begin{aligned}
\xi T &= x_1\alpha_1 + \cdots + x_m\alpha_m \\
&= x_1(a_{11}, \cdots, a_{1n}) + \cdots + x_m(a_{m1}, \cdots, a_{mn}) \\
&= (x_1a_{11} + \cdots + x_ma_{m1}, \cdots, x_1a_{1n} + \cdots + x_ma_{mn})
\end{aligned}$$

in $W = V_n(F)$. Hence, if $(y_1, \cdots, y_n)$ are the coordinates of the transformed vector $\eta = \xi T$, T is given in terms of these coordinates by the homogeneous linear equations

$$y_1 = x_1 a_{11} + x_2 a_{21} + \cdots + x_m a_{m1} = \sum_i x_i a_{i1},$$

(10) $$y_2 = x_1 a_{12} + x_2 a_{22} + \cdots + x_m a_{m2} = \sum_i x_i a_{i2},$$

$$\cdot$$
$$\cdot$$
$$\cdot$$

$$y_n = x_1 a_{1n} + x_2 a_{2n} + \cdots + x_m a_{mn} = \sum_i x_i a_{in}.$$

Hence we have the

Corollary. *Any linear transformation T of $V_m(F)$ into $V_n(F)$ can be described by homogeneous linear equations of the form (10). Specifically, each T determines an $m \times n$ matrix $A = \| a_{ij} \|$, so that T carries the vector ξ with coordinates $x_1, \cdots, x_n$ into the vector $\eta = \xi T$ with coordinates $y_1, \cdots, y_n$ given by (10). Conversely, each $m \times n$ matrix A determines, by means of equations (10), a linear transformation $T = T_A$: $V_m(F) \to V_n(F)$.*

Caution. The rectangular array of the coefficients of (10) is *not* the matrix A appearing in (9); it is the matrix of (9) with its rows and columns interchanged. This $n \times m$ matrix of coefficients of (10), obtained from the $m \times n$ matrix A by interchanging rows and columns, is called the *transpose* of A and is denoted by A^T. If $A = \| a_{ij} \|$ has entry a_{ij} in its ith row and jth column, then the transpose A^T is defined formally by the equations

(11) $$a_{ij}{}^T = a_{ji} \qquad (i = 1, \cdots, n; \quad j = 1, \cdots, m).$$

These results refer to transformations on the spaces $V_m(F)$ and $V_n(F)$ of m- or n-tuples. If V and W are any two vector spaces over F, of dimensions m and n respectively, then any linear transformation $T: V \to W$ can be represented by a matrix A, once we have chosen a basis $\beta_1, \cdots, \beta_m$ in V and a basis $\gamma_1, \cdots, \gamma_n$ in W. For then T is determined by the images $\beta_i T = \sum_j a_{ij} \gamma_j$, and we say that T is represented by the $m \times n$ matrix $A = \| a_{ij} \|$ of these coefficients, relative to the given bases. This amounts to replacing the spaces V and W by the isomorphic spaces of m- and n-tuples, under the isomorphisms $\sum x_i \beta_i \to (x_1, \cdots, x_m)$; $\sum y_j \gamma_j \to (y_1, \cdots, y_n)$.

EXERCISES

1. Describe the geometric effect of each of the following linear transformations
(a) $y' = x,$ $x' = y$;   (b) $y' = x,$ $x' = x$;
(c) $y' = x,$ $x' = 0$;   (d) $y' = ky,$ $x' = kx + kay$;
(e) $y' = by,$ $x' = cx.$

2. Consider the transformation of the plane into itself which carries every point P into a point P' related to P in the way described below.   Determine when the transformation is linear and find its equations.

   (a) P' is two units to the right of P and one unit above (a translation).

   (b) P' is the projection of P on the line of slope $1/2$ through the origin.

   (c) P' lies on the half-line OP joining P to the origin, at a distance from O such that $\overline{OP'} = 4/\overline{OP}$.

   (d) P' is obtained from P by a rotation through $30°$ about the origin, followed by a shear parallel to the y-axis.

   (e) P' is the reflection of P in the line $x = 3$.

3. Find the matrices which represent the symmetries of the equilateral triangle with vertices $(1, 0)$ and $(-1/2, \pm \sqrt{3}/2)$.

4. Describe the geometric effects of the following linear transformations of space:

   (a) $x' = ax$, $y' = by$, $z' = cz$;

   (b) $x' = 0$, $y' = 3y$, $z' = 3z$;

   (c) $x' = x + 2y + 5z$, $y' = y$, $z' = z$;

   (d) $x' = x - y$, $y' = x + y$, $z' = 4z$.

5. What is the matrix of the transformation (6) of the text?

6. Find the matrix which represents the linear transformation described:

   (a) $(1, 1) \rightarrow (0, 1)$ and $(-1, 1) \rightarrow (3, 2)$;

   (b) $(1, 0) \rightarrow (4, 0)$ and $(0, 1) \rightarrow (-1, 2)$;

   (c) $(2, 3) \rightarrow (1, 0)$ and $(3, 2) \rightarrow (1, -1)$;

   (d) $(1, 0, 0) \rightarrow (1, 2, 1)$, $(0, 1, 0) \rightarrow (3, 1, 1)$, $(0, 0, 1) \rightarrow (0, 0, 3)$.

7. By the image of a subspace S of V under a linear transformation T one means the set $(S)T$ of all vectors ξT, for ξ in S. Prove that $(S)T$ is itself a subspace.

8. A linear transformation T takes $(1, 1)$ into $(0, 1, 2)$ and $(-1, 1)$ into $(2, 1, 0)$. What matrix represents T?

2. Matrix Addition

The algebra of linear transformations (matrices) involves three operations: addition of two linear transformations (or matrices), multiplication of a linear transformation by a scalar, and multiplication of two linear transformations (matrices). We shall now define the *vector* operations on matrices, namely, the addition of two matrices, and the multiplication of a matrix by a scalar.

The *sum* $A + B$ of two $m \times n$ matrices $A = \| a_{ij} \|$ and $B = \| b_{ij} \|$ is obtained by adding corresponding entries, as

(12) $$\| a_{ij} \| + \| b_{ij} \| = \| a_{ij} + b_{ij} \|.$$

This sum obeys the usual commutative and associative laws because the terms a_{ij} obey them. The $m \times n$ matrix O which has all entries zero acts as a *zero matrix* under this addition, so that

$$O + A = A + O = A, \qquad \text{for any } m \times n \text{ matrix } A.$$

The additive inverse may be found by simply multiplying each entry by -1. Under addition, $m \times n$ matrices thus form an Abelian group.

The *scalar product* cA of a matrix A by a scalar c is formed by multiplying each entry by c. One may verify the usual laws for vectors:

$$
\text{(13)} \qquad
\begin{aligned}
1 \cdot A &= A, & c(dA) &= (cd)A, \\
(c + d)A &= cA + dA, & c(A + B) &= cA + cB.
\end{aligned}
$$

Theorem 3. *Under addition and scalar multiplication, all $m \times n$ matrices over a field F form a vector space over F.*

Any matrix $\| a_{ij} \|$ may be written as a sum $\sum a_{ij} E_{ij}$, where E_{ij} is the special matrix with entry 1 in the ith row and jth column, entries 0 elsewhere. These matrices E_{ij} are linearly independent, so form a basis for the space of all $m \times n$ matrices. The dimension of this space is therefore mn.

There is a corresponding algebra of linear transformations. One can define the sum $T + U$ of any two linear transformations from a vector space V to a vector space W, by

$$
\text{(14)} \qquad \xi(T + U) = \xi T + \xi U, \qquad \text{for all } \xi \text{ in } V.
$$

Similarly, the scalar product cT is defined by $\xi(cT) = c(\xi T)$. The sum $T + U$ is linear according to definition (1), for

$$
\begin{aligned}
(c\xi + d\eta)(T + U) &= (c\xi + d\eta)T + (c\xi + d\eta)U \\
&= c\xi T + c\xi U + d\eta T + d\eta U \\
&= c\xi(T + U) + d\eta(T + U).
\end{aligned}
$$

The product cT is also linear.

When $V = V_m(F)$ and $W = V_n(F)$, definition (14) implies that $\varepsilon_i(T + U) = \varepsilon_i T + \varepsilon_i U$, whence the matrix C corresponding to $T + U$ in Theorem 2 is the sum of the matrices which correspond to T and U. Since $\varepsilon_i(cT) = c(\varepsilon_i T)$, the operation of scalar multiplication just defined corresponds to that previously defined for $m \times n$ matrices. That is, in the notation introduced following Theorem 2,

$$
\text{(15)} \qquad T_{A+B} = T_A + T_B \qquad \text{and} \qquad T_{cA} = cT_A.
$$

The new definitions have the advantage of being *intrinsic*, in the sense of being independent of the coordinate systems used in V and W (cf. Chap. VII, §8). They also apply to infinite-dimensional vector spaces.

Finally, it should be observed that a linear transformation of a vector space V into a vector space W is just a *homomorphism* of V into W (both being considered as Abelian groups), which preserves multiplication by scalars as well. For this reason, the vector space of all linear transformations from V into W is often referred to as Hom (V, W).

EXERCISES

1. For the matrices R_θ, D_k, S_a of §1, compute $2R_\theta + D_k$, $2S_a - 3D_k$, and $R_\theta - S_a + 5D_k$.

2. Prove that $(A + B)^T = A^T + B^T$, $(cA)^T = cA^T$.

3. Prove the rules (13).

4. Prove directly, without reference to matrices, that the set of all linear transformations $T: V \rightarrow W$ is a vector space under the operations defined in and below (14).

3. Matrix Multiplication

The most important combination of two linear transformations T and U is their *product* TU (first apply T, then U, as in Chap. VI, §2). In this section, we shall consider only the product of two linear transformations T, U of a vector space V into itself. Then TU may be defined as that transformation of V into itself with $\xi(TU) = (\xi T)U$ for every vector ξ.

For instance, if the shear S_a of (8) is followed by a transformation of similitude D_k, which sends (x', y') into $x'' = kx'$, $y'' = ky'$, the combined effect is to take (x, y) into $x'' = kx + kay$, $y'' = ky$. This product $S_a D_k$ is still linear.

Theorem 4. *The product of two linear transformations is linear.*

Proof. By definition, a product TU maps any ξ into $\xi(TU) = (\xi T)U$. By the linearity of T and U, respectively,

$$(16) \qquad (c\xi + d\eta)TU = [c(\xi T) + d(\eta T)]U = c(\xi TU) + d(\eta TU),$$

which is to say that TU also satisfies the defining condition (1) for a linear transformation, Q.E.D.

This result implies that the homogeneous linear equations (10) for T and U may be combined to yield homogeneous linear equations for TU. To be specific, let the transformation

$$(17) \qquad \begin{aligned} x' &= xa_{11} + ya_{21}, \\ y' &= xa_{12} + ya_{22}, \end{aligned} \qquad A = \begin{pmatrix} a_{11} & a_{12} \\ a_{21} & a_{22} \end{pmatrix},$$

with matrix A, be followed by a second linear transformation of the plane, mapping (x', y') on (x'', y''), where

$$(18) \qquad \begin{aligned} x'' &= x'b_{11} + y'b_{21}, \\ y'' &= x'b_{12} + y'b_{22}, \end{aligned} \qquad B = \begin{pmatrix} b_{11} & b_{12} \\ b_{21} & b_{22} \end{pmatrix}.$$

The combined transformation, found by substituting (17) in (18), is

$$(19) \qquad \begin{aligned} x'' &= (a_{11}b_{11} + a_{12}b_{21})x + (a_{21}b_{11} + a_{22}b_{21})y, \\ y'' &= (a_{11}b_{12} + a_{12}b_{22})x + (a_{21}b_{12} + a_{22}b_{22})y. \end{aligned}$$

The matrix of coefficients in this product transformation arises from the original matrices A and B by the important rule

$$(20) \qquad \begin{pmatrix} a_{11} & a_{12} \\ a_{21} & a_{22} \end{pmatrix} \cdot \begin{pmatrix} b_{11} & b_{12} \\ b_{21} & b_{22} \end{pmatrix} = \begin{pmatrix} a_{11}b_{11} + a_{12}b_{21} & a_{11}b_{12} + a_{12}b_{22} \\ a_{21}b_{11} + a_{22}b_{21} & a_{21}b_{12} + a_{22}b_{22} \end{pmatrix}.$$

The entry in the *first row* and the *second column* of this result involves only the *first* row of a's and the *second* column of b's, and so on. This multiplication rule is a labor-saving device which spares one the trouble of using variables in substitutions like (19).

Similar formulas hold for $n \times n$ matrices, for Theorems 2 and 4 show that the product of the transformations $T, U: V_n(F) \to V_n(F)$ must yield a suitable product of their matrices. We shall now compute the "matrix product" AB which corresponds to $T_A T_B$, so as to give the rule

$$(21) \qquad\qquad T_A T_B = T_{AB}.$$

By Theorem 2, $\varepsilon_i T_A = \sum a_{ij}\varepsilon_j$ and $\varepsilon_j T_B = \sum b_{jk}\varepsilon_k$. Hence

$$\varepsilon_i(T_A T_B) = (\varepsilon_i T_A)T_B = \left(\sum_j a_{ij}\varepsilon_j\right) T_B = \sum_j a_{ij}(\varepsilon_j T_B)$$

$$= \sum_j a_{ij} \left(\sum_k b_{jk}\varepsilon_k\right) = \sum_k c_{ik}\varepsilon_k,$$

where

$$(22) \qquad c_{ik} = \sum_j a_{ij}b_{jk} = a_{i1}b_{1k} + a_{i2}b_{2k} + \cdots + a_{in}b_{nk}.$$

Hence the *matrix product* $C = AB$ must be defined by (22) in order to make (21) valid; we adopt this definition.

Definition. *The product AB of the $n \times n$ matrix A by the $n \times n$ matrix B is defined to be the $n \times n$ matrix C having for its entry in the ith row and kth column the sum c_{ik} given by (22).*

The product of two matrices may also be described verbally: the entry c_{ik} in the ith row and the kth column of the product AB is found by multiplying the ith row of A by the kth column of B. To "multiply" a row by a column, one multiplies corresponding entries, then adds the results.

It follows immediately from the correspondence (21) between matrix multiplication and transformation multiplication that the multiplication of matrices is associative. In symbols

$$(23) \qquad\qquad A(BC) = (AB)C,$$

since these matrices correspond to the transformations $T_A(T_B T_C)$ and $(T_A T_B)T_C$, which are equal by the associative law for the multiplication of transformations (Chap. VI, §2).

Not only is matrix multiplication associative; it is distributive on matrix sums. For the matrix $(A + B)C$ has entries d_{ik} given by formulas like (22) as

$$d_{ik} = \sum_j (a_{ij} + b_{ij})c_{jk} = \sum_j a_{ij}c_{jk} + \sum_j b_{ij}c_{jk}.$$

This gives d_{ik} as the sum of an entry g_{ik} of AC and an entry h_{ik} of BC and proves the first of the two distributive laws

(24) $(A + B)C = AC + BC,$ $A(B + C) = AB + AC.$

For scalar products by d one may also verify the laws

(25) $(dA)B = d(AB)$ and $A(dB) = d(AB).$

The laws (24) and (25) are summarized by the statement that matrix multiplication is *bilinear*, for the first halves of these laws combine to give $(dA + d^*A^*)B = d(AB) + d^*(A^*B)$. This is exactly the condition that multiplication by B on the right be a linear transformation $X \to XB$ on the vector space of all $n \times n$ matrices X. The other laws of (24) and (25) assert that multiplication by A on the left is also a linear transformation.

Corresponding to the identity transformation T_I of $V_n(F)$ is the $n \times n$ *identity matrix* I, which has entries $e_{ii} = 1$ along the principal diagonal (upper left to lower right) and zeros elsewhere, since $\varepsilon_i T_I = \varepsilon_i$ for all $i = 1, \cdots , n$. Since I represents the identity transformation, it has the property $IA = A = AI$ for every $n \times n$ matrix I.

We may summarize the foregoing as follows:

Theorem 5.   *The set of all $n \times n$ matrices over a field F is closed under multiplication, which is associative, has an identity, and is bilinear with respect to vector addition and scalar multiplication.*

However, multiplication is not commutative. Thus

$$\begin{pmatrix} -1 & 0 \\ 0 & 1 \end{pmatrix}\begin{pmatrix} 0 & 1 \\ -1 & 0 \end{pmatrix} = \begin{pmatrix} 0 & -1 \\ -1 & 0 \end{pmatrix}.$$

$$\begin{pmatrix} 0 & 1 \\ -1 & 0 \end{pmatrix}\begin{pmatrix} -1 & 0 \\ 0 & 1 \end{pmatrix} = \begin{pmatrix} 0 & 1 \\ 1 & 0 \end{pmatrix}.$$

Hint: What geometric transformations do these matrices induce on the square of Chap. VI, §1?

Not all non-zero matrices have multiplicative inverses; thus the matrix $\begin{pmatrix} 1 & 0 \\ 3 & 0 \end{pmatrix}$, which represents an oblique projection on the x-axis, does not induce a one-one transformation and is not onto; hence (Chap. VI, Theorem 1) it has no left-inverse or right-inverse. Similarly, the law of cancellation fails, for there are plenty of divisors of zero, as in

$$\begin{pmatrix} 1 & 0 \\ 0 & 0 \end{pmatrix} \cdot \begin{pmatrix} 0 & 0 \\ 3 & 2 \end{pmatrix} = \begin{pmatrix} 0 & 0 \\ 0 & 0 \end{pmatrix}, \qquad \begin{pmatrix} 2 & 4 \\ -1 & -2 \end{pmatrix} \cdot \begin{pmatrix} 0 & 2 \\ 0 & -1 \end{pmatrix} = \begin{pmatrix} 0 & 0 \\ 0 & 0 \end{pmatrix}.$$

Formulas (15) and (21) assert the following important principle.

Theorem 6.   *The algebra of linear transformations of $V_n(F)$ is isomorphic to the algebra of all $n \times n$ matrices over F under the correspondence $T_A \leftrightarrow A$ of Theorem 2.*

This suggests that the formal laws, asserted in Theorem 5 for the algebra of matrices, may in fact be valid for the linear transformations of any vector space whatever. This conjecture is readily verified, and leads directly to certain aspects of the "operational calculus," when applied to suitable vector spaces of infinite dimensions.

EXAMPLE 1.   Let V consist of all functions $f(x)$ of a real variable x, and let J be the transformation or "operator" $[f(x)]J = f(x + 1)$. If I is the identity transformation, the operator $\Delta = J - I$ is known as a "difference operator"; it carries $f(x)$ into $f(x + 1) - f(x)$. Both J and Δ are linear, for $[cf(x) + dg(x)]J = c[f(x)]J + d[g(x)]J$. This definition of linearity applies at once, but observe that we cannot set up the linear homogeneous equations in this infinite space. For fixed $a(x)$ the operation $f(x) \rightarrow a(x)f(x)$ is also linear.

EXAMPLE 2.   The derivative operator D applies to the space C^{∞} of all functions $f(x)$ which possess derivatives of all orders; it carries $f(x)$ into $f'(x)$. D is linear. Taylor's Theorem may be symbolically written as $e^D = J$.

EXAMPLE 3.   For functions $f(x, y)$ of two variables there are corresponding linear operators J_x, J_y, D_x, D_y, Δ_x, Δ_y. Thus, $[f(x, y)]J_x = f(x + 1, y)$ and $[f(x, y)]D_x = f_x'(x, y)$.

EXERCISES

1. Compute the products indicated, for the matrices:

$$A = \begin{pmatrix} 1 & 1 \\ 0 & 1 \end{pmatrix}, \quad B = \begin{pmatrix} 1 & -1 \\ 0 & 1 \end{pmatrix}, \quad C = \begin{pmatrix} 1 & 3 \\ 2 & 1 \end{pmatrix}, \quad D = \begin{pmatrix} 4 & 0 \\ 2 & 1 \end{pmatrix};$$

(a) AB, BA, $A^2 + AB - 2B$;

(b) $(A + B - I)(A - B + I) - (A + 2B)(B - A)$;

(c) DB, AC, AD;

(d) Test the associative law for the products $(AC)D$, $A(CD)$.

2. Use matrix products to compute the equations of the following transformations (notation as in §1).

(a) $D_k S_a$,   (b) $S_a D_k$,   (c) $R_\theta S_a$,   for $\theta = 45°$,

(d) $R_\theta S_a D_k$,   for $\theta = 30°$,   (e) $D_k S_a D_k$.

3. When is $S_a D_k = D_k S_a$ (notation as in Ex. 2)?

4. In Ex. 4 of §1 denote by T_n the transformation described in part (n). Compute (using matrices) the following products:

(a) $T_b T_c$,   (b) $T_a T_c$,   (c) $T_b T_a T_b$,   (d) $T_d T_c$,   (e) $T_c T_b T_d$.

5. Prove the laws (25) and the second half of (24).

6. (a) Expand $(A + B)^3$;   (b) Prove that $A^3 A^2 = A^2 A^3$.

7. Prove the associative law for matrix multiplication directly from definition (22).

8. Consider a new "product" $A \times B$ of two matrices, defined by a "row-by-row" multiplication of A by B. Is this product associative?

9. (a) Compute the products BE_1, BE_2, BE_3, E_2E_3, E_1E_3, where

$$B = \begin{pmatrix} 1 & 2 & 1 \\ 1 & 3 & 2 \\ 1 & 4 & 6 \end{pmatrix}, \quad E_1 = \begin{pmatrix} 0 & 0 & 1 \\ 0 & 1 & 0 \\ 1 & 0 & 0 \end{pmatrix}, \quad E_2 = \begin{pmatrix} 1 & 0 & k \\ 0 & 1 & 0 \\ 0 & 0 & 1 \end{pmatrix}, \quad E_3 = \begin{pmatrix} a & 0 & 0 \\ 0 & b & 0 \\ 0 & 0 & c \end{pmatrix}.$$

(b) If A is any 3×3 matrix, how is AE_3 related to A?

(c) Describe the effect caused by multiplying any matrix by E_1; by E_2.

10. Without using matrices, prove the laws $R(S + T) = RS + RT$, $(R + S)T = RT + ST$, and $S(cT) = c(ST)$ for any linear transformations R, S, T of V into itself.

★11. Show that if R, S, T are *any* transformations (linear or not) of a vector space, then $R(S + T) = RS + RT$, but that $(R + S)T = RT + ST$ does not hold in general, unless T is linear.

12. Find all matrices which commute with the matrix E_3 of Ex. 9, when a, b, and c are distinct.

★13. Prove that every matrix which commutes with the matrix D of Ex. 1 can be expressed in the form $aI + bD$.

14. If A is any $n \times n$ matrix, prove that the set $C(A)$ of all $n \times n$ matrices which commute with A is closed under addition and multiplication.

★15. Prove that each $n \times n$ matrix A satisfies an equation of the form

$$A^m + c_{m-1}A^{m-1} + \cdots + c_1A + c_0I = 0, \qquad m \le n^2.$$

★16. (a) Let $A = \| a_{ij} \|$ be an $n \times n$ matrix of real numbers, and let M be the largest of the $| a_{ij} |$. Prove that the entries of A^k are bounded in magnitude by $n^{k-1}M^k$.

(b) Show that the series $I + A + A^2/2! + A^3/3! + \cdots$ is always convergent. (It may be used to define the exponential function e^A of the matrix A.)

In Exercises 17–21, the notation follows that in Examples 1–3 above.

17. (a) Prove D linear;   (b) Show why $e^D = J$.

18. Prove $D_xD_y = D_yD_x$.

★19. (a) Simplify $xD - Dx$, $x\Delta - \Delta x$, $x\Delta^2 - \Delta^2x$.

(b) Simplify $x^iD^j - D^jx^i$, $x^i\Delta^j - \Delta^ix^i$.

★20. Define the Laplacian operator ∇^2 by $\nabla^2 = D_x{}^2 + D_y{}^2$, and find $x\nabla^2 - \nabla^2x$, $y(\nabla^2)^2 - (\nabla^2)^2y$, $\nabla^2(x^2 + y^2) - (x^2 + y^2)\nabla^2$.

★21. Expand $\Delta^n = (J - I)^n$ by a "binomial theorem."

4. Diagonal, Permutation, and Triangular Matrices

A square matrix $D = \| d_{ij} \|$ is called *diagonal* if and only if $i \ne j$ implies $d_{ij} = 0$; that is, if and only if all non-zero entries of D lie on the principal diagonal (from upper left to lower right). To add or to multiply two diagonal matrices, simply add or multiply corresponding entries along the diagonal (why?). If all the diagonal entries d_{ii} of D are non-zero, the diagonal matrix $E = \| e_{ij} \|$ with $e_{ii} = d_{ii}^{-1}$ is the inverse of D, in the sense that $DE = I = ED$. One may then prove

Theorem 7. *All $n \times n$ diagonal matrices with non-zero diagonal entries in a field F form a commutative group under multiplication.*

A *permutation matrix* P is a square matrix which in each row and in each column has some one entry 1, all other entries zero.

The 3×3 permutation matrices are six in number. They are I and the matrices

$$\begin{pmatrix} 0 & 1 & 0 \\ 1 & 0 & 0 \\ 0 & 0 & 1 \end{pmatrix}, \quad \begin{pmatrix} 1 & 0 & 0 \\ 0 & 0 & 1 \\ 0 & 1 & 0 \end{pmatrix}, \quad \begin{pmatrix} 0 & 0 & 1 \\ 0 & 1 & 0 \\ 1 & 0 & 0 \end{pmatrix}, \quad \begin{pmatrix} 0 & 0 & 1 \\ 1 & 0 & 0 \\ 0 & 1 & 0 \end{pmatrix}, \quad \begin{pmatrix} 0 & 1 & 0 \\ 0 & 0 & 1 \\ 1 & 0 & 0 \end{pmatrix}.$$

Since the rows of a matrix are the transforms of the unit vectors, a matrix P is a permutation matrix if and only if the corresponding linear transformation T_P of V_n permutes the unit vectors $\varepsilon_1, \cdots, \varepsilon_n$. The $n \times n$ permutation matrices therefore correspond one-one with the $n!$ possible permutations of n symbols (Chap. VI, §9) and this correspondence is an isomorphism.

Theorem 8. *The $n \times n$ permutation matrices form under multiplication a group isomorphic to the symmetric group on n letters.*

There are other important classes of matrices. A matrix M is *monomial* if each row and column has exactly one non-zero term; any such matrix may be obtained from a permutation matrix by replacing the 1's by any non-zero entries, as for example in

$$(26) \quad M_1 = \begin{pmatrix} 0 & 0 & 5 \\ -2 & 0 & 0 \\ 0 & 3 & 0 \end{pmatrix}, \quad M_2 = \begin{pmatrix} 0 & 7 & 0 \\ 0 & 0 & -3 \\ 4 & 0 & 0 \end{pmatrix}, \quad M_3 = \begin{pmatrix} 0 & 4 \\ -1 & 0 \end{pmatrix}.$$

A square matrix $T = \| t_{ij} \|$ is *triangular* if all the entries below the diagonal are zero; that is, if $t_{ij} = 0$ whenever $i > j$. A matrix S is *strictly triangular* if all the entries on or below the main diagonal are zero. These two patterns may be schematically indicated in the 4×4 case by

$$(27) \quad T = \begin{pmatrix} q & r & s & t \\ 0 & u & v & w \\ 0 & 0 & x & y \\ 0 & 0 & 0 & z \end{pmatrix}, \quad S = \begin{pmatrix} 0 & u & v & w \\ 0 & 0 & x & y \\ 0 & 0 & 0 & z \\ 0 & 0 & 0 & 0 \end{pmatrix},$$

where the letters denote arbitrary entries. Finally, a *scalar matrix* is a matrix which can be written as cI, where I is the identity.

This scheme of prescribing a "pattern" for the non-zero terms of a matrix is not the only method of constructing groups of matrices. Any group of linear transformations may be represented by a corresponding group of matrices. For instance, the group of the square consists of linear transformations. Pick an origin at the center of the square and an x-axis parallel to one side of the square. If the equations giving the motions R, R', H, and D are written out in terms of x and y (see the description in Chap. VI, §1), they will give transformations with the following matrices,

$$R \rightarrow \begin{pmatrix} 0 & -1 \\ 1 & 0 \end{pmatrix}, \quad R' \rightarrow \begin{pmatrix} -1 & 0 \\ 0 & -1 \end{pmatrix}, \quad H \rightarrow \begin{pmatrix} 1 & 0 \\ 0 & -1 \end{pmatrix}, \quad D \rightarrow \begin{pmatrix} 0 & 1 \\ 1 & 0 \end{pmatrix}.$$

The other four elements of the group can be similarly represented. The multiplication table of this group, as given in Chap. VI, §4, might have been computed by simply multiplying the corresponding matrices here (try it!). In other words, the group of the square is *isomorphic* to a group of eight 2×2 matrices.

The preceding examples show that a given matrix A may have an *inverse* A^{-1}, such that $A A^{-1} = A^{-1}A = I$. Such matrices are called *nonsingular;* they will be studied systematically in §6.

EXERCISES

1. What is the effect of multiplying an $n \times n$ matrix A by a diagonal matrix D on the right?

2. If D is diagonal and all the terms on the diagonal are distinct, what matrices A commute with D (when is $AD = DA$)?

3. (a) Exhibit two 4×4 permutation matrices.
   (b) Exhibit three monomial matrices which are neither diagonal nor permutation matrices.

4. Exhibit explicitly the isomorphism between the 3×3 permutation matrices and the symmetric group.

5. Let S_i be the one-dimensional subspace of V_n spanned by the ith unit vector ε_i. Prove that a nonsingular matrix D is diagonal if and only if the corresponding linear transformation T_D maps each subspace S_i onto itself.

6. Find a description like that of Ex. 5 for monomial matrices.

7. (a) Prove that a monomial matrix M can be written in one and only one way in the form $M = DP$, where D is nonsingular and diagonal, and P is a permutation matrix. (*Hint:* Use Ex. 5.)
   (b) Write the matrices M_1 and M_2 of the text in the forms DP and PD.
   ($\star$c) Exhibit a homomorphism mapping the group of monomial matrices onto the group of permutation matrices.

8. Describe the inverse of a monomial matrix M, and find the inverses of M_1 and M_2 in (26).

9. If M is monomial, D diagonal, prove $M^{-1}DM$ diagonal.

10. If P is a permutation matrix and D diagonal, describe explicitly the form of the transform $P^{-1}DP$.

11. How are the rows of PA related to those of A, for P as in Ex. 10?

12. A matrix A is called *nilpotent* if some power of A is 0. Prove that any strictly triangular matrix is nilpotent. (*Hint:* Try the 3×3 case.)

13. Represent the group of symmetries of the rectangle as a group of matrices.

14. For the group of symmetries of the square with vertices at $(\pm 1, \pm 1)$, compute the matrices which represent the symmetries H, D, V. Verify that $HD = DV$.

★15. In Ex. 7, show that the formula $M = DP$ defines a group-homomorphism $M \to P$. Find its kernel.

5. Rectangular Matrices

We shall now discuss the multiplication of rectangular matrices.

An $m \times n$ matrix $A = \| a_{ij} \|$ and an $n \times r$ matrix $B = \| b_{jk} \|$, with the same n, determine as product $AB = \| c_{ik} \|$ an $m \times r$ matrix C with entries

$$c_{ik} = \sum_j a_{ij} b_{jk},$$

where, in the sum, j runs from 1 to n. This "row-by-column" product cannot be formed unless each row of A is just as long as each column of B; hence the assumption that the number n of columns of A equals the number n of rows of B. Thus, if $m = 1$, $n = 2$, $r = 3$,

$$(x_1, x_2) \begin{pmatrix} a_{11} & a_{12} & a_{13} \\ a_{21} & a_{22} & a_{23} \end{pmatrix} = (x_1 a_{11} + x_2 a_{21}, \, x_1 a_{12} + x_2 a_{22}, \, x_1 a_{13} + x_2 a_{23}).$$

As in our formulas (21)–(22), the matrix product AB corresponds under Theorem 2 to the product $T_A T_B$ of the linear transformations $T_A \colon V_m(F) \to V_n(F)$, and $T_B \colon V_n(F) \to V_r(F)$, associated with A and B respectively. Here, as always, the product of a transformation $T \colon V \to W$ by a transformation $U \colon W \to X$ is defined by

$$(28) \qquad\qquad \xi(TU) = (\xi T)U, \qquad \text{for all } \xi \text{ in } V.$$

The algebraic laws for square matrices hold also for rectangular matrices, provided these matrices have the proper dimensions to make all products involved well defined. For example, the $m \times m$ identity matrix I_m and the $n \times n$ identity I_n satisfy

$$(29) \qquad\qquad I_m A = A = A I_n \qquad \text{(if } A \text{ is } m \times n\text{)}.$$

Matrix multiplication is again bilinear, as in (24) and (25). The associative law is

$$(30) \qquad A(BC) = (AB)C \qquad (A \text{ is } m \times n; \, B, \, n \times r; \, C, \, r \times s).$$

Again, it is best proved by appeal to an interpretation of rectangular matrices as transformations.

As in (11), the *transpose* A^T of an $m \times n$ matrix A is an $n \times m$ matrix A^T with entries $a_{ij}^T = a_{ji}$ ($i = 1, \cdots, n; \, j = 1, \cdots, m$). The ith row of this transpose A^T is the ith column of the original A, and vice versa. One may also obtain A^T by reflecting A in its main diagonal.

To calculate the transpose C^T of a product $AB = C$, use

$$c_{ik}{}^T = c_{ki} = \sum_j a_{kj}b_{ji} = \sum_j b_{ji}a_{kj} = \sum_j b_{ij}{}^T a_{jk}{}^T,$$

the result is just the (i, k) element of the product $B^T A^T$. (Note the change in order.) This proves the first of the laws

(31) $(AB)^T = B^T A^T,$ $(A + B)^T = A^T + B^T,$ $(cA)^T = cA^T.$

The correspondence $A \leftrightarrow A^T$ therefore preserves sums and inverts the order of products, so is sometimes called an anti-automorphism. Since $(A^T)^T = A$, this anti-automorphism is called "involutory."

A systematic use of rectangular matrices has several advantages. For example, a vector ξ in the space $V_n(F)$ of n-tuples over F may be regarded as a $1 \times n$ matrix X with just one row,

(32) $X = (x_1, \cdots, x_n),$ X a "row matrix."

One may also regard the transform XT_A of the vector X by the linear transformation T_A as an ordinary matrix product XA of the row matrix X by A, as in the special case shown in the equation displayed above (28). In effect, the equations $y_j = \sum_i x_i a_{ij}$ of (10) state that the row matrix Y is the product of the row matrix X by the matrix A. Thus the linear transformation $T_A: V_m(F) \to V_n(F)$ can be written in the compact form

(33) $Y = XA,$ $X \in V_m(F),$ $Y \in V_n(F).$

The transpose X^T of a row matrix is a *column* matrix.† The equation (33) for a linear transformation could also be written in terms of column matrices, for on taking the transpose of each side of (33) we get $Y^T = A^T X^T$. The inner product $x_1 y_1 + \cdots + x_n y_n$ of two vectors (Chap. VII, §9) is simply the matrix product of the row matrix X by the column matrix Y^T, so that

(34) $(X, Y) = XY^T$ $(X, Y$ row matrices$).$

The row-by-column multiplication of matrices A and B is actually a matrix multiplication of the ith row of A by the kth column of B so that the definition of a product may be written as

(35) $AB = \| c_{ik} \|$ with $c_{ik} = A_i B^{(k)},$

where we have employed the notation

(36) $A_i =$ the ith row of A, $B^{(k)} =$ the kth column of B.

---

† Again, if $X = (x_1, \cdots, x_n)$ is a row matrix and C a column matrix of the same length, the product $XC = \Sigma x_i c_i$ may be regarded as a linear function of X (for fixed C). This makes column matrices into elements of the dual vector space $V_n(F)^*$.

The whole ith row $(c_{i1}, \cdots, c_{in})$ of the product AB uses only the ith row in A and the various columns of B, hence is the matrix product of A_i by all of B. Similarly, the kth column of AB arises only from the kth column of B. In the notation of (36) these rules are

$$(37) \qquad\qquad (AB)_i = A_iB, \qquad (AB)^{(k)} = AB^{(k)}.$$

The second rule may be visualized by writing out B as the row of its columns, for then

$$(38) \quad A \cdot \| B^{(1)} \quad B^{(2)} \cdots B^{(r)} \| = \| AB^{(1)} \quad AB^{(2)} \cdots AB^{(r)} \|.$$

These columns may also be grouped into sets of columns forming larger submatrices. Thus, a 6×5 matrix B could be considered as a 6×2 matrix $D_1 = \| B^{(1)} \quad B^{(2)} \|$ laid side by side with a 6×3 matrix $D_2 = \| B^{(3)} \quad B^{(4)} \quad B^{(5)} \|$ to form the whole 6×5 matrix $B = \| D_1 \quad D_2 \|$. By (38), the rule for multiplication becomes

$$(39) \quad A \cdot \| D_1 \quad D_2 \| = \| AD_1 \quad AD_2 \|; \qquad D_1 \text{ and } D_2 \text{ } n\text{-rowed blocks.}$$

If we decompose the $n \times r$ matrix B into n rows $B_1, \cdots, B_n$, and if $Y = (y_1, \cdots, y_n)$ is a row matrix, the product YB is the row matrix

$$\begin{aligned} YB &= (y_1b_{11} + \cdots + y_nb_{n1}, \cdots, y_1b_{1r} + \cdots + y_nb_{nr}) \\ &= y_1(b_{11}, \cdots, b_{1r}) + \cdots + y_n(b_{n1}, \cdots, b_{nr}) \\ &= y_1B_1 + \cdots + y_nB_n. \end{aligned}$$

The product YB is thus formed by multiplying the row Y by the "column" of rows B_i. For example, the ith row of AB is by definition the product of the row matrix $A_i = (a_{i1}, \cdots, a_{in})$ by B, hence

$$(40) \qquad (AB)_i = a_{i1}B_1 + \cdots + a_{in}B_n, \qquad i = 1, \cdots, m;$$

thus each row of AB is a linear combination of the rows of B. These formulas are special instances of a method of multiplying matrices which have been subdivided into "blocks" or submatrices. It is convenient to sketch other instances of this method.

$$\left(\begin{array}{ccc|ccc} a_{11} & \cdots & a_{1s} & a_{1,s+1} & \cdots & a_{1n} \\ \cdot & & \cdot & \cdot & & \cdot \\ \cdot & & \cdot & \cdot & & \cdot \\ \cdot & & \cdot & \cdot & & \cdot \\ a_{m1} & \cdots & a_{ms} & a_{m,s+1} & \cdots & a_{mn} \\ \underbrace{}_{M_1} & & & \underbrace{}_{M_2} & & \end{array} \right) \left. \left(\begin{array}{ccc} b_{11} & \cdots & b_{1r} \\ \cdot & & \cdot \\ \cdot & & \cdot \\ \cdot & & \cdot \\ b_{s1} & \cdots & b_{sr} \\ \hline b_{s+1,1} & \cdots & b_{s+1,r} \\ \cdot & & \cdot \\ \cdot & & \cdot \\ \cdot & & \cdot \\ b_{n1} & \cdots & b_{nr} \end{array} \right) \right\} \begin{array}{c} N_1 \\ \\ \\ N_2 \end{array} \right.$$

Let the n columns of a matrix A consist of the s columns of a sub-matrix M_1 followed by a submatrix M_2 with the remaining $n - s$ columns. Make a parallel subdivision of the rows of the matrix B, so that B appears as an $s \times r$ matrix N_1 on top of an $(n - s) \times r$ matrix N_2. The product formula for $AB = C$ subdivides into two corresponding sections

$$(41) \quad c_{ik} = (a_{i1}b_{1k} + \cdots + a_{is}b_{sk}) + (a_{i,s+1}b_{s+1,k} + \cdots + a_{in}b_{nk}).$$

The first parenthesis uses only the ith row from the first block M_1 of A, and only the kth column from the top block N_1 of B. Therefore this first parenthesis is exactly d_{ik}, the entry in the ith row and kth column of the block product M_1N_1. In like manner the second parenthesis of (41) is the term d_{ik}^* of the product M_2N_2. Therefore $c_{ik} = d_{ik} + d_{ik}^*$, so the whole product AB is the matrix sum, $M_1N_1 + M_2N_2$. Thus,

$$(42) \qquad \left\| M_1 \quad M_2 \right\| \cdot \left\| \begin{matrix} N_1 \\ N_2 \end{matrix} \right\| = M_1N_1 + M_2N_2.$$

This formula is a row-by-column *multiplication of blocks*, just like the row-by-column multiplication of matrix entries. A similar result holds for any subdivision of columns of A, with a corresponding row sub-division of B. When both rows and columns are subdivided, the rule for multiplication is a combination of (42) and rule (39),

$$(43) \quad \begin{pmatrix} M_{11} & M_{12} \\ M_{21} & M_{22} \end{pmatrix} \cdot \begin{pmatrix} N_{11} & N_{12} \\ N_{21} & N_{22} \end{pmatrix}$$
$$= \begin{pmatrix} M_{11}N_{11} + M_{12}N_{21} & M_{11}N_{12} + M_{12}N_{22} \\ M_{21}N_{11} + M_{22}N_{21} & M_{21}N_{12} + M_{22}N_{22} \end{pmatrix}.$$

This assumes that the subdivisions fit: that the number of columns in M_{11} equals the number of rows in N_{11}. This rule (43) is exactly the rule for the multiplication of 2×2 matrices, as stated in §3, (20), except that the entries M_{ij} and N_{ij} are submatrices or "blocks," and not scalars. We conclude that matrix multiplication under any fitting block subdivision proceeds just like ordinary matrix multiplication.

EXERCISES

1. Let

$$A = \begin{pmatrix} 1 & 0 & 0 \\ 0 & \frac{1}{2} & \frac{1}{2} \end{pmatrix}, \qquad B = \begin{pmatrix} i & 0 & -i \\ 0 & 1 & 1+i \end{pmatrix}, \qquad X = (1, -1), \qquad Y = (i, 0).$$

(a) Find XA, XB, YA, YB;

(b) Find $3A - 4B$, $A + (1+i)B$, $(X - (1+i)Y)(iA + 5B)$;

(c) Find BA^T, AB^T, XAB^T, BA^TY^T.

2. Show that, if X is any row vector, then XX^T is the inner product of X with itself, while X^TX is the matrix A with $a_{ij} = x_ix_j$.

3. Find AB, BA, AC, and BC, if

$$A = \begin{pmatrix} 2 & 3 & 0 & 0 \\ 5 & 2 & 0 & 0 \\ 0 & 0 & 4 & 0 \\ 0 & 0 & 0 & 2 \end{pmatrix}, \quad B = \begin{pmatrix} 1 & 0 & 0 & 0 \\ 0 & 1 & 0 & 0 \\ 1 & 2 & 1 & 0 \\ 3 & 4 & 0 & 1 \end{pmatrix}, \quad C = \begin{pmatrix} 0 & 1 \\ 1 & 0 \\ 2 & 0 \\ 0 & 2 \end{pmatrix}.$$

4. Let I^* be the $(r + n) \times n$ matrix formed by putting an $n \times n$ identity matrix on top of an $r \times n$ matrix of zeros. What is the effect of multiplying any $n \times (r + n)$ matrix by I^*?

★5. Prove the "block multiplication rule" (43).

6. Inverses

Linear transformations may be divided into two categories, according as they are or are not one-one onto. For instance, the oblique projection $(x, y, z) \to (x, y + z, 0)$ of three-dimensional Euclidean space onto the (x, y)-plane is not one-one.

Definition. *A linear transformation T of a vector space V to itself is called* nonsingular *if and only if it is one-one from V onto V. Otherwise T is called* singular.

A nonsingular linear transformation T is a one-one correspondence of V onto V which preserves the algebraic operations of sum and scalar product, so is an isomorphism of the vector space V to itself. Hence a nonsingular linear transformation of V may be called an *automorphism* of V.

The most direct way to prove the main facts about singular and nonsingular linear transformations is to apply the theory of linear independence derived in Chap. VII, using a fixed basis $\alpha_1, \cdots, \alpha_n$ for the vector space V on which a given transformation T operates.

Theorem 9. *A linear transformation T of a vector space V with finite basis $\alpha_1, \cdots, \alpha_n$ is nonsingular if and only if the vectors $\alpha_1 T, \cdots, \alpha_n T$ are linearly independent in V. When this is the case, T has a (two-sided) linear inverse T^{-1}, with $TT^{-1} = T^{-1}T = I$.*

Proof. First suppose T nonsingular. If there is a linear relation $\sum x_i(\alpha_i T) = O$ between the $\alpha_i T$, then

$$(x_1 \alpha_1 + \cdots + x_n \alpha_n)T = x_1(\alpha_1 T) + \cdots + x_n(\alpha_n T) = O.$$

Since $OT = O$, and T is one-one, this implies $x_1 \alpha_1 + \cdots + x_n \alpha_n = O$ and hence, by the independence of the α's, $x_1 = \cdots = x_n = 0$. Therefore the $\alpha_i T$ are linearly independent.

Conversely, assume that the vectors $\beta_1 = \alpha_1 T, \cdots, \beta_n = \alpha_n T$ are linearly independent, and recall that a transformation T is one-one onto if and only if it has a two-sided inverse (Chap. VI, §2). Since V is n-dimensional, the n independent vectors $\beta_1, \cdots, \beta_n$ are a basis of V. By Theorem 1, there is a linear transformation S of V with

$$\beta_1 S = \alpha_1, \quad \beta_2 S = \alpha_2, \quad \cdots, \quad \beta_n S = \alpha_n.$$

Thus for each $i = 1, \cdots, n$, $\beta_i(ST) = \beta_i$. Since the $\beta_1, \cdots, \beta_n$ are a basis, there is by Theorem 1 only one linear transformation R with $\beta_i R = \beta_i$ for every i, and this transformation is the identity. Hence $ST = I$. Similarly $\alpha_i(TS) = \beta_i S = \alpha_i$, and, because the α's are a basis, $TS = I$. Thus S is the inverse of T, and T is nonsingular.

Thus to test the nonsingularity of T, one may test the linear independence of the images of *any* finite basis of V, as by the methods of Chap. VII, §6.

Corollary 1. *Let T be a linear transformation of a finite-dimensional vector space V. If T is nonsingular, then (i) T has a two-sided linear inverse, (ii) $\xi T = O$ and ξ in V imply $\xi = O$, (iii) T is one-one from V into V, (iv) T transforms V onto V. If T is singular, then (i′) T has neither a left- nor a right-inverse, (ii′) $\xi T = O$ for some $\xi \neq O$, (iii′) T is not one-one, (iv′) T transforms V into a proper subspace of V.*

Proof. Condition (i) was proved in Theorem 9. Again, if $\xi T = O$ for some $\xi \neq O$, then since $OT = O$, T would not be one-one, contrary to the definition of "nonsingular." This proves (ii); (iii) and (iv) are parts of the definition. Again, if T is singular, then for any basis $\alpha_1, \cdots, \alpha_n$ of V, the $\alpha_i T$ are linearly dependent by Theorem 9. Therefore

$$O = x_1\alpha_1 T + \cdots + x_n\alpha_n T = (x_1\alpha_1 + \cdots + x_n\alpha_n)T = \xi T$$

for some $x_1, \cdots, x_n$ not all zero—hence (the α_i being independent) for some $\xi \neq O$, which proves (ii′). Since $OT = O$, it follows that T is not one-one, proving (iii′). Again, since the $\alpha_i T$ are linearly dependent and V is n-dimensional, they span a proper subspace of V, by Theorem 4, Corollary 2 of Chap. VII, proving (iv′). Finally, by Theorem 1 of Chap. VI, (iii′) and (iv′) are equivalent to (i′). Q.E.D.

Note that since the conditions enumerated in Corollary 1 are incompatible in pairs, all eight conditions are "if and only if" (i.e., necessary and sufficient) conditions. Thus if (iv) holds, then (iv′) cannot hold, hence T cannot be singular, hence it must be nonsingular.

Corollary 2. *If the product TU of two linear transformations of a finite-dimensional vector space V is the identity, then T and U are both nonsingular, $T = U^{-1}$, $U = T^{-1}$, and $UT = I$.*

Proof. Since $TU = I$, T has a right-inverse, hence is nonsingular by (i′) above, and has an inverse T^{-1} by (i). Then $T^{-1} = T^{-1}(TU) = (T^{-1}T)U = U$, as asserted, and the other conclusions follow. Q.E.D.

In view of the multiplicative isomorphism of Theorem 6 between linear transformations of $V_n(F)$ and $n \times n$ matrices over F, the preceding results can be translated into results about matrices. We define an $n \times n$ matrix A to be *nonsingular* if and only if it corresponds under Theorem 2 to a nonsingular linear transformation T_A of $V_n(F)$; otherwise we shall call A singular. But the transformation T_A is, by Theorem 2, that transformation which takes the unit vectors of $V_n(F)$ into rows of A. Hence the condition of Theorem 9 becomes (cf. the Corollary of Theorem 5, Chap. VII):

Corollary 3.   *An $n \times n$ matrix over a field F is nonsingular if and only if its rows are linearly independent—or, equivalently, if and only if they form a basis for $V_n(F)$.*

Similarly, conditions (i)–(i') of Corollary 1 translate into the following result.

Corollary 4.   *An $n \times n$ matrix A is nonsingular if and only if it has a matrix inverse A^{-1}, such that*

$$(44) \qquad A A^{-1} = A^{-1}A = I \qquad (A, A^{-1}, I \quad all \quad n \times n).$$

If A has an inverse, so does its transpose, for on taking the transpose of either side of (44) one gets by (31) $(A^{-1})^T A^T = A^T (A^{-1})^T = I$, so that

$$(45) \qquad\qquad\qquad (A^{-1})^T = (A^T)^{-1}.$$

Thus, if A is nonsingular, so is A^T; moreover, the reverse is true similarly. But by Corollary 4, A^T is nonsingular if and only if its rows are linearly independent. These rows are precisely the columns of A; hence we have

Corollary 5.   *A square matrix is nonsingular if and only if its columns are linearly independent.*

If Corollary 2 is translated from linear transformations to matrices, by Theorem 6, we obtain

Corollary 6.   *Every left-inverse of a square matrix is also a right-inverse.*

If matrices A and B both have inverses, so does their product

$$(46) \qquad\qquad (AB)^{-1} = B^{-1}A^{-1} \qquad (note\ the\ order!).$$

For $(AB)(B^{-1}A^{-1}) = A(BB^{-1})A^{-1} = A I A^{-1} = A A^{-1} = I$.

Inverses of nonsingular matrices may be computed by solving suitable simultaneous linear equations. If we write the coordinates of the basis vectors as

$$(47) \quad I_1 = (1, 0, 0, \cdots, 0), \qquad I_2 = (0, 1, 0, \cdots, 0),$$
$$\cdots, I_n = (0, 0, \cdots, 0, 1),$$

then in a given matrix $A = \| a_{ij} \|$ each row A_i is given as a linear combination

$$A_i = \sum_j a_{ij} I_j$$

of the basis vectors. One may try to solve these equations for the "unknowns" I_j in terms of the A_i; the result will be linear expressions for the I_j as

(48) $$I_j = c_{j1}A_1 + \cdots + c_{jn}A_n = \sum_{k=1}^{n} c_{jk}A_k.$$

By (40), this equation states that the matrix $C = \| c_{jk} \|$ satisfies $CA = I$, hence that $C = A^{-1}$. Another construction for A^{-1} appears in §8 below.

EXAMPLE.   To compute the inverse of the matrix shown, write its rows as $A_1 = I_1 + 2I_2 - 2I_3$, $A_2 = -I_1 + 3I_2$, $A_3 = -2I_2 + I_3$. These three simultaneous equations have a solution $I_1 = 3A_1 + 2A_2 + 6A_3$, $I_2 = A_1 + A_2 + 2A_3$, $I_3 = 2A_1 + 2A_2 + 5A_3$. The coefficients c_{jk} in these linear combinations give the inverse matrix, for one may verify that

$$\begin{pmatrix} 1 & 2 & -2 \\ -1 & 3 & 0 \\ 0 & -2 & 1 \end{pmatrix}$$

$$\begin{pmatrix} 3 & 2 & 6 \\ 1 & 1 & 2 \\ 2 & 2 & 5 \end{pmatrix} \begin{pmatrix} 1 & 2 & -2 \\ -1 & 3 & 0 \\ 0 & -2 & 1 \end{pmatrix} = \begin{pmatrix} 1 & 0 & 0 \\ 0 & 1 & 0 \\ 0 & 0 & 1 \end{pmatrix}.$$

Linear transformations from a finite-dimensional vector space V to a second such space W (over the same field) can well be one-one but not onto, or vice versa. The same is true of linear transformations from an infinite-dimensional vector space to itself. For example, the linear transformation $(x_1, x_2, x_3, \cdots) \to (0, x_1, x_2, x_3, \cdots)$ on the space of infinite sequences of real numbers is one-one but not onto, hence has many (linear) right-inverses, but no left-inverse.

However, a two-sided inverse, when it exists, is necessarily linear even if V is a space of infinite dimensions:

Theorem 10.   *If the linear transformation* $T: V \to W$ *is a one-one transformation of V onto W, its inverse is linear.*

Proof.   Let ψ denote the unique inverse transformation of W onto V, not assumed to be linear. Take vectors ξ and η in W and scalars c and d. Since ψT is the identity transformation of W, and T is linear

$$(c\xi + d\eta)\psi T = c\xi + d\eta = c(\xi\psi T) + d(\eta\psi T) = [c(\xi\psi) + d(\eta\psi)]T.$$

Apply ψ to both sides; since $T\psi$ is also the identity, one finds that

(49) $$(c\xi + d\eta)\psi = c(\xi\psi) + d(\eta\psi),$$

an equation which asserts that ψ is linear. Q.E.D.

A one-one linear transformation T of V onto W is an isomorphism of V to W, in the sense of Chap. VII, §8.

Corollary 1.   *An isomorphism T of V onto W carries any set of independent vectors $\alpha_1, \cdots, \alpha_r$ of V into independent vectors in W, and any set $\beta_1, \cdots, \beta_s$ of vectors spanning V into vectors spanning W.*

Proof.   If there is a linear relation

$$x_1(\alpha_1 T) + \cdots + x_r(\alpha_r T) = 0$$

between the $\alpha_i T$, we may apply T^{-1} to find $x_1\alpha_1 + \cdots + x_r\alpha_r = 0$, hence $x_1 = \cdots = x_r = 0$; the $\alpha_i T$ are independent. The proof of the second half is similar.

For any transformation $T: V \to W$, the *image* or *transform* $S' = (S)T$ under T of a subspace S of V is defined as the set of all transforms ξT of vectors in S. This image is always a subspace of W, for each linear combination $c(\xi T) + d(\eta T) = (c\xi + d\eta)T$ of vectors ξT and ηT in S' is again in S'.

Corollary 2.   *For an isomorphism $T: V \to W$, the image under T of any finite-dimensional subspace S of V has the same dimension as S. Thus T carries lines into lines, and planes into planes.*

EXERCISES

1. Find inverses for the matrices A, B, C, D of Ex. 1, §3.

2. (a) Prove that $A = \begin{pmatrix} a & b \\ c & d \end{pmatrix}$ is nonsingular if and only if $ad - bc \neq 0$.

(b) Show that, if A is nonsingular, its inverse is $\Delta^{-1}\begin{pmatrix} d & -b \\ -c & a \end{pmatrix}$, where $\Delta = ad - bc$.

3. Find inverses for the linear transformations R_θ, D_k, S_a of §1.

4. Find inverses (if any) for the linear transformations of Ex. 4, §1.

5. (a) If $\theta = 45°$, compute the matrix of the transformation $R_\theta^{-1}U_bR_\theta$ (see §1), where U_b is the transformation $x' = bx$, $y' = y$.

(b) Describe geometrically the effect of this transformation.

(c) Do the same for $R_\theta^{-1}S_aR_\theta$ (with $\theta = 45°$).

6. If A satisfies $A^2 - A + I = 0$, prove that A^{-1} exists and is $I - A$.

7. Find inverses for the matrices E_1, E_2, and E_3 of Ex. 9, §3.

8. Find inverses for the matrices A and B of Ex. 3, §5. (*Hint:* Use blocks.)

9. (a) Compute a formula for the inverse of a 2×2 triangular matrix.

(b) The same for a 3×3. (*Hint:* Try a triangular inverse.)

(c) Prove that every triangular matrix with no zero terms on the diagonal has a triangular inverse.

10. Given A, B, A^{-1}, B^{-1}, and C, find the multiplicative inverse of

(a) $\begin{pmatrix} A & 0 \\ 0 & B \end{pmatrix}$,   (b) $\begin{pmatrix} A & C \\ 0 & B \end{pmatrix}$,   (c) $\begin{pmatrix} A & 0 \\ C & B \end{pmatrix}$.

11. Prove that all nonsingular $n \times n$ matrices form a group with respect to matrix multiplication.

12. If a product AB of square matrices is nonsingular, prove that both factors A and B are nonsingular.

★13. Prove without appeal to linear transformations that a matrix A has a left-inverse if and only if its rows are linearly independent.

14. Prove Corollary 2 of Theorem 10.

15. Exhibit a linear transformation of the space of sequences $(x_1, x_2, x_3, \cdots)$ *onto* itself which is not one-one.

★16. If a linear transformation $T: V \to W$ has a right-inverse, prove that it has a right-inverse which is linear (without assuming finite-dimensionality).

7. Rank and Nullity

In general, (see Chap. VI, §2) each transformation (function) $T: S \to S_1$ has given sets S and S_1 as *domain* and *codomain*, respectively. The *range* of T is the set of *transforms* (image of the domain under T).

In case T is a *linear* transformation of a vector space V into a second vector space W the range (set of all ξT) cannot be an arbitrary subset of W.

Lemma 1. *The range of a linear transformation* $T: V \to W$ *is itself a vector space* (*hence a subspace of* W).

Proof. Since $c(\xi T) = (c\xi)T$ and $\xi T + \eta T = (\xi + \eta)T$, the set of transforms is closed under the vector operations.

Lemma 2. *Let* T_A *be the linear transformation corresponding to the* $m \times n$ *matrix* A. *Then the range of* T_A *is the row space of* A.

Proof. The transformation $T_A: V_m(F) \to V_n(F)$ carries each vector $X = (x_1, \cdots, x_m)$ of $V_m(F)$ into $Y = XA$ in $V_n(F)$, so that the range of T_A consists of all n-tuples of the form

$$Y = XA = \left(\sum x_i a_{i1}, \cdots, \sum x_i a_{in} \right) = \sum x_i (a_{i1}, \cdots, a_{in}).$$

These are exactly the different linear combinations of the rows $A_i = (a_{i1}, \cdots, a_{in})$ of A. The range of T_A is thus the set of all linear combinations of the rows of A. But this is the row space of A, as defined in Chap. VII, §5. Q.E.D.

The *rank* of a matrix A has been defined (Chap. VII, §6) as the (linear) dimension of the row space of A; it is therefore the dimension of the range of T_A. More generally, the *rank* of any linear transformation T is defined as the dimension (finite or infinite) of the range of T.

Since the dimension of the subspace spanned by m given vectors is the maximum number of linearly independent vectors in the set, the rank of A also is the maximum number of linearly independent *rows* of A. For this reason, the rank of A as defined above is often called the *row-rank* of A, as distinguished from the *column-rank*, which is the maximum number of linearly independent columns of A.

Dual to the concept of the row space of a matrix or range of a linear transformation is that of its *null-space*.

Definition.   *The* null-space *of a linear transformation T is the set of all vectors ξ such that $\xi T = O$. The null-space of a matrix A is the set of all row matrices X which satisfy the homogeneous linear equations $XA = O$.*

Lemma 3.   *The null-space of any linear transformation (or matrix) is a subspace of its domain.*

Proof.   If $\xi T = O$ and $\eta T = O$, then for all c, c',

$$(c\xi + c'\eta)T = c(\xi T) + c'(\eta T) = O + O = O.$$

Hence $c\xi + c'\eta$ is in the null-space, which is therefore a subspace, Q.E.D.

The dimension of the null-space of a given matrix A or a linear transformation T is called the *nullity* of A or T. Nullity and rank are connected by a fundamental equation, valid for both matrices and linear transformations. Because of the correspondence between matrices and linear transformations, we need supply the proof only for one case.

Theorem 11.   *Rank + Nullity = Dimension of domain.*

Thus for an $m \times n$ matrix, (row) rank plus (row) nullity equals m.

Proof.   If the nullity of T is s, its null-space N has a basis $\alpha_1, \cdot \cdot \cdot, \alpha_s$ of s elements, which can be extended to a basis $\alpha_1, \cdot \cdot \cdot, \alpha_s, \beta_1, \cdot \cdot \cdot, \beta_r$ for the whole domain of T. Since every $\alpha_i T = O$, the vectors $\beta_j T$ span the range R of T. Moreover, $x_1(\beta_1 T) + \cdot \cdot \cdot + x_r(\beta_r T) = O$ implies that $x_1\beta_1 + \cdot \cdot \cdot + x_r\beta_r$ is in N, so that $x_1 = \cdot \cdot \cdot = x_r = 0$. Hence the vectors $\beta_j T$ are independent and form a basis for R. We conclude that the dimension $m = s + r$ of the domain is the sum of the dimensions s of N and r of R, which is all we need.

Theorem 12.   *For a linear transformation $T: V_n(F) \to V_n(F)$ to be nonsingular, each of the following conditions is necessary and sufficient:*

(a) *rank* $T = n$; (b) *nullity* $T = 0$.

Proof.   Condition (a) states that T carries $V_n(F)$ onto itself; while condition (b) states that $\xi T = O$ implies $\xi = O$ in $V_n(F)$. Thus Theorem 12 is just a restatement of conditions (iv) and (ii) of Corollary 1 to Theorem 9.

Quotient-spaces.   We have already noted, in §2, that any linear transformation $T: V \to W$ between vector spaces is also a *homomorphism* from V to W, regarded as Abelian groups under addition. Since O is the group identity, it follows that the *null-space* of T is precisely the *kernel* of T, regarded as a group-homomorphism.

Therefore, given any subspace S of a vector space V, it is not surprising that we can paraphrase the discussion of Chap. VI, §13, to obtain a *quotient-space* $V/S = X$. Recall that, for any group G and (normal) subgroup N, the elements of the quotient-group G/N are simply the cosets xN of N in G. Hence, given a subspace S of the vector space V, each vector $\alpha \in V$ determines a *coset* of S, defined as the set $\alpha + S$ of all sums $\alpha + \sigma$ for variable $\sigma \in S$. Thus $\alpha = \alpha + O$ is one of the vectors in this coset; call it a "representative" of the coset. Two cosets $\alpha + S$ and $\beta + S$ are equal (as sets) if and only if $(\alpha - \beta) \in S$; when this holds, α and β represent (are members of) the *same* coset. Geometrically, the different cosets of a subspace S are just its "parallel subspaces" under translation.

Now define the sum of two cosets to be the coset

$$(\alpha + S) + (\beta + S) = (\alpha + \beta) + S;$$

as in Lemma 2 of Chap. VI, §13, this sum does not depend on the choice of the representatives α and β. Next, define the product of a coset $\alpha + S$ by a scalar c to be the coset

$$c(\alpha + S) = c\alpha + S.$$

Since $(\alpha - \beta) \in S$ implies $(c\alpha - c\beta) \in S$, this product also does not depend on the choice of the representative of the given coset. It is readily verified that these two definitions make the set V/S of all the cosets of S in V into a vector space, called the *quotient-space* of V by S. Moreover, if the function P is defined by $\alpha P = \alpha + S$, then P is a linear transformation with null-space exactly S and range all of V/S. This transformation P is called the *canonical projection* of V onto its quotient-space; we have thus proved

Theorem 12a. *Given any subspace S of a vector space V, there exists a quotient-space $X = V/S$ and a linear transformation $P: V \to X$ whose nullspace is S and whose range is X.*

EXERCISES

1. Find the ranges, null-spaces, ranks, and nullities of the transformations given in §1, Exercises 1a–1d and 4a–4b.
2. Construct a transformation of $V_3(\mathbf{R})$ into itself which will have its range spanned by the vectors $(1, 3, 2)$ and $(3, -1, 1)$.
3. Construct a transformation of $V_4(\mathbf{R})$ into itself which has a null-space spanned by $(1, 2, 3, 4)$ and $(2, 2, 4, 4)$.
4. Prove that the row-rank of a product AB never exceeds the row-rank of B.
5. If the $n \times n$ matrix A is nonsingular, show that for every $n \times n$ matrix B the matrices AB, B and BA all have the same rank.

6. Prove that rank $(A + B) \leq$ rank $(A) +$ rank (B).

7. Given the ranks of A and B, what is the rank of $\begin{pmatrix} A & O \\ O & B \end{pmatrix}$?

8. Prove in detail that, under the operations displayed in the text, the cosets of any subspace S of a vector space V do form a vector-space.

★**9.** Let $T: V \to W$ be any linear transformation with null-space S. Show that $T = PR$, where $P: V \to V/S$ is the canonical projection defined in the text and $R: V/S \to W$ is an *isomorphism* from V/S onto the range of T.

8. Elementary Matrices

The elementary row operations on a matrix A, introduced in Chap. VII, §5, may be interpreted as premultiplications of A by suitable factors. For example, two rows in a matrix may be permuted by premultiplying the matrix by a matrix obtained by permuting the same rows of the identity matrix I. Thus

$$\begin{pmatrix} 0 & 1 \\ 1 & 0 \end{pmatrix}\begin{pmatrix} a_1 & a_2 \\ b_1 & b_2 \end{pmatrix} = \begin{pmatrix} 0 \cdot a_1 + 1 \cdot b_1 & 0 \cdot a_2 + 1 \cdot b_2 \\ 1 \cdot a_1 + 0 \cdot b_1 & 1 \cdot a_2 + 0 \cdot b_2 \end{pmatrix} = \begin{pmatrix} b_1 & b_2 \\ a_1 & a_2 \end{pmatrix}.$$

To add the second row to the first row or to multiply the second row by c, simply do the same for an identity factor in front:

$$\begin{pmatrix} 1 & 1 \\ 0 & 1 \end{pmatrix}\begin{pmatrix} a_1 & a_2 \\ b_1 & b_2 \end{pmatrix} = \begin{pmatrix} a_1 + b_1 & a_2 + b_2 \\ b_1 & b_2 \end{pmatrix},$$

$$\begin{pmatrix} 1 & 0 \\ 0 & c \end{pmatrix}\begin{pmatrix} a_1 & a_2 \\ b_1 & b_2 \end{pmatrix} = \begin{pmatrix} a_1 & a_2 \\ cb_1 & cb_2 \end{pmatrix}.$$

Similar results hold for $m \times n$ matrices; the prefactors used to represent the operations are known as *elementary matrices*.

Definition.   *An elementary $m \times m$ matrix E is any matrix obtained from the $m \times m$ identity matrix I by one elementary row operation.*

There are thus three types of elementary matrices, samples of which are

$$(50) \qquad \begin{pmatrix} 1 & 0 & 0 & 0 \\ 0 & 0 & 0 & 1 \\ 0 & 0 & 1 & 0 \\ 0 & 1 & 0 & 0 \end{pmatrix} \quad \begin{pmatrix} 1 & 0 & 0 & 0 \\ 0 & 1 & 0 & 0 \\ 0 & 0 & 3 & 0 \\ 0 & 0 & 0 & 1 \end{pmatrix} \quad \begin{pmatrix} 1 & 0 & 0 & 0 \\ d & 1 & 0 & 0 \\ 0 & 0 & 1 & 0 \\ 0 & 0 & 0 & 1 \end{pmatrix}.$$
$$\qquad\qquad\qquad H_{24} \qquad\qquad\quad I + 2E_{33} \qquad\quad I + dE_{21}$$

In general, let I_k denote the kth row of the $m \times m$ identity matrix I. Then the interchange in I of row i with row j gives the elementary permutation matrix $H = \| h_{ij} \|$ whose rows H_k are

$$(51) \qquad H_i = I_j, \qquad H_j = I_i, \qquad H_k = I_k \qquad (k \neq i, j).$$

Similarly, multiplication of row i in I by a non-zero scalar c gives the matrix M whose rows M_k are given by

(52) $$M_i = cI_i \quad (c \neq 0), \quad M_k = I_k \quad (k \neq i).$$

If E_{ij} is, as before, the matrix having the single entry 1 in the ith row and the jth column, and all other entries zero, this matrix M can be written as $M = I + (c - 1)E_{ii}$. Finally, the elementary operation of adding d times the ith row to the jth row, when applied to I, gives the elementary matrix $F = I + dE_{ji}$, whose rows F_k are given by

(53) $$F_j = I_j + dI_i, \quad F_k = I_k \quad (k \neq j).$$

Theorem 13. *Each elementary row operation on an $m \times n$ matrix A amounts to premultiplication by the corresponding elementary $m \times m$ matrix E.*

This may be proved easily by direct computation of the product EA. Consider, for example, the elementary operation of adding the ith row to the jth row of A. The rows F_k of the corresponding elementary matrix F are then given by (53). The rows of any product EA are always found from the rows of the first factor, by formula (37), so

$$(FA)_j = F_jA = (I_i + I_j)A = I_iA + I_jA = (IA)_i + (IA)_j,$$
$$(FA)_k = F_kA = I_kA = (IA)_k \quad (k \neq j).$$

These equations state that the rows of FA are obtained from the rows of $IA = A$ by adding the ith row to the jth row. In other words, the elementary operation in question does carry A into FA, as asserted in Theorem 13.

Corollary 1. *Every elementary matrix E is nonsingular.*

Proof. E is obtained from I by certain operations. The reverse operation corresponds to some elementary matrix E^* and carries E back into I. By Theorem 13 it carries E into E^*E, so $E^*E = I$, E has a left-inverse E^*, and so is nonsingular.

Corollary 2. *If two $m \times n$ matrices A and B are row-equivalent, then $B = PA$, where P is nonsingular.*

For by Theorem 13, $B = E_nE_{n-1} \cdots E_1A$, where the E_i are elementary, and so nonsingular.

Matrix inverses can be calculated using elementary matrices. For let A be any nonsingular square matrix. By Corollary 3 of Theorem 8 of Chap. VII, A can be reduced to I by elementary row operations. Hence, by Theorem 13, for suitable elementary matrices E_i,

$$E_sE_{s-1} \cdots E_1A = I.$$

Multiply each side of this equation by A^{-1} on the right. Then

(54) $$E_s E_{s-1} \cdots E_1 I = A^{-1}.$$

The matrix on the left is the result of applying to the identity I the sequence of elementary operations $E_1, \cdots, E_s$. This proves

Theorem 14. *If a square matrix A is reduced to the identity by a sequence of row operations, the same sequence of operations applied to the identity matrix I will give a matrix which is the inverse of A.*

This is an efficient construction for the inverse. Given any A, it will by a finite sequence of rational operations either produce an inverse for A or reduce A to an equivalent singular matrix. In the latter event A has no inverse. For matrices larger than 3×3 this method is more efficient than the devices from determinant theory sometimes used to find A^{-1} (cf. Chap. X).

Incidentally, any nonsingular matrix P is the inverse $(P^{-1})^{-1}$ of another nonsingular matrix; hence, as in (54), it can be written as a product of elementary matrices. This combines with Corollary 1 of Theorem 13 to yield the following result.

Theorem 15. *A square matrix P is nonsingular if and only if it can be written as a product of elementary matrices,*

(55) $$P = E_s E_{s-1} \cdots E_1.$$

Corollary 1. *Two $m \times n$ matrices A and B are row-equivalent if and only if $B = PA$, for some nonsingular matrix P.*

For B is row-equivalent to A if and only if (by Theorem 13) $B = E_n E_{n-1} \cdots E_1 A$, where the E_i are elementary. And by Theorem 15 this amounts to $B = PA$, with P nonsingular.

Theorem 15 has a simple geometrical interpretation in the two-dimensional case. The only 2×2 elementary matrices are

$$H_{12} = \begin{pmatrix} 0 & 1 \\ 1 & 0 \end{pmatrix}, \qquad M_1 = \begin{pmatrix} c & 0 \\ 0 & 1 \end{pmatrix}, \qquad M_2 = \begin{pmatrix} 1 & 0 \\ 0 & c \end{pmatrix},$$

$$F_{12} = \begin{pmatrix} 1 & 0 \\ d & 1 \end{pmatrix}, \qquad F_{21} = \begin{pmatrix} 1 & d \\ 0 & 1 \end{pmatrix}.$$

The corresponding linear transformations are, as in §1:

(H_{12}) a reflection of the plane in the 45° line through the origin;
(M_i, for c positive) a compression (or elongation) parallel to the x- or y-axis;
(M_i, for c negative) a compression followed by a reflection in the axis;
(F_{ij}) a shear parallel to one of the axes.

This gives

Corollary 2. *Any nonsingular homogeneous linear transformation of the plane may be represented as a product of shears, one-dimensional compressions (or elongations), and reflections.*

This primarily geometric conclusion has been obtained by algebraic argument on matrices. Analogous results may be stated for a space of three or more dimensions.

The elementary row operations on a matrix involve only manipulations within the given field F. If the elements of a matrix A are rational numbers, while the field is that of all real numbers, the elementary operations can be carried out just as if the field contained only the rational numbers. In either field we get the same echelon form, hence the same number of independent rows.

Theorem 16. *If a matrix A over a field F has its entries all contained in a smaller field F', then the rank of A relative to F is the same as the rank of A relative to the smaller field F'.*

The operations with row-equivalence are exactly those used to solve simultaneous linear equations (Chap. II, §3, and Chap. VII, §5). To state the connection, consider m equations

$$\sum_j a_{ij}x_j = b_i \qquad (i = 1, \cdots, m; \quad j = 1, \cdots, n)$$

in the n unknowns x_j. The coefficients of the unknowns form an $m \times n$ matrix $A = \| a_{ij} \|$, while the constant terms b_i constitute a column vector B^T. The equations may be written in matrix form as $AX^T = B^T$, where X^T is the column vector of unknowns (the transpose of the vector $X = (x_1, \cdots, x_n)$). The column of constants B^T may be adjoined to the given matrix A to form an $m \times (n + 1)$ matrix $\| A, B^T \|$, the so-called *augmented matrix* of the given system of equations. Operations on the *rows* of this matrix correspond to operations carrying the given *equations* into equivalent equations, and so *two systems of equations $AX^T = B^T$ and $A^*X^T = B^{*T}$ have the same solutions X^T if their augmented matrices are row-equivalent.*

EXERCISES

1. Find the row-equivalent echelon form for each of the matrices displayed in Ex. 9(a) of §3.
2. (a) Display the possible 3×3 elementary matrices;
   (b) Draw a diagram to represent each $n \times n$ elementary matrix of the form (51)–(53).
3. Find the inverse of each of the 4×4 elementary matrices H_{24}, $I + 2E_{33}$, $I + dE_{21}$ displayed in the text.

4. Prove Theorem 13 for 2×2 matrices by direct computation for the five matrices displayed after Theorem 15.

5. Find the inverses of $\begin{pmatrix} 1 & 0 & 3 \\ 2 & 4 & 1 \\ 1 & 3 & 0 \end{pmatrix}$ and $\begin{pmatrix} 0 & 1 & 2 \\ 1 & 0 & 2 \\ 1 & 2 & 0 \end{pmatrix}$.

6. Write each of the following matrices as a product of elementary matrices:

   (a) $\begin{pmatrix} 3 & 6 \\ 2 & 1 \end{pmatrix}$,   (b) $\begin{pmatrix} 4 & -2 \\ 3 & -5 \end{pmatrix}$,   (c) the first matrix of Ex. 5.

7. Represent the transformation $x' = 2x - 5y$, $y' = -3x + y$ as a product of shears, compressions, and reflections.

★8. For a three-dimensional space, state and prove an analogue of Corollary 2 to Theorem 15. Using Ex. 3, §5, Chap. VII; sharpen your result.

9. Prove that any nonsingular 2×2 matrix can be represented as a product of the matrices $\begin{pmatrix} 0 & 1 \\ 1 & 0 \end{pmatrix}$, $\begin{pmatrix} 1 & 1 \\ 0 & 1 \end{pmatrix}$, and $\begin{pmatrix} c & 0 \\ 0 & 1 \end{pmatrix}$, where $c \neq 0$ is any scalar. What does this result mean geometrically?

10. Show that the rank of a product never exceeds the rank of either factor.

11. Prove that a system of linear equations $AX^T = B^T$ has a solution if and only if the rank of A equals the rank of the augmented matrix $\| A, B^T \|$.

12. Let $AX^T = B^T$ be a system of nonhomogeneous linear equations with a particular solution $X^T = X_0{}^T$. Prove that every solution X^T can be written as $X^T = X_0{}^T + Y^T$, where Y^T is a solution of the homogeneous equations $AY^T = 0$, and conversely.

13. Prove: If a system of linear equations with coefficients in a field F has no solutions in F, it has no solutions in any larger field.

9. Equivalence and Canonical Form

Operations analogous to elementary row operations can also be applied to columns. By an *elementary column operation* on an $m \times n$ matrix A is thus meant either (i) the interchange of any two columns of A, (ii) the multiplication of any column by any non-zero scalar, or (iii) the addition of any multiple of one column to another column.

The replacement of A by its transpose A^T changes elementary column operations into elementary row operations, and vice versa. In particular, A can be transformed into B by a succession of elementary *column* operations if and only if the transpose A^T can be transformed into B^T by a succession of elementary *row* operations. Applying Corollary 1 of Theorem 15, this means that $B^T = PA^T$, or $B = (B^T)^T = (PA^T)^T = AP^T = AQ$, where $Q = P^T$ is nonsingular. Conversely, $B = AQ$ for a nonsingular Q makes B column-equivalent to A. Hence, application of column operations is equivalent to *post*multiplication by nonsingular factors. The explicit postfactors corresponding to each elementary operation may be found by applying this operation to the identity matrix, much as in Theorem 13.

Column and row operations may be applied jointly. We may define two $m \times n$ matrices A and B to be *equivalent* if and only if A can be changed to B by a succession of elementary row *and* column operations; and we then get the following result.

Theorem 17. *An $m \times n$ matrix A is equivalent to a matrix B if and only if $B = PAQ$ for suitable nonsingular $m \times m$ and $n \times n$ matrices P and Q.*

Using simultaneous row and column operations, matrices can be reduced to a very simple form.

Theorem 18. *Any $m \times n$ matrix is equivalent to a diagonal matrix D in which the diagonal entries are either 0 or 1, all the 1's preceding all the 0's on the diagonal.*

Explicitly, if r is the number of non-zero entries in D, where clearly $r \leqq m$, $r \leqq n$, then D may be displayed in block form as

$$(56) \qquad D = \begin{pmatrix} I_r & O_{r,n-r} \\ O_{m-r,r} & O_{m-r,n-r} \end{pmatrix}, \; I_r \text{ the } r \times r \text{ identity matrix,}$$

where $O_{i,j}$ denotes the $i \times j$ matrix of zeros.

The proof is by induction on the number m of rows of A. If all entries of A are zero, there is nothing to prove. Otherwise, by permuting rows and columns we can bring some non-zero entry c to the a_{11} position. After the first row is multiplied by c^{-1}, the entry a_{11} is 1. All other entries in the first column can be made zero by adding suitable multiples of the first row to each other row, and the same may be done with other elements of the first row. This reduces A to an equivalent matrix of the form

$$(57) \qquad \qquad B = \begin{pmatrix} 1 & O \\ O & C \end{pmatrix}, \; C \text{ an } (m-1) \times (n-1) \text{ matrix.}$$

Upon applying the induction assumption to C we are done.

Theorem 19. *Equivalent matrices have the same rank.*

Proof.   We already know (Chap. VII, Theorem 6) that row-equivalent matrices have the same row space, and hence the same rank. Hence we need only show that column-equivalent matrices A and $B = AQ$ (Q nonsingular) have the same rank. Again, by Theorem 11, this is true if A and B have the same nullity, which is certainly true if they have the same null-space. But $XA = O$ clearly implies $XB = XAQ = OQ = O$, and conversely, $XB = O$ implies $XA = XAQQ^{-1} = XBQ^{-1} = OQ^{-1} = O$. That is, *column-equivalent matrices have the same null-space.*

Corollary 1. *An $m \times n$ matrix A is equivalent to one and only one diagonal matrix of the form (56); the rank r of A determines the number r of units on the diagonal.*

Corollary 2. *Equivalent matrices have the same column rank.*

Proof. The column rank of A (the maximum number of independent columns of A) equals the (row) rank of its transpose A^T. But the equivalence of A to B entails the equivalence of the transposes A^T and B^T. By the theorem, A^T and B^T have the same rank, so A and B have the same column rank.

In the canonical form (56) the rank is the same as the column rank; since both ranks are unaltered by equivalence, we deduce

Corollary 3.   *The (row) rank of a matrix always equals its column rank.*

Corollary 4.   *Two $m \times n$ matrices are equivalent if and only if they have the same rank.*

If equivalent, they have the same rank (Theorem 19); if they have the same rank, both are equivalent to the same canonical D; hence to each other.

Corollary 5.   *An $n \times n$ matrix A is nonsingular if and only if it is equivalent to the identity matrix I.*

For, by Corollary 4, A is equivalent to I if and only if it has rank n; by Theorem 12, this is true if and only if A is nonsingular.

EXERCISES

1. Check Corollary 3 of Theorem 19 by computing both the row and the column ranks (a) in Ex. 1 of Chap. VII, §6; (b) in Exs. 7a–7b of Chap. VII, §6.
2. Find an equivalent diagonal matrix for each matrix of Ex. 2, Chap. VII, §6.
3. Do the same for the matrices of Ex. 7, Chap. VII, §6.
4. Let T be a linear transformation of an m-dimensional vector space V into an n-space W. Show that by suitably choosing bases in V and in W the equations of T take on the form $y_i = x_i$ $(i = 1, \cdots, r), y_j = 0$ $(j = r + 1, \cdots, n)$.
5. (a) Prove that the transpose of any elementary matrix is elementary.
   (b) Use this to give an independent proof of the fact that the transpose of any nonsingular matrix is nonsingular.
★6. If A and B are $n \times n$ matrices of ranks r and s, prove that the rank of AB is never less than $(r + s) - n$. (*Hint:* Use the canonical form for A.)
★7. (a) Prove Sylvester's law of nullity: the nullity of a product AB never exceeds the sum of the nullities of the factors and is never less than the nullity of A; if A is square, it is also at least the nullity of B.
   (b) Give examples to show that both of these limits can be attained by the nullity of AB.
8. Show that any nonsingular $n \times n$ matrix P can be written as $P = TU^T$, where T and U are triangular matrices.
9. Prove: An $m \times n$ matrix A has rank at most 1 if and only if it can be represented as a product $A = BC$, where B is $m \times 1$ and C is $1 \times n$.

10. Prove that any matrix of rank r is the sum of r matrices of rank 1.

⋆**11.** Let the sequence $E_1, \cdots, E_r$ of elementary row operations, suitably interspersed with the elementary column operations $E_1', \cdots, E_s'$, reduce A to I. Show that $A^{-1} = QP$, where $P = E_r \cdots E_1$ and $Q = E_1' \cdots E_s'$ are obtained from I by the same sequences of elementary operations.

12. Show that if $PAQ = D$, as in Theorem 18, then the system $AX^T = B^T$ of simultaneous linear equations (§8) may be solved by solving $DY^T = PB^T$ and then computing $X^T = QY^T$.

⋆10. Quaternions

The algebraic laws valid for square matrices apply to other algebraic systems, such as the quaternions of Hamilton. These quaternions constitute a four-dimensional vector space over the field of real numbers, with a basis of four special vectors denoted by 1, i, j, k. The algebraic operations for quaternions are the usual two vector operations (vector addition and scalar multiplication), plus a new operation of quaternion multiplication.

Definition. *A quaternion is a vector* $x = x_0 + x_1 i + x_2 j + x_3 k$, *with real coefficients* x_0, x_1, x_2, x_3. *The product of any two of the quaternions* 1, i, j, k *is defined by the requirement that* 1 *act as an identity and by the table*

$$
(58) \qquad
\begin{aligned}
i^2 = j^2 &= k^2 = -1, \\
ij = -ji = k, \qquad jk &= -kj = i, \qquad ki = -ik = j.
\end{aligned}
$$

If c and d are any scalars, while l, m are any two of 1, i, j, k, the product $(cl)(dm)$ is defined as $(cd)(lm)$. These rules, with the distributive law, determine the product of any two quaternions.

Thus, if $x = x_0 + x_1 i + x_2 j + x_3 k$ and $y = y_0 + y_1 i + y_2 j + y_3 k$ are any two quaternions, then their product is

$$
(59) \qquad
\begin{aligned}
xy = x_0 y_0 &- x_1 y_1 - x_2 y_2 - x_3 y_3 \\
&+ (x_0 y_1 + x_1 y_0 + x_2 y_3 - x_3 y_2)i \\
&+ (x_0 y_2 + x_2 y_0 + x_3 y_1 - x_1 y_3)j \\
&+ (x_0 y_3 + x_3 y_0 + x_1 y_2 - x_2 y_1)k.
\end{aligned}
$$

Though the multiplication of quaternions is noncommutative, they satisfy every other postulate for a field. Number systems sharing this property are called division rings.

Definition. *A division ring is a system* R *of elements closed under two single-valued binary operations, addition and multiplication, such that: (i) under addition,* R *is a commutative group with an identity* 0; (ii) *under multiplication, the elements other than* 0 *form a group;* (iii) *both distributive laws hold:*

$$
a(b + c) = ab + ac \qquad \text{and} \qquad (a + b)c = ac + bc.
$$

From these postulates, the rule $a0 = 0a = 0$ and thence the associative law for products with a factor 0 can be deduced easily. It follows that any commutative division ring is a field. We note also that analogues of the results of §§1–7 are valid over division rings if one is careful about the side on which the scalar factors appear. Thus for the product $c\xi$ of a vector ξ by a scalar c we write the scalar to the left, but in defining (§2) the product of a transformation T by a scalar we write the scalar on the right $\xi(Tc) = (c\xi)T$, and we likewise multiply a matrix by a scalar on the right. The space of linear transformations T of a left vector space over a division ring R is thus a *right* vector space over R.

Theorem 20.   *The quaternions form a division ring.*

The proof of every postulate, except for the existence of multiplicative inverses (which implies the cancellation law, by Theorem 3 of Chap. VI) and the associative law of multiplication is trivial. To prove that every non-zero quaternion $x = x_0 + x_1 i + x_2 j + x_3 k$ has an inverse, define the *conjugate* of x as $x^* = x_0 - x_1 i - x_2 j - x_3 k$. It is then easily shown that the *norm* of x, defined by $N(x) = xx^*$, satisfies

$$(60) \quad N(x) = xx^* = x^*x = x_0{}^2 + x_1{}^2 + x_2{}^2 + x_3{}^2 > 0 \qquad \text{if } x \neq 0.$$

Hence x has the inverse $x^*/N(x)$.

The proof of the associative law is most easily accomplished using complex numbers. Indeed, it is easily seen from (60) that the quaternions $x = x_0 + x_1 i$ with $x_2 = x_3 = 0$ constitute a subsystem isomorphic with the field of complex numbers. Moreover

$$(61) \qquad x = (x_0 + x_1 i) + (x_2 + x_3 i)j = z_1 + z_2 j,$$

where z_1 and z_2 behave like ordinary complex numbers. Actually, all the rules of (58) are contained in the expansion (61), the associative and distributive laws, and the rules

$$(62) \qquad z_1 j = j z_1^*, \qquad j^2 = -1,$$

where $z_1^* = x_0 - x_1 i$ is the complex (and quaternion!) conjugate of $z_1 = x_0 + x_1 i$. Indeed, the product of two quaternions in the form (61) is

$$(z_1 + z_2 j)(w_1 + w_2 j) = (z_1 w_1 - z_2 w_2^*) + (z_1 w_2 + z_2 w_1^*)j.$$

Using this formula, the associative law is readily verified.

Every quaternion x satisfies a quadratic equation $f(t) = 0$ with roots x and x^*, and with real coefficients. This equation is

$$f(t) = (t - x)(t - x^*) = t^2 - (x + x^*)t + xx^* = t^2 - 2x_0 t + N(x).$$

Any quaternion $x = x_0 + x_1 i + x_2 j + x_3 k$ can be decomposed into its real part x_0 and its "pure quaternion" part $x_1 i + x_2 j + x_3 k$. These have various interesting properties (cf. Exercises 2c, 15); one of the most curious concerns the multiplication of the pure quaternions $\xi = x_1 i + x_2 j + x_3 k$ and $\eta = y_1 i + y_2 j + y_3 k$. By definition

(63) $$\xi\eta = \xi \times \eta - (\xi, \eta),$$

where $\xi \times \eta = (x_2 y_3 - x_3 y_2)i + (x_3 y_1 - x_1 y_3)j + (x_1 y_2 - x_2 y_1)k$ is the usual *outer product* (or "vector product") of ξ and η, and $(\xi, \eta) = x_1 y_1 + x_2 y_2 + x_3 y_3$ is the "inner product" defined in Chap. VII. Largely because of the identity (63), much of present day three-dimensional vector analysis was couched in the language of quaternions in the half-century 1850–1900.

It was proved by Eilenberg and Niven in 1944 that any polynomial equation $f(x) = a_0 + a_1 x + \cdots + a_n x^n = 0$, with quaternion coefficients, $a_n \neq 0$, and $n > 0$, has a quaternion solution x.

EXERCISES

1. Solve $xc = d$ for (a) $c = i$, $d = 1 + j$; (b) $c = 2 + j$, $d = 3 + k$.
2. (a) Prove that $x^2 = -1$ has an infinity of quaternions x as solutions.
   (b) Show why this does not contradict the Corollary of Theorem 3 of Chap. III on the number of roots of a polynomial.
   (c) Show that the real quaternions are those whose squares are positive while the pure quaternions are those whose squares are negative real numbers. Infer that the set of quaternions satisfying $x^2 < 0$ is closed under addition and subtraction.
   (d) Show that if q is not real, $x^2 = q$ has exactly two quaternion solutions.
3. Let $a = 1 + i + j$, $b = 1 + j + k$.
   (a) Find $a + b$, ab, $a - b$, $ia - 2b$, a^*, aa^*.
   (b) Solve $ax = b$, $xa = b$, $x^2 = b$, $bx + (2j + k) = a$.
4. Derive the multiplication table (62) from (58).
5. (a) Show that the norm $N(x) = xx^*$ of x is $x_0^2 + x_1^2 + x_2^2 + x_3^2$.
   (b) Show that $x^*y^* = (yx)^*$.
6. Show that in the group of non-zero quaternions under multiplication, the "center" consists precisely of the real non-zero quaternions.
7. Prove that the solution of a quaternion equation $xa = b$ is uniquely determined if $a \neq 0$.
8. If a quaternion x satisfies a quadratic equation $x^2 + a_0 x + b_0 = 0$, with real coefficients a_0 and b_0, prove that every quaternion $q^{-1}xq$ satisfies the same quadratic equation (if $q \neq 0$).
9. Prove that the multiplication of quaternions is associative. (*Hint:* Use (61) and (62).)
10. In the algebra of quaternions prove the elements ± 1, $\pm i$, $\pm j$, $\pm k$ form a multiplicative group. (This group, which could be defined directly, is known as the *quaternion group*.)
11. (a) Enumerate the subgroups of the quaternion group (Ex. 10), and show they are all normal.
    (b) Show that the quaternion group is not isomorphic with the group of the square.

12. (a) Prove that the quaternions $x_0 + x_1 i + x_2 j + x_3 k$ with rational coefficients x_i form a division ring.

  (b) Show that this is not the case for quaternions with complex coefficients. (*Note:* Do not confuse the scalar $\sqrt{-1} \in \mathbf{C}$ with the quaternion unit i.)

13. In a division ring, show that the commutative law for addition follows from the other postulates. (*Hint:* Expand $(a + b)(1 + 1)$ in two different ways.)

14. How many of the conditions of Theorem 2, Chap. II, can you prove in a general division ring, if a/b is interpreted as ab^{-1}?

15. Show that the "outer product" of two vectors is not associative.

16. If the integers a and b are both sums of four squares of integers, show that the product ab is also a sum of four squares. (*Hint:* Use Ex. 5.)

17. Derive all of the rules (58) from $i^2 = j^2 = k^2 = ijk = -1$.

18. Does $(AB)^T = B^T A^T$ hold for matrices with quaternion entries?

IX. Linear Groups

1. Change of Basis

The coordinates of a vector ξ in a space V depend upon the choice of a basis in V (see Chap. VII, §8); hence any change in the basis will cause a change in the coordinates of ξ. For example, in the real plane $V_2(\mathbf{R})$, the vector $\beta = 4\varepsilon_1 + 2\varepsilon_2$ has by definition the coordinates $(4, 2)$ relative to the basis of unit vectors $\varepsilon_1, \varepsilon_2$. The vectors

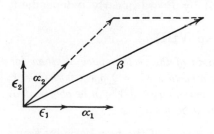

Figure 1

$$(1) \quad \alpha_1 = 2\varepsilon_1, \qquad \alpha_2 = \varepsilon_1 + \varepsilon_2$$

also form a basis; in terms of this basis, β is expressed as $\beta = \alpha_1 + 2\alpha_2$. The coefficients 1 and 2 are the coordinates of β, relative to this new basis (that is, relative to the oblique coordinate system shown in Figure 1).

More generally, the coordinates x_1^*, x_2^* of any vector ξ relative to the "new" basis α_1, α_2, may be found from the "old" coordinates x_1, x_2 of ξ as follows. By definition (Chap. VII, §8), these coordinates are the coefficients in the expressions

$$\xi = x_1\varepsilon_1 + x_2\varepsilon_2, \qquad \xi = x_1^*\alpha_1 + x_2^*\alpha_2$$

of ξ in terms of the two bases. Solving the vector equations (1) for ε_1 and ε_2, we find

$$\varepsilon_1 = \tfrac{1}{2}\alpha_1, \qquad \varepsilon_2 = \alpha_2 - \tfrac{1}{2}\alpha_1.$$

Substituting in the first expression for ξ the values of ε_1 and ε_2, we find

$$\xi = x_1(\tfrac{1}{2}\alpha_1) + x_2(\alpha_2 - \tfrac{1}{2}\alpha_1) = \tfrac{1}{2}(x_1 - x_2)\alpha_1 + x_2\alpha_2.$$

Hence the new coordinates of ξ are given by the linear homogeneous equations

$$(2) \qquad\qquad x_1^* = (x_1 - x_2)/2, \qquad x_2^* = x_2.$$

Conversely, the old coordinates can be expressed in terms of the new, as $x_1 = 2x_1^* + x_2^*, x_2 = x_2^*.$

Similar relations hold in n dimensions. If $\alpha_1, \cdots, \alpha_n$ is a given basis with its vectors arranged in a definite order, and $\alpha_1^*, \cdots, \alpha_n^*$ a new (ordered) basis, then each vector α_i^* of the new basis can be expressed as a linear combination of vectors of the old basis, in the form

$$(3) \quad \alpha_i^* = p_{i1}\alpha_1 + \cdots + p_{in}\alpha_n = \sum_{j=1}^{n} p_{ij}\alpha_j, \quad i = 1, \cdots, n.$$

Formally, the expression (3) can be written as the matrix equation $\alpha^* = \alpha P^T$, where P^T is the transpose of P.

The matrix $P = \| p_{ij} \|$ of the coefficients in these expressions has as its ith row the row of old coordinates $(p_{i1}, \cdots, p_{in})$ of the vector α_i^*. Since the vectors α_i^* form a basis, the rows of P are linearly independent, and hence the matrix P is nonsingular (Chap. VIII, Theorem 9). Conversely, if $P = \| p_{ij} \|$ is any nonsingular matrix, and $\alpha_1, \cdots, \alpha_n$ any basis of V, the vectors α_i^* determined as in (3) by P are linearly independent, hence form a new basis of V.

We have proved (by Theorem 9, Chap. VIII)

Theorem 1. *If $\alpha_1, \cdots, \alpha_n$ is a basis of the vector space V, then for each nonsingular matrix $P = \| p_{ij} \|$, the n vectors $\alpha_i^* = \sum p_{ij}\alpha_j$, with $i = 1, \cdots, n$, constitute a new basis of V, and every basis of V can be obtained in this fashion from exactly one nonsingular $n \times n$ matrix P.*

One may also express the old basis in terms of the new basis by equations $\alpha_k = \sum q_{ki}\alpha_i^*$ with a coefficient matrix $Q = \| q_{ki} \|$. Upon substituting the values of α_i^* in terms of the α's, we obtain

$$\alpha_k = \sum_i q_{ki} \left(\sum_j p_{ij}\alpha_j \right) = \sum_j \left(\sum_i q_{ki}p_{ij} \right)\alpha_j.$$

But there is only one such expression for the vectors α_k in terms of themselves; namely, $\alpha_k = \alpha_k$. Hence the coefficient $\sum q_{ki}p_{ij}$ of α_j here must be 0 or 1, according as $k \neq j$ or $k = j$. These coefficients are exactly the (k, j) entries in the matrix product QP; hence $QP = I$, and $Q = P^{-1}$ is the inverse of P.

The parallel result for change of coordinates is as follows:

Theorem 2. *If the basis $\alpha_1, \cdots, \alpha_n$ of the vector space V is changed to a new basis $\alpha_1^*, \cdots, \alpha_n^*$ expressed in the form $\alpha_i^* = \sum_j p_{ij}\alpha_j$, then the coordinates x_i of any vector ξ relative to the old basis α_i determine the new coordinates x_i^* of ξ relative to the α_i^* by the linear homogeneous equations*

$$(4) \qquad\qquad x_j = x_1^* p_{1j} + \cdots + x_n^* p_{nj} = \sum_{i=1}^{n} x_i^* p_{ij}.$$

Proof. By definition (Chap. VII, §8), the coordinates x_i^* of ξ relative to the basis α_i^* are the coefficients in the expression $\xi = \sum x_i^* \alpha_i^*$ of ξ as a linear combination of the α_i^*. Substitution of the formula (3) for α_i^* yields

$$\xi = \sum_i x_i^* \left(\sum_j p_{ij}\alpha_j \right) = \sum_j \left(\sum_i x_i^* p_{ij} \right)\alpha_j.$$

The coefficient of each α_j here is the old coordinate x_j of ξ; hence the equation (4).

The equations (4) may be written in matrix form as $X = X^*P$, where $X = (x_1, \cdots, x_n)$ is the row matrix of old coordinates and $X^* = (x_1^*, \cdots, x_n^*)$ is the row matrix of new coordinates. Since the α_i and α_i^* are bases, P is nonsingular, and one may solve for X^* in terms of X as $X^* = XP^{-1}$.

If one compares this matrix equation with the matrix formulation $\alpha^* = \alpha P^T$ of (3) already mentioned, one gets the interesting relation

(5)   Bases: $\alpha^* = \alpha P^T$;   Coordinates: $X^* = XP^{-1}$.

The matrix P^{-1} of the second equation is the *transposed inverse* of the matrix P^T of the first. (This situation is sometimes summarized by the statement that the change of coordinates is contragredient to the corresponding change of basis.)

EXERCISES

1. Let T carry the usual unit vectors ε_i (in V_2 or V_3) into the vectors α_i specified below. Find the corresponding equations for the new coordinates in terms of the old coordinates, and for the old coordinates in terms of the new coordinates. In cases (a) and (b) draw a figure.
   (a) $\alpha_1 = (1, 1)$, $\alpha_2 = (1, -1)$;   (b) $\alpha_1 = (2, 3)$, $\alpha_2 = (-2, -1)$;
   (c) $\alpha_1 = (1, 1, 0)$, $\alpha_2 = (1, 0, 1)$, $\alpha_3 = (0, 1, 1)$;
   (d) $\alpha_1 = (i, 1, i)$, $\alpha_2 = (0, 1, i)$, $\alpha_3 = (0, i, 1)$,   where $i^2 = -1$.
2. If a new basis α_j^* is given indirectly by equations of the form $\alpha_i = \Sigma_j q_{ij}\alpha_j^*$, work out the equations for the corresponding change of coordinates.
3. Give the equations for the transformation of coordinates due to rotation of axes in the plane through an angle θ.

2. Similar Matrices and Characteristic Vectors

A linear transformation $T: V \to V$ of a vector space V may be represented by various matrices, depending on the choice of a basis (coordinate system) in V. Thus, in the plane the transformation defined by $\varepsilon_1 \to 3\varepsilon_1$, $\varepsilon_2 \to -\varepsilon_1 + 2\varepsilon_2$ is represented, in the usual coordinate system of V_2, by the matrix A where rows are the coordinates of the transforms of ε_1 and ε_2, as displayed below:

$$A = \begin{pmatrix} 3 & 0 \\ -1 & 2 \end{pmatrix}, \qquad D = \begin{pmatrix} 3 & 0 \\ 0 & 2 \end{pmatrix}.$$

But relative to the new basis $\alpha_1 = 2\varepsilon_1$, $\alpha_2 = \varepsilon_1 + \varepsilon_2$ discussed in §1 the transformation is $\alpha_1 \rightarrow 3\alpha_1$ and $\alpha_2 \rightarrow 2\alpha_2$; hence it is represented by the simpler diagonal matrix D displayed above. We shall say that two such matrices A and D are similar.

To generalize this result, let us recall how a matrix represents a transformation. Take any (ordered) basis $\alpha_1, \cdots, \alpha_n$ of a vector space V and any linear transformation $T: V \rightarrow V$. Then the images under T of the basis vectors α_i may be written by formula (9) of Chap. VIII as

$$(6) \qquad\qquad \alpha_i T = \sum_j a_{ij}\alpha_j, \qquad A = \| a_{ij} \|.$$

Hence T is represented, relative to the base α, by the $n \times n$ matrix A. This relation can also be expressed in terms of coordinates. Let $\xi = \sum x_i \alpha_i$ be a vector of V with the n-tuple $X = (x_1, \cdots, x_n)$ of coordinates relative to the basis α. Then the image $\eta = \xi T$ is

$$\xi T = \left(\sum x_i \alpha_i \right) T = \sum x_i (\alpha_i T) = \sum_i \sum_j x_i a_{ij} \alpha_j = \sum_j \left(\sum_i x_i a_{ij} \right) \alpha_j.$$

The coordinates y_i of η are then just the coefficients of α_j, so that

$$y_j = \sum_i x_i a_{ij}$$

and the coordinate vector Y of η is just the matrix product $Y = XA$. Briefly

$$(7) \qquad Y = XA, \qquad \text{where} \qquad \begin{array}{l} X = \alpha\text{-coordinates of } \xi, \\ Y = \alpha\text{-coordinates of } \eta = \xi T. \end{array}$$

Either of the equivalent statements (6), (7) means that T is *represented, relative to the basis* α, *by the matrix* A.

Now let $\alpha_1^*, \cdots, \alpha_n^*$ be a second basis. Then, by Theorem 1, the new basis is expressed in terms of the old one by a nonsingular $n \times n$ matrix P as in (3); and the new coordinates of ξ and $\eta = \xi T$ are given in terms of the old coordinates, by Theorem 2, as $X^* = XP^{-1}$, and $Y^* = YP^{-1}$. Then by (7)

$$Y^* = YP^{-1} = XAP^{-1} = X^*(PAP^{-1}).$$

Hence, by (7) again, the matrix B representing T in the new coordinate system has the form PAP^{-1}. The equivalence relation $B = PAP^{-1}$ is formally like that of conjugate elements in a group (Chap. VI, §12); it is of fundamental importance, and called the relation of similarity.

Definition. *Two $n \times n$ matrices A and B with entries in a field F are* similar *(over F) if and only if there is a nonsingular $n \times n$ matrix P over F with $B = PAP^{-1}$.*

Our discussion above proves

Theorem 3. *Two $n \times n$ matrices A and B over a field F represent the same linear transformation $T: V \to V$ on an n-dimensional vector space V over F, relative to (possibly) different coordinate systems, if and only if the matrices A and B are similar.*

More explicitly, we may restate this as

Theorem 3'. *Let the linear transformation $T: V \to V$ be represented by a matrix A relative to a basis $\alpha_1, \cdots, \alpha_n$ of V, let $P = \| p_{ij} \|$ be a nonsingular matrix, and $\alpha_i^* = \Sigma_j \, p_{ij}\alpha_j$ the corresponding new basis of V. Then T is represented relative to the new basis by the matrix PAP^{-1}.*

The algebra of matrices applies especially smoothly to diagonal matrices: to add or multiply any two diagonal matrices, one simply adds (or multiplies) corresponding diagonal entries. For this and other reasons, it is important to know which matrices are similar to diagonal matrices—and also, which pairs of diagonal matrices are similar to each other. The answer to these questions involves the notions of characteristic vector and characteristic root—also often called eigenvector and eigenvalue.

Definition. *A* characteristic vector *of a linear transformation $T: V \to V$ is a non-zero vector $\xi \in V$ such that $\xi T = c\xi$ for some scalar c. A* characteristic root *of T is a scalar c such that $\xi T = c\xi$ for some vector ξ not O. A characteristic vector or characteristic root of a square matrix A is a characteristic vector or root of the associated transformation $T_A: V_n \to V_n$. The set of all characteristic roots of T (or T_A) is called its* spectrum.

Thus each characteristic vector ξ of T determines a characteristic root c, and each characteristic root belongs to at least one characteristic vector. Since similar matrices correspond to the same linear transformation under different choices of bases, *similar matrices have the same characteristic roots.* Explicitly, the n-tuple $X \neq O$ is a characteristic vector of the $n \times n$ matrix A if $XA = cX$ for some scalar c. If the matrix $B = PAP^{-1}$ is similar to A, then $(XP^{-1})B = XP^{-1}PAP^{-1} = c(XP^{-1})$, so that XP^{-1} is a characteristic vector of B belonging to the same characteristic root c. Note also that any non-zero scalar multiple of a characteristic vector is a characteristic vector.

The connection between characteristic vectors and diagonal matrices is provided by

Theorem 4. *An $n \times n$ matrix A is similar to a diagonal matrix D if and only if the characteristic vectors of A span $V_n(F)$; when this is the case, the characteristic roots of A are the diagonal entries in D.*

In particular, this means that the characteristic roots of a diagonal matrix are the entries on the diagonal.

Proof. Suppose first that A is similar to a diagonal matrix D with diagonal entries $d_1, \cdots, d_n$. The unit vectors $\varepsilon_1 = (1, 0, \cdots, 0)$, $\cdots, \varepsilon_n = (0, \cdots, 0, 1)$ are then characteristic vectors for D, since $\varepsilon_1 D = d_1 \varepsilon_1, \cdots, \varepsilon_n D = d_n \varepsilon_n$. Also, the diagonal entries $d_1, \cdots, d_n$ are the corresponding characteristic roots of D and hence of A. They are the only characteristic roots, for let $X = (x_1, \cdots, x_n) \neq 0$ be any characteristic vector of D, so that $XD = cX$ for a suitable characteristic root c. Now $XD = (d_1 x_1, \cdots, d_n x_n)$, so that $d_i x_i = c x_i$ for all i. Since some $x_i \neq 0$, this proves that $d_i = c$ for this i, and the characteristic root c is indeed some d_i.

Conversely, suppose there are enough characteristic vectors of the matrix A to span the whole space $V_n(F)$ on which T_A operates. Then (Chap. VII, Theorem 3, Corollary 2) we can extract a subset of characteristic vectors $\beta_1, \cdots, \beta_n$ which is a basis for $V_n(F)$. Since each β_i is characteristic, $\beta_1 T_A = c_1 \beta_1, \cdots, \beta_n T_A = c_n \beta_n$, for characteristic roots $c_1, \cdots, c_n$. Hence, relative to the basis $\beta_1, \cdots, \beta_n$, T_A is represented as in (6) by the diagonal matrix D with diagonal entries $c_1, \cdots, c_n$, and A is similar to this matrix D.

Corollary. *If P is a matrix whose rows are n linearly independent characteristic vectors of the $n \times n$ matrix A, then P is nonsingular and PAP^{-1} is diagonal.*

Proof. We are given n linearly independent n-tuples $X_1, \cdots, X_n$ which are characteristic vectors of A, so that $X_i A = c_i X_i$ for characteristic roots $c_1, \cdots, c_n$. The matrix P with rows $X_1, \cdots, X_n$ is nonsingular because the rows are linearly independent. By the block multiplication rule

$$(8) \quad \begin{pmatrix} X_1 \\ \cdot \\ \cdot \\ \cdot \\ X_n \end{pmatrix} A = \begin{pmatrix} c_1 X_1 \\ \cdot \\ \cdot \\ \cdot \\ c_n X_n \end{pmatrix} = \begin{pmatrix} c_1 & & 0 \\ & \cdot & \\ & & \cdot \\ 0 & & c_n \end{pmatrix} \begin{pmatrix} X_1 \\ \cdot \\ \cdot \\ \cdot \\ X_n \end{pmatrix}.$$

This asserts that $PA = DP$, and hence that $PAP^{-1} = D$, where D is the diagonal matrix with diagonal entries $c_1, \cdots, c_n$. The matrix P is, in fact, exactly the matrix required for the change of basis involved in the direct proof of Theorem 4, Q.E.D.

On the other hand, there are matrices which are not similar to any diagonal matrix (cf. Ex. 5 below).

To explicitly construct a diagonal matrix (if it exists!) similar to a given matrix, one thus searches for characteristic roots and vectors. This search is greatly facilitated by the following consideration.

If a scalar λ is a characteristic root of the $n \times n$ matrix A, and if I is the $n \times n$ identity matrix, then $XA = \lambda X = \lambda XI$ and consequently

$X(A - \lambda I) = O$ for some non-zero n-tuple X. The n homogeneous linear equations with matrix $A - \lambda I$ thus have a nontrivial solution; hence by Theorem 9 of Chap. VIII, we have

Theorem 5.   *The scalar λ is a characteristic root of the matrix A if and only if the matrix $A - \lambda I$ is singular.*

For example, the 2×2 matrix

$$(9) \qquad A - \lambda I = \begin{pmatrix} a_{11} - \lambda & a_{12} \\ a_{21} & a_{22} - \lambda \end{pmatrix}$$

is readily seen to be singular if and only if

$$(10) \qquad \lambda^2 - (a_{11} + a_{22})\lambda + a_{11}a_{22} - a_{12}a_{21} = 0.$$

(This merely states that the determinant of $A - \lambda I$ is zero.) Hence we find all characteristic roots by solving this equation. Moreover, for each root λ there is at least one characteristic vector, found by solving

$$x_1 a_{11} + x_2 a_{21} = \lambda x_1$$
$$x_1 a_{12} + x_2 a_{22} = \lambda x_2.$$

EXAMPLE.   Find a diagonal matrix similar to the matrix $\begin{pmatrix} -3 & 4 \\ 2 & -1 \end{pmatrix}$.
The polynomial (10) is $\lambda^2 + 4\lambda - 5$. The roots of this are 1 and -5; hence the characteristic vectors satisfy one or the other of the systems of homogeneous equations

$$\begin{aligned} -3x + 2y &= x \\ 4x - y &= y, \end{aligned} \qquad \text{or} \qquad \begin{aligned} -3x + 2y &= -5x \\ 4x - y &= -5y. \end{aligned}$$

Solving these, we get characteristic vectors $(1, 2)$ and $(1, -1)$. Using these as a new basis, the transformation takes on a diagonal form. The new diagonal matrix may be written, according to Theorem 3′, as a product

$$\begin{pmatrix} 1 & 2 \\ 1 & -1 \end{pmatrix} \begin{pmatrix} -3 & 4 \\ 2 & -1 \end{pmatrix} \begin{pmatrix} 1 & 2 \\ 1 & -1 \end{pmatrix}^{-1} = \begin{pmatrix} 1 & 0 \\ 0 & -5 \end{pmatrix}.$$

EXERCISES

1. Show that the equations $2x' = (1 + b)x + (1 - b)y$, $2y' = (1 - b)x + (1 + b)y$ represent a compression on the 45° line through the origin. Compute the characteristic roots and the characteristic vectors of the transformation and interpret them geometrically.

2. Compute the characteristic roots and the characteristic vectors of the following matrices over the complex field:

   (a) $\begin{pmatrix} 2 & 4 \\ 5 & 3 \end{pmatrix}$;   (b) $\begin{pmatrix} 3 & 2 \\ -2 & 3 \end{pmatrix}$;   (c) $\begin{pmatrix} 1 & 2 \\ 2 & -2 \end{pmatrix}$;   (d) $\begin{pmatrix} -1 & 2i \\ -2i & 2 \end{pmatrix}$.

3. For each matrix A given in Ex. 2 find, when possible, a nonsingular matrix P for which PAP^{-1} is diagonal.

4. (a) Find the complex characteristic roots of the matrix representing a rotation of the plane through an angle θ.

   (b) Prove that the matrix representing a rotation of the plane through an angle θ ($0 < \theta < \pi$) is not similar to any real diagonal matrix.

5. Prove that no matrix $\begin{pmatrix} 1 & c \\ 0 & 1 \end{pmatrix}$ is similar to a real or complex diagonal matrix, if $c \neq 0$. Interpret the result geometrically.

6. Show that the slopes γ of the characteristic vectors of a 2×2 matrix A satisfy the quadratic equation

$$a_{21}\gamma^2 + (a_{11} - a_{22})\gamma - a_{12} = 0.$$

7. Prove that the set of all characteristic vectors belonging to a fixed characteristic root of a given matrix constitutes a subspace, when O is included among the characteristic vectors.

8. Prove that any 2×2 real symmetric matrix not a scalar matrix has two distinct real characteristic values.

9. (a) Show that two $m \times n$ matrices A and B are equivalent if and only if they represent the same linear transformation $T: V \to W$ of an m-dimensional vector space V into an n-dimensional vector space W, relative to different bases in V and in W.

   (b) Interpret Theorem 18, Chap. VIII, in the light of this remark.

★10. Let both A and B be similar to diagonal matrices. Prove that $AB = BA$ if and only if A and B have a common basis of characteristic vectors. (Frobenius.)

11. (a) Show that, if $A = \begin{pmatrix} a & b \\ c & d \end{pmatrix}$ is similar to an orthogonal matrix, then $ad - bc = \pm 1$ (For definition of orthogonal, see page 242).

   (b) Show that if $ad - bc = 1$, then A is similar to an orthogonal matrix if and only if $A = \pm I$ or $-2 < a + d < 2$.

   (c) Show that if $ad - bc = -1$, then A is similar to an orthogonal matrix if and only if $a + d = 0$.

3. The Full Linear and Affine Groups

All nonsingular linear transformations of an n-dimensional vector space $V_n(F)$ form a group because the products and inverses of such transformations are again linear and nonsingular (Chap. VIII, Theorem 9). This group is called the *full linear group* $L_n = L_n(F)$. In the one-one correspondence of linear transformations to matrices, products correspond to products, so the full linear group $L_n(F)$ is isomorphic to the group of all nonsingular $n \times n$ matrices with entries in the field F.

The translations form another important group. A translation of the plane moves all the points of the plane the same distance in a specified direction. The distance and direction may be represented by a vector κ of the appropriate magnitude and direction; the translation then carries the end-point of each vector ξ into the end-point of $\xi + \kappa$. A *translation* in any space $V_n(F)$ is a transformation $\xi \to \xi + \kappa$, for κ fixed. Relative to any coordinate system the coordinates y_i of the translated vector are $y_1 = x_1 + k_1, \cdots, y_n = x_n + k_n$ where the k_i are coordinates of κ. The product of a translation $\xi \to \eta = \xi + \kappa$ by $\eta \to \zeta = \eta + \lambda$ is found by substitution to be the translation $\xi \to \zeta = \xi + (\kappa + \lambda)$. It corresponds exactly to the sum of the vectors κ and λ. Similarly, the inverse of a translation $\xi \to \xi + \kappa$ is $\eta \to \eta - \kappa$. Thus we have proved the following special case of Cayley's Theorem (Chap. VI, Theorem 8):

Theorem 6. *All the translations $\xi \to \xi + \kappa$ of V_n form an Abelian group isomorphic to the additive group of the vectors κ of V_n.*

A linear transformation T followed by a translation yields

$$(11) \qquad \xi \to \eta = \xi T + \kappa \qquad (T \text{ linear, } \kappa \text{ a fixed vector}).$$

An *affine* transformation H of $V_n(F)$ is any transformation of this form. The affine transformations include the linear transformations (with $\kappa = 0$) and the translations (with $T = I$). If one affine transformation (11) be followed by a second, $\eta \to \eta U + \lambda$, the product is

$$(12) \qquad \xi \to (\xi T + \kappa) U + \lambda = \xi(TU) + (\kappa U + \lambda).$$

The result is again affine because $\kappa U + \lambda$ is a fixed vector of $V_n(F)$. Every translation is one-one and onto, hence it has an inverse; hence the affine transformation (11) will be one-one and onto if and only if its linear part T is one-one. Its inverse will consequently be the affine transformation $\eta \to \xi = \eta T^{-1} - \kappa T^{-1}$, found by solving (11) for ξ. This proves

Theorem 7. *The set of all nonsingular affine transformations of $V_n(F)$ constitutes a group, the affine group $A_n(F)$. It contains as subgroups the full linear group and the group of translations.*

What are the equations of an affine transformation relative to a basis? The linear part T yields a matrix $A = \| a_{ij} \|$; the translation vector has as coordinates a row $K = (k_1, \cdots, k_n)$. The affine transformation thus carries a vector with coordinates $X = (x_1, \cdots, x_n)$ into a vector with coordinates,

$$(13) \quad Y = XA + K, \qquad y_j = \sum_{i=1}^{n} x_i a_{ij} + k_j \qquad (j = 1, \cdots, n).$$

A transformation is affine if and only if it is expressed, relative to some basis, by nonhomogeneous linear equations such as these.

The product of the transformation (13) by $Z = YB + L$ is

$$(14) \qquad Z = X(AB) + KB + L \qquad (K, L \text{ row matrices});$$

the formula is parallel to (12). The same multiplication rule holds for a matrix of order $n + 1$ constructed from the transformation (13) by bordering the matrix A to the right by a column of zeros, below by the row K, below and to the right by the single entry 1:

$$(15) \qquad \{Y = XA + K\} \leftrightarrow \begin{pmatrix} A & O \\ K & 1 \end{pmatrix} \qquad \begin{matrix} (O \text{ is } n \times 1) \\ (K \text{ is } 1 \times n). \end{matrix}$$

The rule for block multiplication (Chap. VIII, §5, (43)) gives

$$(16) \qquad \begin{pmatrix} A & O \\ K & 1 \end{pmatrix}\begin{pmatrix} B & O \\ L & 1 \end{pmatrix} = \begin{pmatrix} AB + O \cdot L & A \cdot O + O \cdot 1 \\ KB + 1 \cdot L & K \cdot O + 1 \cdot 1 \end{pmatrix}$$
$$= \begin{pmatrix} AB & O \\ KB + L & 1 \end{pmatrix};$$

the result is precisely the bordered matrix belonging to the product transformation (14). This proves

Theorem 8. *The group of nonsingular affine transformations of an n-dimensional space is isomorphic to the group of all those nonsingular $(n + 1) \times (n + 1)$ matrices in which the last column is $(0, \cdots, 0, 1)$. The isomorphism is explicitly given by the correspondence (15).*

Each affine transformation $\xi H = \xi T + \kappa$ determines a unique linear transformation T, and the product of two affine transformations determines as in (12) the product of the corresponding linear parts. This correspondence $H \to T$ maps the group of nonsingular affine transformations H onto the full linear group, and is a homomorphism in the sense of group theory (Chap. VI, §11). In any homomorphism the objects mapped on the identity form a normal subgroup; in this case the affine transformations H with $T = I$ are exactly the translations. This proves

Theorem 9. *The group of translations is a normal subgroup of the affine group.*

Equation (13) was interpreted above as a transformation of points (vectors), which carried each point $X = (x_1, \cdots, x_n)$ into a new point Y having coordinates $(y_1, \cdots, y_n)$ in the same coordinate system. We could equally well have interpreted equation (13) as a change of *coordinates*. We call the first interpretation an *alibi* (the point is moved elsewhere) and the second an *alias* (the point is renamed).

Thus, in the plane, the equations

$$y_1 = x_1 + 2, \qquad y_2 = x_2 - 1$$

can be interpreted (alibi) as a point transformation which translates the whole plane two units east and one unit south, or (alias) as a change of coordinates, in which the original coordinate network is replaced by a parallel network, with new origin two units west and one unit north of the given origin.

A similar double interpretation applies to all groups of substitutions.

EXERCISES

1. (a) Represent each of the following affine transformations by a matrix

$$H_1: \quad x' = 3x + 6y + 2, \quad y' = 3y - 4;$$
$$H_2: \quad x' = x + y + 3, \quad y' = x - y + 5.$$

(b) Compute the products H_1H_2, H_2H_1.

(c) Find the inverses of H_1 and H_2.

2. Prove that the set of all affine transformations $x' = ax + by + e$, $y' = cx + dy + f$, with $ad - bc = 1$, is a normal subgroup of the affine group $A_2(F)$.

★3. Given the circle $x^2 + y^2 = 1$, prove that every non-singular affine transformation of the plane carries this circle into an ellipse or a circle.

4. Which of the following sets of $n \times n$ matrices over a field are subgroups of the full linear group?

  (a) All scalar matrices cI,   (b) All diagonal matrices,

  (c) All nonsingular diagonal matrices,   (d) All permutation matrices,

  (e) All monomial matrices,   (f) All triangular matrices,

  (g) All strictly triangular matrices,   (h) All matrices with zeros in the

  (i) All matrices in which at least one   second row,

     row consists of zeros.

5. Exhibit a group of matrices isomorphic with the group of all translations of $V_n(F)$.

6. If $\mathbf{Z}_2$ is the field of integers modulo 2, list all matrices in $L_2(\mathbf{Z}_2)$.

(b) Construct a multiplication table for this group $L_2(\mathbf{Z}_2)$.

★7. What is the order of the full linear group $L_2(\mathbf{Z}_p)$ when $\mathbf{Z}_p$ is the field of integers mod p?

8. Let G be the group of all matrices $A = \begin{pmatrix} a & b \\ 0 & d \end{pmatrix}$ with $ad \neq 0$. Show that the correspondence $A \to a$ is a homomorphism.

9. Map the group of nonsingular 3×3 triangular matrices homomorphically on the nonsingular 2×2 triangular matrices. (*Hint:* Proceed as in Ex. 8, but use *blocks*.)

10. If two fields F and K are isomorphic, prove that the groups $L_n(F)$ and $L_n(K)$ are isomorphic.

11. If $n < m$, prove that $L_n(F)$ is isomorphic to a subgroup of $L_m(F)$.

12. Prove that the identity is the only affine transformation which commutes with every affine transformation. (*Hint:* Use Ex. 8, Chap. VIII, §11.)

★13. If $L_n(F)$ is the full linear group, show that two affine transformations H_1 and H_2 fall into the same right coset of $L_n(F)$ if and only if $OH_1 = \Theta H_2$ (O is the origin!).

14. Prove that the quotient group $A_n(F)/T_n(F)$ is isomorphic to $L_n(F)$, where A_n denotes the affine group, T_n the group of translations.

15. (a) Show that all one-one transformations $y = (ax + b)/(cx + d)$ with $ad \neq bc$ form a group (called the *linear fractional group*).

(b) Prove that this group is isomorphic to the quotient group of the full linear group modulo the subgroup of non-zero scalar matrices.

($\star$c) Extend the results to matrices larger than 2×2.

16. (a) Show that the set of all nonsingular matrices of the form $\begin{pmatrix} A & 0 \\ 0 & B \end{pmatrix}$, with

A $r \times r$ and B $s \times s$, is a group isomorphic with the direct product $L_r(F) \times L_s(F)$.

(b) What is the geometric character of the linear transformations of $V_3(\mathbf{R})$ determined by such a matrix, if $r = 2$, $s = 1$?

4. The Orthogonal and Euclidean Groups

In Euclidean geometry, length plays an essential role. Hence we seek those linear transformations of Euclidean vector spaces which preserve the lengths $|\xi|$ of all vectors ξ.

Definition.   *A linear transformation T of a Euclidean vector space is orthogonal if it preserves the length of every vector ξ, so that $|\xi T| = |\xi|$.*

We now determine all orthogonal transformations $Y = XA$ of the Euclidean plane. The transforms

$$(1, 0) \begin{pmatrix} a_1 & a_2 \\ b_1 & b_2 \end{pmatrix} = (a_1, a_2), \qquad (0, 1) \begin{pmatrix} a_1 & a_2 \\ b_1 & b_2 \end{pmatrix} = (b_1, b_2)$$

of the unit vectors $(1, 0)$ and $(0, 1)$ have length 1 since A is orthogonal. According to the Pythagorean formula for length, this means

(18) $$a_1{}^2 + a_2{}^2 = 1, \qquad b_1{}^2 + b_2{}^2 = 1.$$

In addition, the vector $(1, 1)$ has a transform $(a_1 + b_1, a_2 + b_2)$ of length $\sqrt{2}$, so $(a_1 + b_1)^2 + (a_2 + b_2)^2 = 2$. Expanding, and subtracting (18), we find

(18') $$a_1 b_1 + a_2 b_2 = 0.$$

By (18) there is an angle θ with $\cos \theta = a_1$, $\sin \theta = a_2$. Then by (18'), $\tan \theta = a_2/a_1 = -b_1/b_2$ whence by (18) $b_2 = \pm \cos \theta$, $b_1 = \pm \sin \theta$. The two choices of sign give exactly the two matrices

(19) $$\begin{pmatrix} \cos \theta & \sin \theta \\ -\sin \theta & \cos \theta \end{pmatrix} \qquad \begin{pmatrix} \cos \theta & \sin \theta \\ \sin \theta & -\cos \theta \end{pmatrix}$$

By Chap. VIII, formulas (5)–(5'), these represent rotation through an angle θ and reflection in a line making an angle $\alpha = \theta/2$ with the x-axis, respectively. Hence *every orthogonal transformation of the plane is a rotation or a reflection.*

Geometrically, the inverse of the first orthogonal transformation (19) is obtained by replacing θ by $-\theta$; hence it is the *transpose* of the original. This fact (unlike the trigonometric formulas) generalizes to $n \times n$ orthogonal matrices.

Theorem 10. *An orthogonal transformation T has, for every pair of vectors ξ, η, the properties*
  (i) *T preserves distance, or $| \xi - \eta | = | \xi T - \eta T |$,*
 (ii) *T preserves inner products, or $(\xi, \eta) = (\xi T, \eta T)$,*
(iii) *T preserves orthogonality, or $\xi \perp \eta$ implies $\xi T \perp \eta T$,*
(iv) *T preserves magnitude of angles, or $\cos \angle(\xi, \eta) = \cos \angle(\xi T, \eta T)$.*

Proof.   Since T is linear, the definition gives (i). Because $\xi \perp \eta$ means $(\xi, \eta) = 0$ and because angle is also definable in terms of inner products (Chap. VII, (41)), properties (iii) and (iv) will follow immediately from (ii). As for (ii), the "bilinearity" of the inner product proves that $(\xi + \eta, \xi + \eta) = (\xi, \xi) + 2(\xi, \eta) + (\eta, \eta)$. This equation may be solved for (ξ, η) in terms of the "lengths" such as $| \xi | = (\xi, \xi)^{1/2}$, in the form

$$(20) \qquad\qquad 2(\xi, \eta) = | \xi + \eta |^2 - | \xi |^2 - | \eta |^2.$$

The orthogonal transformation T leaves invariant the lengths on the right, hence also the inner product on the left of this equation. This proves (ii), Q.E.D.

Conversely, a transformation T known to preserve all inner products must preserve length and hence be orthogonal, for length is defined in terms of an inner product.

Next we ask, which matrices correspond to orthogonal linear transformations? The question is easily answered, at least relative to normal orthogonal bases.

Theorem 11.   *Relative to any normal orthogonal basis, a real $n \times n$ matrix A represents an orthogonal linear transformation if and only if each row of A has length one, and any two rows, regarded as vectors, are orthogonal.*

Proof.   Any orthogonal transformation T must by Theorem 10 carry the given basis $\varepsilon_1, \cdots, \varepsilon_n$ into a basis $\alpha_1 = \varepsilon_1 T, \cdots, \alpha_n = \varepsilon_n T$ which is normal and orthogonal. Conversely, if T has this property, then for any vector $\xi = x_1 \varepsilon_1 + \cdots + x_n \varepsilon_n$ having the transform $\xi T = x_1 \alpha_1 + \cdots + x_n \alpha_n$, we know by Theorem 21 of Chap. VII that the length is given by the usual formula as

$$| \xi | = (x_1^2 + \cdots + x_n^2)^{1/2} = | \xi T |,$$

whence T is orthogonal. The proof is completed by the remark (cf. Chap. VIII, §1) that the ith row of A represents the coordinates of $\alpha_i = \varepsilon_i T_A$ relative to the original basis $\varepsilon_1, \cdots, \varepsilon_n$.

In coordinate form, the conditions on A stated in the theorem are equivalent to the equations

$$(21) \qquad \sum_{k=1}^{n} a_{ik}a_{ik} = 1 \quad \text{for all } i, \qquad \sum_{k=1}^{n} a_{ik}a_{jk} = 0 \quad \text{if } i \neq j.$$

The conclusions (21) are exactly those already found explicitly in (18) and (18′) for a two-rowed matrix. If we write A_i for the ith row of the matrix A and A_i^T for its transpose, the inner product of A_i by A_j is the matrix product $A_i A_j^T$ (see (34), Chap. VIII), so the conditions (21) may be written as

$$(21') \qquad\qquad A_i A_i^T = 1, \qquad A_i A_j^T = 0 \qquad (i \neq j).$$

In the row-by-column product $A A^T$ of A by its transpose, the equations (21′) state that the ith row times the jth column is $A_i A_j^T = \delta_{ij}$, where δ_{ij} is the element in the ith row and the jth column of the identity matrix $I = \| \delta_{ij} \|$, with diagonal entries $\delta_{ii} = 1$ and all nondiagonal entries zero. (The symbol δ_{ij} is called the *Kronecker delta*.) We have proved

Theorem 12.   *A real $n \times n$ matrix represents an orthogonal transformation if and only if $A A^T = I$.*

The equation $A A^T = I$ has meaning over any field, so that the concept of an orthogonal matrix can be defined in general.

Definition.   *A square matrix A over any field is called orthogonal if and only if $A A^T = I$.*

This means that the transpose A^T of an orthogonal matrix A is a right-inverse of A; hence by Theorem 9 of Chap. VIII, every orthogonal matrix A is nonsingular, with $A^{-1} = A^T$. Therefore $A^T A = I$. This equation may be written as $A^T (A^T)^T = I$, whence A^T is orthogonal: the transpose of any orthogonal matrix A is also orthogonal. From this it also follows that a matrix A is orthogonal if and only if each *column A* has length one, and any two *columns* are orthogonal,

$$(22) \qquad \sum_{k=1}^{n} a_{ki}a_{ki} = 1 \quad \text{for all } i, \qquad \sum_{k=1}^{n} a_{ki}a_{kj} = 0 \quad \text{if } i \neq j.$$

All $n \times n$ orthogonal matrices form a group. This is clear since the inverse $A^{-1} = A^T$ of an orthogonal matrix is orthogonal and the product of the two orthogonal matrices A and B is orthogonal: $(AB)^T = B^T A^T = B^{-1}A^{-1} = (AB)^{-1}$. This subgroup of the full linear group $L_n(F)$ is called the *orthogonal group O_n*; it is isomorphic to the group of all orthogonal transformations of the given Euclidean space, if $F = \mathbf{R}$.

By a *rigid motion* of a Euclidean vector space E is meant a nonsingular transformation U of E which preserves distance, i.e., which satisfies

$| \xi U - \eta U | = | \xi - \eta |$ for all vectors ξ, η. Any translation of E preserves vector differences $\xi - \eta$, hence their lengths, and so is a rigid motion. Therefore if an affine transformation $\xi \to \xi T + \kappa$ is rigid, so is $\xi \to (\eta - \kappa) = \xi T$; conversely, if T is rigid, so is $\xi \to \eta = \xi T + \kappa$. But by Theorem 10, a linear transformation is rigid if and only if it is orthogonal. We conclude, *an affine transformation* (11) *is a rigid motion if and only if T is orthogonal.* It follows as in the proof of Theorem 7, since the orthogonal transformations form a group, that the totality of rigid affine transformations constitutes a subgroup of the affine group, called the *Euclidean group*. It is the basis of Euclidean geometry.†

Various other geometrical groups exist. A familiar one is the group of similarity transformations T, consisting of those linear transformations T which alter all lengths by a numerical factor $c_T \neq 0$, so that $| \xi T | = c_T | \xi |$. One may prove that they do in fact form a group which contains the orthogonal group as subgroup. The "extended" similarity group consists of all affine transformations $\xi \to \xi T + \kappa$ in which T is a similarity transformation.

EXERCISES

1. Test the following matrices for orthogonality. If a matrix is orthogonal, find its inverse:

(a) $\begin{pmatrix} 1/2 & \sqrt{3}/2 \\ -\sqrt{3}/2 & 1/2 \end{pmatrix}$, (b) $\begin{pmatrix} 1/2 & \sqrt{3}/2 \\ \sqrt{3}/2 & 1/2 \end{pmatrix}$, (c) $\begin{pmatrix} .6 & .8 \\ .8 & -.6 \end{pmatrix}$.

2. Find an orthogonal matrix whose first row is a scalar multiple of $(5, 12, 0)$.

3. If the columns of an orthogonal matrix are permuted, prove that the result is still orthogonal.

4. If A and B are orthogonal, prove that $\begin{pmatrix} A & 0 \\ 0 & B \end{pmatrix}$ is also.

5. Multiply the following two matrices, and test the resulting product for orthogonality.

$$\begin{pmatrix} \cos \phi & \sin \phi & 0 \\ -\sin \phi & \cos \phi & 0 \\ 0 & 0 & 1 \end{pmatrix}, \quad \begin{pmatrix} 1 & 0 & 0 \\ 0 & \cos \theta & \sin \theta \\ 0 & -\sin \theta & \cos \theta \end{pmatrix}.$$

6. Show that the Euclidean group is isomorphic to a group of matrices.

7. Prove that all translations form a normal subgroup of the Euclidean group.

8. As an alternative proof of (ii) in Theorem 10, show from first principles that $4(\xi, \eta) = | \xi + \eta |^2 - | \xi - \eta |^2$.

9. Show that an affine transformation H commutes with every translation if and only if H is itself a translation.

10. Prove that any similarity transformation S can be written in the form $S = cT$ as a product of a positive scalar and an orthogonal transformation T in one and only one way.

† It is a fact that any rigid motion is necessarily affine; hence the Euclidean group is actually the group of all rigid motions.

11. Give necessary and sufficient conditions that a matrix A represent a similarity transformation relative to a normal orthogonal basis (cf. Theorems 11–12).

12. (a) Prove that all similarity transformations form a group S_n.
   (b) Prove that O_n is a normal subgroup of S_n.
   (c) Prove that the quotient group S_n/O_n is isomorphic to the multiplicative group of all positive real numbers.

13. How many 3×3 orthogonal matrices are there with coefficients in $\mathbf{Z}_2$? in $\mathbf{Z}_3$?

14. (a) Show that the correspondence $A \to \theta(A) = (A^{-1})^T$ is an automorphism of the full linear group $L_n(F)$.
   (b) Show that $\theta^2(A) = A$ for all A.
   (c) For which matrices does $\theta(A) = A$?

5. Invariants and Canonical Forms

The full linear, the affine, the orthogonal, and the Euclidean groups form examples of linear groups. Another is the similarity group (§4, Ex. 12). In the following sections, we shall see how far one can go in "simplifying" polynomials, quadratic forms, and various geometrical figures, by applying suitable transformations from these groups. These simplifications will be analogous to the simplification made in reducing a general matrix to row-equivalent reduced echelon form, whose rank was proved to be an invariant under the transformations considered. The notions of a simplified "canonical form" and "invariant" can be formulated in great generality, as follows.†

Let G be a group of transformations (Chap. VI, §2) on any set or "space" S. Call two elements x and y of S *equivalent* under G (in symbols, xE_Gy) if and only if there is some transformation T of G which carries x into y. Then T^{-1} carries y back into x, so yE_Gx, and the relation of equivalence is symmetric. Similarly, using the other group properties, one proves that equivalence under any G is also a reflexive and transitive relation (an equivalence relation). A subset C of S is called a set of *canonical forms* under G if each $x \in S$ is equivalent under G to one and only one element c in C; this element c is then *the* canonical form of x. A function $F(x)$ defined for all elements x of S and with values in some convenient other set, say a set of numbers, is an *invariant* under G if $F(xT) = F(x)$ for every point x in S and every transformation T in G; in other words, F must have the same value at all equivalent elements. A collection of invariants $F_1, \cdots,$ F_n is a *complete set of invariants* under G if $F_1(x) = F_1(y), \cdots, F_n(x) = F_n(y)$ imply that x is equivalent to y.

For example, let the space S be the set M_n of all $n \times n$ matrices over some field. We already have at hand three different equivalence relations for such matrices; these are listed below, together with three

---

† The reader is advised to return again to this discussion when he has finished the chapter.

new cases which will be discussed in subsequent sections (§8, §10, and §12, respectively).

A row-equivalent to B	$B = PA$,	P nonsingular,
A equivalent to B	$B = PAQ$,	P, Q nonsingular,
A similar to B	$B = PAP^{-1}$,	P nonsingular,
A congruent to B	$B = PAP^T$,	P nonsingular,
A orthogonally equivalent to B	$B = PAP^{-1}$,	P orthogonal,
A unitary equivalent to B	$B = PAP^{-1}$,	P unitary.

The first line is to be read "A is row-equivalent to B if and only if there exists P such that $B = PA$, with P nonsingular," and similarly for the other lines.

Each of these equivalence relations is the equivalence relation E_G determined by a suitable group acting on M_n, and arises naturally from one of the various interpretations of a matrix.

The first relation, that of row equivalence, arises from the study of a fixed subspace of $V_n(F)$ represented as the row space of a matrix A; in this case the full linear group of matrices P acts on A by $A \to PA$, and the reduced echelon form is a canonical form under this group. The rank of A is a (numerical) invariant under this group, but it does not give a complete system of invariants, because two matrices A and B with the same rank need not be row-equivalent.

The second relation of equivalence (in the technical sense $B = PAQ$, not to be confused with the general notion of an equivalence relation) arises when we are studying the various matrix representations of a linear transformation of one vector space into a second such space (cf. §2, Ex. 9). Here, by Theorem 18 of Chap. VIII, the rank is a complete system of invariants under the group $A \to PAQ$. The set of all diagonal matrices with entries 1 and 0 along the diagonal, the 1's preceding the 0's, is a set of canonical forms. Note that we might equally well have chosen a *different* set of canonical forms—say the same sort of diagonal matrices, but with the 0's preceding the 1's on the diagonal.

The relation of similarity arises when we study the various matrix representations of a linear transformation of a vector space into itself; in this case the full linear group acts on A by $A \to PAP^{-1}$. Under similarity the rank of the matrix A is an invariant, since two similar matrices are certainly equivalent, and rank is even invariant under equivalence. The set of all characteristic roots of a matrix is also an invariant under similarity, by §2, but is not a complete system of invariants. The formulation of a complete set of canonical forms under similarity is one of the major problems of matrix theory; for the field of complex numbers, it gives rise to the Jordan canonical form of a matrix.

The relation of congruence ($B = PAP^T$), as will appear subsequently, arises from the representation of a quadratic form by a (symmetric) matrix.

As still another example of equivalence under a group consider the simplification of a quadratic polynomial $f(x) = ax^2 + bx + c$, with $a \neq 0$, by the group of all translations $y = x + k$. Substituting $x = y - k$, we find the result of translating $f(x)$ to be

$$g(y) = a(y - k)^2 + b(y - k) + c = ay^2 + (b - 2ak)y + ak^2 - bk + c.$$

In particular, we obtain the familiar "completion of the square"—the new polynomial will have no linear terms if and only if $k = b/2a$, and in this case the polynomial is

$$(23) \qquad g(y) = ay^2 - d/(4a), \qquad \text{where} \qquad d = b^2 - 4ac.$$

Thus $f(x)$ is equivalent under the group of translations to one and only one polynomial of the form $ay^2 + h$, so that the quadratic polynomials without linear terms are canonical forms under this group. On the other hand, any transformed polynomial has the same leading coefficient a and the same discriminant $d = (b - 2ak)^2 - 4a(ak^2 - bk + c)$ as the original polynomial $f(x)$. Hence the first coefficient and the discriminant of $f(x)$ are invariants under the group. They constitute a complete set of invariants, because the canonical form can be expressed in terms of them as shown in (23).

To give a last example, recall that the full linear group $L_n(F)$ is a group of transformations on the vector space $V_n(F)$. Each transformation of this group carries a subspace S of $V_n(F)$ into another subspace. By Corollary 2 of Theorem 10, Chap. VIII, the dimension of any subspace S is an invariant under the full linear group. This one invariant is actually a complete set of invariants for subspaces of $V_n(F)$ under the full linear group (see Ex. 5 below).

EXERCISES

1. Find canonical forms for all *monic* quadratic polynomials $x^2 + bx + c$ under the group of translations.
2. Find canonical forms for all quadratic polynomials $ax^2 + bx + c$ with $a \neq 0$ under the affine group $y = hx + k$, $h \neq 0$.
3. In Ex. 2, show that $d/a = b^2/a - 4c$ is an affine invariant.
4. Show that, over any field in which $1 + 1 \neq 0$, any quartic polynomial is equivalent under translation to a polynomial in which the cubic term is absent.
5. Let V be an n-dimensional vector space. Show that a complete system of invariants for ordered pairs of subspaces (S_1, S_2) of V under the full linear group is given by the dimensions of S_1, of S_2, and of their intersection.
6. Consider the set of homogeneous quadratic functions ax^2 with rational a under the group $x \to rx$, with $r \neq 0$ and rational. Show that the set of

integral coefficients a which are products of distinct primes ("square free") provide canonical forms for this set.

7. If $f(x)$ is any polynomial in one variable, prove that the degree of f and the number of real roots are both invariant under the affine group.

8. For a polynomial in n variables, show that the coefficient of the term of highest degree is invariant under the group of translations.

9. Show that a real cubic polynomial is equivalent under the affine group to one and only one polynomial of the form $x^3 + ax + b$.

★10. Find canonical forms for the quadratic forms $x^2 + bx + c$ under the group of translations, in case b and c are elements from the field $\mathbf{Z}_2$ of integers modulo 2.

6. Linear and Bilinear Forms

A *linear form* in n variables over a field F is a polynomial of the form

$$(24) \qquad f(x_1, \cdots, x_n) = b_1 x_1 + \cdots + b_n x_n + c,$$

with coefficients $b_1, \cdots, b_n$ and c in F; to exclude the trivial case, we assume that some coefficient b_j is not zero. The form is *homogeneous* if $c = 0$. Any form (24) may be regarded as a function $f(X)$ of the vector $X = (x_1, \cdots, x_n)$ of $V_n(F)$. Distinct forms determine distinct functions, for the function $f(X)$ determines the coefficients of the form by the formulas $f(0, \cdots, 0) = c$, $f(1, 0, \cdots, 0) = b_1 + c, \cdots, f(0, \cdots, 0, 1) = b_n + c$.

To any linear form we may apply a nonsingular affine transformation

$$(25) \qquad x_i = \sum_j a_{ij} y_j + k_i, \qquad \| a_{ij} \| \text{ nonsingular,}$$

to yield upon substitution in (24) the new linear form

$$(26) \qquad g(y_1, \cdots, y_n) = \sum_j \left(\sum_i b_i a_{ij} \right) y_j + \left(\sum_i b_i k_i + c \right).$$

We say that f and g are *equivalent* forms under the affine group, if there exists such a nonsingular affine transformation carrying f into g.

A canonical form may be obtained readily. First, since some $b_j \neq 0$, the translation $x_j = y_j - c/b_j$, and $x_i = y_i$ for $i \neq j$ will remove the constant term. The permutation $z_1 = y_j$, $z_j = y_1$, and $z_i = y_i$ for $i \neq 1$ or j will then give a new form like (24) with $b_1 \neq 0$ and $c = 0$. If this form is written with the variables x_j, the new affine transformation with the equations

$$y_1 = b_1 x_1 + \cdots + b_n x_n, \qquad y_2 = x_2, \cdots, y_n = x_n$$

is nonsingular, and carries any f with $c = 0$ to the equivalent function $g(y_1, \cdots, y_n) = y_1$. Therefore *all nonzero linear forms are equivalent under the affine group.*

Consider now the equivalence of real linear forms under the Euclidean group (i.e., with $A = \| a_{ij} \|$ in (25) an orthogonal matrix). Call $d = (b_1^2 + \cdots + b_n^2)^{1/2}$ the *norm* of the form (24). As before, we can remove the constant c by a translation. By the choice of d, $(b_1/d, \cdots, b_n/d)$ is a vector of unit length. Hence there is an orthogonal matrix $\| h_{ij} \|$ with this vector as its first row. The transformation $y_i = \sum h_{ij} x_j$ is then in the Euclidean group; since $dy_1 = b_1 x_1 + \cdots + b_n x_n$, it carries the form f, with $c = 0$, into the form $g = dy_1$.

This form dy_1 is a canonical form for linear forms under the Euclidean group. To show this, we need only prove that the norm d is invariant under the Euclidean group. Now the norm d of f is just the length of the coefficient vector $\beta = (b_1, \cdots, b_n)$, and (26) shows that in the transformed form the coefficient vector is the transform βA of the original coefficient vector by the orthogonal matrix $\| a_{ij} \|$; hence the norm is indeed invariant. We have proved

Theorem 13. *Under the Euclidean group, every linear form (24) is equivalent to one and only one of the canonical forms dy, with positive d, where $d = (b_1^2 + \cdots + b_n^2)^{1/2}$ is an invariant under this group.*

A (homogeneous) *bilinear form* in two sets of variables $x_1, \cdots, x_n$ and $y_1, \cdots, y_n$ is a polynomial of the form

$$(27) \qquad b(x_1, \cdots, x_n, y_1, \cdots, y_n) = \sum_{i,j=1}^{n} x_i a_{ij} y_j;$$

it is determined by the matrix of coefficients $A = \| a_{ij} \|$. In terms of the vectors $X = (x_1, \cdots, x_n)$ and $Y = (y_1, \cdots, y_n)$ the bilinear form may be written as the matrix product

$$(28) \qquad\qquad b(X, Y) = X A Y^T.$$

As a function of X and Y, it is linear in each argument separately.

Conversely, let V and W be two vector spaces of the same dimension n over a field F, and let $B(\xi, \eta)$ be any function, with values in F, defined for arguments $\xi \in V$ and $\eta \in W$, which is bilinear in the sense that, for a_1 and $a_2 \in F$,

$$(29) \quad B(a_1 \xi_1 + a_2 \xi_2, \eta) = a_1 B(\xi_1, \eta) + a_2 B(\xi_2, \eta), \qquad \xi_1, \xi_2 \in V, \eta \in W;$$
$$(29') \quad B(\xi, a_1 \eta_1 + a_2 \eta_2) = B(\xi, \eta_1)a_1 + B(\xi, \eta_2)a_2, \qquad \xi \in V, \eta_1, \eta_2 \in W.$$

Choose a basis $\alpha_1, \cdots, \alpha_n$ in V and a basis $\beta_1, \cdots, \beta_n$ in W and let the scalars a_{ij} be defined as $a_{ij} = B(\alpha_i, \beta_j)$. Then for any vectors ξ and η in V and W, expressed in terms of the respective bases, we have

$$B(\xi, \eta) = B(x_1 \alpha_1 + \cdots + x_n \alpha_n, y_1 \beta_1 + \cdots + y_n \beta_n)$$

and hence by (29) and (29′),

$$B(\xi, \eta) = \sum_{i,j} x_i B(\alpha_i, \beta_j) y_j = \sum_{i,j} x_i a_{ij} y_j.$$

In other words, any bilinear function B on V and W has a unique expression, relative to given bases, as a bilinear form (27).

A change of basis in both spaces corresponds to nonsingular transformations $X = X^*P$ and $Y = Y^*Q$ of each set of variables. These transformations replace (28) by a new bilinear form $X^*(PAQ^T)Y^{*T}$, with a new matrix PAQ^T. Since any nonsingular matrix may be written as the transpose Q^T of a nonsingular matrix, we see that two bilinear forms are equivalent (under changes of bases) if and only if their matrices are equivalent. Hence, by Theorem 18 of Chap. VIII on the equivalence of matrices, *any bilinear form is equivalent to one and only one of the canonical forms*

$$x_1 y_1 + \cdots + x_r y_r.$$

The integer r, which is the rank of the matrix of the form, is a (complete set of) invariants.

EXERCISES

1. Find a canonical form for homogeneous real linear functions under the similarity group.
2. Treat the same question (a) under the diagonal group of transformations $y_1 = d_1 x_1, \cdots, y_n = d_n x_n$, (b) under the monomial group of all transformations $Y = XM$ with a monomial matrix M.
3. Prove that any bilinear form of rank r is expressible as

$$\sum_i (b_{i1} x_1 + \cdots + b_{in} x_n)(c_{i1} y_1 + \cdots + c_{in} y_n), \quad \text{where} \quad i = 1, \cdots, r;$$

   that is, as the sum of r products of linear forms.
4. Treat, as in the text, bilinear forms in $x_1, \cdots, x_m; y_1, \cdots, y_n$ for $m \neq n$.
5. Find new variables x^*, y^*, z^* and u^*, v^*, w^* which will reduce to canonical form the bilinear function

$$xu + xv + xw + yu + yv + yw + zu + zv + zw.$$

7. Quadratic Forms

The next four sections are devoted to the study of canonical forms for quadratic functions under various groups of transformations. The simplest problems of this type arise in connection with central conics in the plane (ellipses or hyperbolas with "tilted" axes). Such conics have equations $Ax^2 + Bxy + Cy^2 = 1$, in which the left-hand side is a "quadratic form." Such quadratic forms (homogeneous quadratic expressions in the variables) arise in many other instances: in the equations for quadric surfaces in space, in the projective equations for conics in homogeneous coordinates, in the formula $|X|^2 = (x_1{}^2 + x_2{}^2 + \cdots + x_n{}^2)$ for the square of the length of a vector, in the formula $(m/2)(u^2 + v^2 + w^2)$ for the kinetic energy of a moving body in space with three velocity components u, v, and w, in differential geometry, in the formula for the length of arc ds in spherical coordinates of space, $ds^2 = dr^2 + r^2 d\phi^2 + r^2 \sin \phi d\theta^2$.

Such quadratic forms can be expressed by matrices. To obtain a matrix from a quadratic form such as $5x^2 + 6xy + 2y^2$, first adjust the form so that the coefficients of xy and yx are equal, as $5x^2 + 3xy + 3yx + 2y^2$. The result can be written as a matrix product,

$$(x, y) \begin{pmatrix} 5 & 3 \\ 3 & 2 \end{pmatrix} \begin{pmatrix} x \\ y \end{pmatrix} = (x, y) \begin{pmatrix} 5x + 3y \\ 3x + 2y \end{pmatrix} = 5x^2 + 6xy + 2y^2.$$

The 2×2 matrix of coefficients which arises here is symmetric, in the sense that it is equal to its transpose.

In general, a square matrix A is called *symmetric* if it is equal to its own transpose, $A^T = A$; in other words, $\|a_{ij}\|$ is symmetric if and only if $a_{ij} = a_{ji}$ for all i and j. Similarly, a matrix C is *skew-symmetric* if $C^T = -C$. To split a matrix B into symmetric and skew-symmetric parts, write

$$(30) \qquad B = (B + B^T)/2 + (B - B^T)/2 = S + K,$$

where $S = (B + B^T)/2$, $K = (B - B^T)/2$. By the laws for the transpose, $(B \pm B^T)^T = B^T \pm B^{TT} = B^T \pm B$, so S is symmetric and K skew. No other decomposition $B = S_1 + K_1$ with S_1 symmetric and K_1 skew is possible, because any such decomposition would give $B^T = S_1{}^T + K_1{}^T = S_1 - K_1$, $B + B^T = 2S_1$, $B - B^T = 2K_1$, and $S_1 = S$, $K_1 = K$. Formulas (30) apply over any field in which $2 = 1 + 1 \neq 0$, but are meaningless for matrices over the field $\mathbf{Z}_2$, where $1 + 1 = 0$. In conclusion, any matrix can be expressed uniquely as the sum of a symmetric matrix and a skew matrix, provided $1 + 1 \neq 0$.

A *homogeneous quadratic form* in n variables $x_1, \cdots, x_n$ is by definition a polynomial

$$\sum_i \sum_j x_i b_{ij} x_j$$

in which each term is of degree two. This form may be written as a matrix product XBX^T. If the matrix B of coefficients is skew-symmetric, $b_{ij} = -b_{ji}$ and the form equals zero. In general, write the matrix B as $B = S + K$, according to (30); the form then becomes

$$XBX^T = X(S + K)X^T = XSX^T + XKX^T = XSX^T \qquad (K \text{ skew}).$$

Hence if $1 + 1 \neq 0$, any quadratic form may be expressed uniquely, with S denoted by A, as

$$(31) \qquad \sum_{i=1}^n \sum_{j=1}^n x_i a_{ij} x_j = XAX^T, \qquad A = \|a_{ij}\| \text{ symmetric.}$$

If a vector ξ has coordinates $X = (x_1, \cdots, x_n)$, each quadratic form determines a quadratic function $Q(\xi) = XAX^T$ of the vector ξ. A change of basis in the space gives new coordinates X^* related to the old coordinates by an equation $X = X^*P$, with P nonsingular. In terms of the new coordinates of ξ the quadratic function becomes

$$Q(\xi) = XAX^T = (X^*P)A(X^*P)^T = X^*(PAP^T)X^{*T},$$

this is another quadratic form with a new matrix PAP^T. The new matrix, like A, is symmetric; $(PAP^T)^T = P^{TT}A^TP^T = PAP^T$.

Theorem 14. *A change of coordinates replaces a quadratic form with matrix A by a quadratic form with matrix PAP^T, where P is nonsingular.*

Symmetric matrices A and B are sometimes called *congruent* when (as in this case) $B = PAP^T$ for some nonsingular P.

Reinterpreted, Theorem 14 asserts that the problem of reducing a homogeneous quadratic form to canonical form, under the full linear group of nonsingular linear homogeneous substitutions on its variables, is equivalent to the problem of finding a canonical form for symmetric matrices A under the group $A \to PAP^T$.

EXERCISES

1. Prove that A^TA and AA^T are always symmetric.
2. Prove: If A is skew-symmetric, then A^2 is symmetric.
3. Represent each matrix of Ex. 1, §3, Chap. VIII, in the form $S + K$.
4. Find the symmetric matrix associated with each of the following quadratic forms:
   (a) $2x^2 + 3xy + 6y^2$,   (b) $8xy + 4y^2$,
   (c) $x^2 + 2xy + 4xz + 3y^2 + yz + 7z^2$,   (d) $4xy$,
   (e) $x^2 + 4xy + 4y^2 + 2xz + z^2 + 4yz$.
5. (a) Prove: If S is symmetric and A orthogonal, then $A^{-1}SA$ is symmetric.
   (b) If K is skew-symmetric and A orthogonal, then $A^{-1}KA$ is skew-symmetric.
6. Study the symmetry of the matrix $AB - BA$ in the following cases:
   (a) A and B both symmetric; (b) A and B both skew-symmetric;
   (c) A symmetric and B skew-symmetric.
7. Prove: If A and B are symmetric, then AB is symmetric if and only if $AB = BA$.
8. (a) Prove: Over the field $\mathbf{Z}_2$ (integers mod 2) every skew-symmetric matrix is symmetric.
   (b) Exhibit a matrix over $\mathbf{Z}_2$ which is not a sum $S + K$ (cf. (30)).
9. Let D be a diagonal matrix with no repeated entries. Show that $AD = DA$ if and only if A is also diagonal.
10. If $Q(\xi)$ is a quadratic function, prove that
$$Q(\alpha + \beta + \gamma) - Q(\alpha + \beta) - Q(\beta + \gamma) - Q(\gamma + \alpha)$$
$$+ Q(\alpha) + Q(\beta) + Q(\gamma) = 0.$$

11. A bilinear form $B(\xi, \eta)$, with ξ, η both in V, is symmetric when $B(\xi, \eta) = B(\eta, \xi)$. Prove that, if B is a symmetric bilinear form, then $Q(\xi) = B(\xi, \xi)$ is a quadratic form, with $2B(\xi, \eta) = Q(\xi + \eta) - Q(\xi) - Q(\eta)$.

12. Show that a real $n \times n$ matrix A is symmetric if and only if the associated linear transformation $T = T_A$ of Euclidean n-space satisfies $(\xi T, \eta) = (\xi, \eta T)$ for any two vectors ξ and η.

*13. Show that if the real matrix S is skew-symmetric and $I + S$ is nonsingular, then $(I - S)(I + S)^{-1}$ is orthogonal.

8. Quadratic Forms under the Full Linear Group

The familiar process of "completing the square" may be used as a device for simplifying a quadratic form by linear transformations. For two variables, the procedure gives

$$ax^2 + 2bxy + cy^2 = a[x^2 + 2(b/a)xy + (b^2/a^2)y^2] + [c - (b^2/a)]y^2$$
$$= a[x + (b/a)y]^2 + [c - (b^2/a)]y^2.$$

The term in brackets suggests the new variables $x' = x + (b/a)y$, $y' = y$. Under this linear change of variables, the form becomes $ax'^2 + [c - (b^2/a)]y'^2$; the cross term has been eliminated.

This argument requires $a \neq 0$. If $a = 0$, but $c \neq 0$, a similar transformation works. Finally, if $a = c = 0$, the original form is $2bxy$, and the corresponding equation $2bxy = 1$ represents an equilateral hyperbola. In this case, the transformation $x = x' + y'$, $y = x' - y'$ will reduce the form to

$$2b(x' + y')(x' - y') = 2b(x'^2 - y'^2);$$

the result again contains only square terms. (*Hint:* How is the transformation used here related to a rotation of the axes of the hyperbola?)

An analogous preparatory device may be applied to forms in more than two variables.

Lemma. *By a nonsingular linear transformation, any quadratic form $\sum x_i a_{ij} x_j$ not identically zero can be reduced to a form with leading coefficient $a_{11} \neq 0$, provided only that $1 + 1 \neq 0$.*

Proof. By hypothesis, at least one coefficient $a_{ij} \neq 0$. If there is a diagonal term $a_{ii} \neq 0$, one can get a new coefficient $a_{11}' \neq 0$ by interchanging the variables x_1 and x_i (this is a nonsingular transformation because its matrix is a permutation matrix). In the remaining case, all diagonal terms a_{ii} are zero, but there are indices $i \neq j$, with $a_{ij} \neq 0$. By permuting the variables we can make $a_{12} \neq 0$; by the symmetry of the matrix $a_{12} = a_{21}$. The given quadratic form is then $a_{12}x_1x_2 + a_{21}x_2x_1 = 2a_{12}x_1x_2$, plus terms involving other variables. Just as in the case of the equilateral hyperbola this may be reduced to a form $2a_{12}(y_1^2 - y_2^2)$, with a leading coefficient $2a_{12} \neq 0$, by a transformation

$$x_1 = y_1 - y_2, \qquad x_2 = y_1 + y_2, \qquad x_3 = y_3, \; \cdots \;, x_n = y_n.$$

This transformation is nonsingular, for by elimination one easily shows that it has an inverse

$$y_1 = (x_1 + x_2)/2, \qquad y_2 = (x_2 - x_1)/2, \qquad y_3 = x_3, \; \cdots \;, y_n = x_n.$$

Query: Where does this argument use the hypothesis $1 + 1 \neq 0$?

Now for the completion of the square in any quadratic form! By the Lemma, we make $a_{11} \neq 0$, so the form can be written as $a_{11}(\sum x_i b_{ij} x_j)$, where $b_{ij} = a_{ij}/a_{11}$ and $b_{11} = 1$. Because of the symmetry of the matrix, the terms which actually involve x_1 are then

$$x_1{}^2 + 2 \sum_{j=2}^{n} b_{1j} x_1 x_j = \Big(x_1 + \sum_{j=2}^{n} b_{1j} x_j \Big)^2 - \Big(\sum_{j=2}^{n} b_{1j} x_j \Big)^2.$$

The formation of this "perfect square" suggests the transformation

$$y_1 = x_1 + \sum_{j=2}^{n} b_{1j} x_j, \qquad y_2 = x_2, \; \cdots \;, y_n = x_n;$$

then y_1 will appear only as $y_1{}^2$. The original form is now $a_{11} y_1{}^2 + \sum y_j c_{jk} y_k$, where the indices j and k run from 2 to n. This residual part in $y_2, \; \cdots \;, y_n$ is a quadratic form in $n - 1$ variables; to this form the same process applies. This may be repeated (an induction argument!) till the new coefficients in one of the residual quadratic forms are all zero. Hence we have

Theorem 15. *By nonsingular linear transformations of the variables, a quadratic form over any field with $1 + 1 \neq 0$ can be reduced to a diagonal quadratic form,*

$$(32) \qquad d_1 y_1{}^2 + d_2 y_2{}^2 + \cdots + d_r y_r{}^2, \qquad \text{each } d_i \neq 0.$$

The number r of non-zero diagonal terms is an invariant called the rank *of the given form Q.*

The invariance of the rank r is immediate, for r is the rank of the diagonal matrix D of the reduced form (32). This rank must equal the rank of the matrix A of the original quadratic form, for by Theorem 14 our transformations reduce A to $D = PAP^T$, and we already know (Chap. VIII, Theorem 19) that rank is invariant under the more general transformation $A \to PAQ$.

A quadratic form XAX^T in n variables is called nonsingular if its rank is n, because this means that the matrix A is nonsingular.

In the diagonal form (32), the rank r is an invariant, but the coefficients are not, because different methods of reducing the form may well yield different sets of coefficients $d_1, \; \cdots \;, d_r$. We shall now get a complete set of invariants for the special case of the real field.

EXERCISES

1. Over the field of rational numbers reduce each of the quadratic forms of §7, Ex. 4 to diagonal form.
2. Reduce $2x^2 + xy + 3y^2$ to diagonal form over the field of integers modulo 5.
3. Over the field Z_5, prove that every quadratic form may be reduced by linear transformations to a form $\sum d_i y_i^2$, with each coefficient $d_i = 0$, 1, or 2.
4. Over the field of rational numbers show that the quadratic form $x_1^2 + x_2^2$ can be transformed into both of the distinct diagonal forms $9y_1^2 + 4y_2^2$ and $2z_1^2 + 8z_2^2$.
5. Find a P such that PAP^T is diagonal, if

(a) $A = \begin{pmatrix} 3 & 1 \\ 1 & 0 \end{pmatrix}$,   (b) $A = \begin{pmatrix} 1 & 2 \\ 2 & 4 \end{pmatrix}$,   (c) $A = \begin{pmatrix} 0 & 1 & 0 \\ 1 & 0 & 2 \\ 0 & 2 & 0 \end{pmatrix}$.

6. Find all linear transformations which carry the real quadratic form $x_1^2 + \cdots + x_n^2$ into $y_1^2 + \cdots + y_n^2$.
7. Show rigorously that the quadratic form xy is not equivalent to a diagonal form under the group $L_2(Z_2)$.

9. Real Quadratic Forms under the Full Linear Group

Conic sections and quadratic surfaces are described in analytic geometry by real quadratic polynomial functions. Over the real field, each term of the diagonal form (32) can be simplified further by making the substitution $y_i' = (\pm d_i)^{1/2} y_i$, so that the term $d_i y_i^2$ becomes $\pm y_i'^2$. Carrying out these substitutions simultaneously on all the variables will reduce the quadratic form to $\sum \pm y_i^2$. In this sum the variables may be permuted so that the positive squares come first. This proves

Theorem 16.   *Any quadratic function over the field of real numbers can be reduced by nonsingular linear transformation of the variables to a form*

(33) $z_1^2 + \cdots + z_p^2 - z_{p+1}^2 - \cdots - z_r^2$.

Theorem 17.   *The number p of positive squares which appear in the reduced form (33) is an invariant of the given function Q, in the sense that p depends only on the function and not on the method used to reduce it (Sylvester's law of inertia).*

Proof.   Suppose that there is another reduced form

(34) $y_1^2 + \cdots + y_q^2 - y_{q+1}^2 - \cdots - y_r^2$

with q positive terms. Since both are obtained from the same Q by nonsingular transformations, there is a nonsingular transformation carrying (33) into (34). We may regard the equations of this transformation as a change of coordinates ("alias"); then (33) and (34) represent the same quadratic function $Q(\xi)$ of a fixed vector ξ with coordinates z_i relative to one basis, y_j relative to another.

Suppose $q < p$. Then $Q(\xi) \geq 0$ whenever $z_{p+1} = \cdots = z_r = 0$ in (33). The ξ's satisfying these $r - p$ equations form an $n - (r - p)$ dimensional subspace S_1 (in this subspace there are $n - (r - p)$ coordinates $z_1, \cdots, z_p, z_{r+1}, \cdots, z_n$). Similarly, (34) makes $Q(\xi) < 0$ for each $\xi \neq 0$ with coordinates $y_1 = \cdots = y_q = y_{r+1} = \cdots = y_n = 0$. These conditions determine an $(r - q)$-dimensional subspace S_2. The sum of the dimensions of these subspaces S_1 and S_2 is

$$n - (r - p) + (r - q) = n + (p - q) > n.$$

Therefore S_1 and S_2 have a non-zero vector ξ in common, for, according to Theorem 16 of Chap. VII, the dimension of the intersection $S_1 \cap S_2$ is positive. For this common vector ξ, $Q(\xi) \geq 0$ by (33) and $Q(\xi) < 0$ by (34), a manifest contradiction. The assumption $q > p$ would lead to a similar contradiction, so $q = p$, completing the proof.

This result shows that any real quadratic form can be reduced by linear transformations to one and only one form of the type (33). The expressions $\sum \pm z_i^2$ of this type are therefore *canonical* for quadratic forms under the full linear group. This canonical form itself is uniquely determined by the so-called *signature* $\{+, \cdots, +, -, \cdots, -\}$ which is a set of p positive and $r - p$ negative signs, r being the *rank* of the form. This set of signs is determined by r and by $s = p - (r - p) = 2p - r$ (s is the number of positive signs diminished by the number of negative signs). Sometimes this integer s is called the signature. Together, r and s form a complete system of numerical invariants, because two forms are equivalent if and only if they reduce to the same canonical form (33).

Theorem 18. *Two real quadratic forms are equivalent under the full linear group if and only if they have the same rank and the same signature.*

A real quadratic form $Q = XAX^T$ in n variables is called *positive definite* when $X \neq 0$ implies $Q > 0$; a real symmetric matrix A is called positive definite under the same conditions. Considering the canonical reduced form (33), it is evident that this is the case if and only if the reduced form is $z_1^2 + \cdots + z_n^2$. This is because a sum of n squares is positive unless all terms are individually zero, and because for $X = \varepsilon_n$, the nth unit vector, $XAX^T \leq 0$ in (33) unless $p = n$. That is, we have proved

Theorem 19. *A real quadratic form is positive definite if and only if its canonical form is $z_1^2 + \cdots + z_n^2$.*

By Theorem 14, this means that $A = PIP^T$, which gives the following further result.

Theorem 20. *A real symmetric matrix A is positive definite if and only if there exists a real nonsingular matrix P such that $A = PP^T$.*

A quadratic form XAX^T defines in n-dimensional real space a locus, consisting of all points X satisfying $XAX^T = 1$. The canonical form (33) means that a suitable nonsingular linear transformation will reduce this locus to one with an equation

$$z_1^2 + \cdots + z_p^2 - z_{p+1}^2 - \cdots - z_r^2 = 1.$$

For example, in the plane, the reduced equations of rank 2 are

$$x^2 + y^2 = 1, \qquad x^2 - y^2 = 1, \qquad -x^2 - y^2 = 1.$$

They represent, respectively, a circle, an equilateral hyperbola, or no locus. The only form of rank 0 is $0 = 1$; those of rank 1 are $x^2 = 1$ (which represents the two lines $x = \pm 1$) or $-x^2 = 1$ (no locus). In Chap. VIII it was proved (Theorem 15, Corollary 2) that any nonsingular linear transformation of the plane can be represented as a product of shears, compressions, and reflections. Hence any "central conic" with an equation $ax^2 + bxy + cy^2 = 1$ can be reduced to one of the forms we have listed by a succession of shears, compressions, and reflections. Geometrically, this result is reasonable: an ellipse could be compressed along one axis to make a circle; but, clearly, no sequence of linear transformations could reduce a circle $x^2 + y^2 = 1$ to an equilateral hyperbola $x^2 - y^2 = 1$. This is the geometric significance of the invariance of the signature in this case.

The signature is useful in studying the maxima and minima of functions of two variables. Let $z = f(x, y)$ be a function for which both first partial derivatives f_x' and f_y' vanish at $x = x_0$, $y = y_0$, so that there are no first-degree terms in the Taylor's series expansion of z in powers of $h = (x - x_0)$ and $k = (y - y_0)$. This expansion is

$$f(x_0 + h, y_0 + k) = f(x_0, y_0) + (1/2)[ah^2 + 2bhk + ck^2] + \cdots ;$$

the coefficients being the partial derivatives

$$a = f_{xx}''(x_0, y_0), \qquad b = f_{xy}''(x_0, y_0), \qquad c = f_{yy}''(x_0, y_0).$$

For small values of h and k the controlling term is the one in brackets; it is a quadratic form in h and k with real coefficients. If this form has rank 2, it can be expressed in terms of transformed variables h' and k', as $\pm h'^2 \pm k'^2$. If both signs are plus, nearby values of $f(x_0 + h, y_0 + k)$ must always exceed $f(x_0, y_0)$, and z has a relative *minimum*. If both signs are minus, z has a *maximum*. If one sign is plus and one sign is minus, the quadratic form may take on both positive and negative values, so x_0, y_0 is neither a maximum nor a minimum, but a *saddle-point* (like a saddle or a pass between two mountain peaks, where motion in one direction increases the altitude z, in another decreases z). Maxima, minima, and saddle-points of f are therefore distinguished by the signature of the quadratic form. Similar results hold for *critical points* of functions of three or more variables.

EXERCISES

1. Prove: A homogeneous quadratic form with complex coefficients is always equivalent under the full linear group (using complex coefficients) to a sum of squares $z_1^2 + \cdots + z_r^2$.
2. Prove that two quadratic forms in n variables with complex coefficients are equivalent under the full linear group if and only if they have the same rank.
3. Reduce the following real quadratic forms to the canonical form of Theorem 16. Find the rank and signature of each form.
   (a) $9x_1^2 + 12x_1x_2 + 79x_2^2$,   (b) $2x_1^2 - 12x_1x_2 + 18x_2^2$,
   (c) $-2x_1^2 - 4x_1x_2 + 22x_2^2 + 12x_2x_3 + 6x_3x_1 - x_3^2$.
4. Describe the geometrical loci corresponding to the various possible canonical forms for real quadratic forms in three dimensions.
5. (a) List all the types of nonsingular quadratic forms in four variables.
   (b) Describe geometrically at least two of the corresponding loci in $V_4(\mathbf{R})$.
6. Prove that the real quadratic function $ax^2 + bxy + cy^2$ is positive definite if and only if $a > 0$ and $4ac - b^2 > 0$.
7. Prove that the bilinear function XAY^T is an "inner product" if and only if A is symmetric and positive definite.
8. A quadratic form is called *positive semidefinite* if its rank equals its signature. State and prove an analogue of Theorem 19 for such forms.
9. Do the same for Theorem 20.

10. Quadratic Forms under the Orthogonal Group

How far can a real quadratic form be simplified by transformations restricted to be orthogonal? An orthogonal transformation $Y = XP$ changes XAX^T into $Y(P^{-1}AP^{-1T})Y^T$, because P is orthogonal, the new matrix may be written† $P^{-1}AP^{-1T} = P^{-1}AP$.

In the plane an orthogonal transformation (rotation or reflection) of an ellipse will never yield a circle; at most one can hope to rotate the axes of the ellipse into standard position. The major axis might be characterized as the longest diameter. To reformulate this maximum property, consider any real quadratic function $Q(\xi) = ax^2 + cy^2$ with $a \leq c$ and no xy term. Then $Q(\xi) \leq cx^2 + cy^2 = c(x^2 + y^2)$: this means that the maximum value assumed by Q for all points on the unit circle $x^2 + y^2 = 1$ is c, and this maximum is taken on at the point $y = 1$, $x = 0$. Conversely, the latter statement insures the absence of an xy term in Q.

---

† Two symmetric matrices A and $P^{-1}AP$, with P orthogonal, are sometimes called *orthogonally congruent*.

Lemma.   *If a real quadratic function $Q = ax^2 + 2bxy + cy^2$ has among all points on the unit circle $x^2 + y^2 = 1$ a maximum value at $x = 0, y = 1$, then $b = 0$.*

Proof.   Consider Q as a (two-valued) function of one variable x, where y is given implicitly in terms of x by $x^2 + y^2 = 1$. Differentiating, we get $2x + 2y(dy/dx) = 0$, so the derivative $y' = dy/dx$ is $y' = -x/y$. The derivative of Q is

$$Q' = (ax^2 + 2bxy + cy^2)' = 2ax + 2by + 2bxy' + 2cyy'.$$

Putting in the value of y' and setting $y = 1$, $x = 0$, one finds $Q' = 2b$. But at the maximum $y = 1$, $x = 0$, this derivative must be zero, hence $2b = 0$, Q.E.D.

Now return to quadratic forms in n variables. In n-space the unit hypersphere $\sum x_i^2 = 1$ is a closed and bounded set S; its points are all vectors of length one. On this hypersphere the values taken on by a real quadratic form $Q(\xi) = \sum_{i,j} x_i a_{ij} x_j$ have an upper bound $\sum_{i,j} |a_{ij}|$. Therefore, since $Q(\xi)$ is a continuous function of ξ, $Q(\xi)$ has a maximum† λ_1 on S. In other words, among all vectors ξ of unit length there is one, ξ_0, at which $Q(\xi)$ takes as its maximum value λ_1. Since ξ_0 has length 1, we may choose $\alpha_1 = \xi_0$ as the first vector of a new normal orthogonal basis $\alpha_1, \cdots, \alpha_n$ (Theorem 20, Chap. VII). In terms of the new coordinates $y_1, \cdots, y_n$ of ξ relative to this basis the quadratic form is now expressed as $Q(\xi) = \sum y_i b_{ij} y_j$ with a new matrix of coefficients b_{ij}. The maximum value λ_1 of Q is given by the vector α_1 with coordinates $(1, 0, \cdots, 0)$; so by substitution the maximum value λ_1 is b_{11}. This maximum will remain the maximum if we further restrict the variables so that all but two, y_1 and y_i, are zero. Therefore, $y_1 = 1$, $y_i = 0$ is the maximum of the form $b_{11} y_1^2 + 2b_{1i} y_1 y_i + b_{ii} y_i^2$, subject to the condition $y_1^2 + y_i^2 = 1$. The Lemma (with x replaced by y_i) then asserts that the cross product coefficient b_{1i} is zero. This argument applies to each $i = 2, \cdots, n$. Therefore Q, in these coordinates y_i, loses all cross product terms involving y_1 and becomes

$$(35) \qquad Q(\xi) = \lambda_1 y_1^2 + \sum_{i=2}^{n} \sum_{j=2}^{n} y_i b_{ij} y_j, \qquad B = \| b_{ij} \| = B^T.$$

The first coefficient λ_1 is *not* a vector, but a scalar (the maximum of $Q(\xi)$ on the sphere $|\xi| = 1$).

The difference $Q^*(\xi) = Q(\xi) - \lambda_1 y_1^2$ in (35) is a quadratic form in $n - 1$ variables $y_2, \cdots, y_n$. These variables are coordinates in the space S_{n-1} spanned by the $n - 1$ new basis vectors $\alpha_2, \cdots, \alpha_n$. In this space

---

† Here, as in calculus, we assume the fact that a function continuous on a bounded closed set has a maximum value on this set.

(which is the orthogonal complement of the first basis vector ξ_0) we may reapply the same device of choosing a new normal orthogonal basis which makes $Q^*(\xi)$ a maximum for $|\xi| = 1$; this splits another diagonal term off the form. One finally finds a basis of *principal axes* for which

$$(36) \quad Q(\xi) = \lambda_1 z_1^2 + \lambda_2 z_2^2 + \cdots + \lambda_n z_n^2, \qquad \lambda_1 \geq \lambda_2 \geq \cdots \geq \lambda_n.$$

Here $z_1, \cdots, z_n$ are the coordinates of ξ relative to a basis $\alpha_1, \beta_2, \gamma_3, \cdots$ which has been chosen step by step by successive maximum requirements. The first vector α_1 gives $Q(\xi)$ its maximum value λ_1, subject only to the restriction $|\xi| = 1$. The second basis vector β_2 was chosen as a vector in the space orthogonal to α_1; that is, $\eta = \beta_2$ makes $Q(\eta)$ a maximum λ_2 among all vectors η for which $|\eta| = 1$, $(\eta, \alpha_1) = 0$. The third basis vector yields a maximum for $Q(\zeta)$ among all vectors $|\zeta| = 1$ orthogonal to α_1 and β_2; and so on. These successive maximum problems may be visualized (in inverted form) on an ellipsoid with three different axes $a > b > c > 0$. The shortest principal axis c is the minimum diameter; the next principal axis b is the minimum diameter among all those perpendicular to the shortest axis, etc.

The coefficients λ_i of (36) may be thus characterized as the solutions of certain maximum problems which depend only on Q, and not on a particular coordinate system. An ambiguity in the reduction process could arise only if the first maximum (or some later maximum) were given by two or more distinct vectors ξ_0 and η_0 of length 1. Even in this case the λ_i can still be proved unique (Chap. X, §4).

This proves the following Principal Axis Theorem.

Theorem 21.   *Any real quadratic form in n variables assumes the diagonal form (36), relative to a suitable normal orthogonal basis.*

This new basis $\alpha_1^*, \cdots, \alpha_n^*$ can, by Theorem 1, be expressed in terms of the original basis $\varepsilon_1 = (1, 0, \cdots, 0), \cdots, \varepsilon_n = (0, \cdots, 0, 1)$ as $\alpha_i^* = \sum_j p_{ij} \varepsilon_j$; furthermore, since the vectors $\alpha_1^*, \cdots, \alpha_n^*$ are normal and orthogonal, the matrix $p = \| p_{ij} \|$ of coefficients is an orthogonal matrix. As in Theorem 2, the old coordinates $x_1, \cdots, x_n$ are then expressed in terms of the new coordinates $x_1^*, \cdots, x_n^*$ as $x_j = \sum_i x_i^* p_{ij}$; in other words, we have made an orthogonal transformation of the variables in the quadratic form. The "alias" result of Theorem 21 thus may be rewritten in "alibi" form as

Corollary 1.   *Any real homogeneous quadratic function of n variables can be reduced to the diagonal form (36) by an orthogonal point-transformation.*

Either of these two results is known as the "principal axis theorem." If the quadratic form is replaced by its symmetric matrix, the theorem asserts

Corollary 2.   *For any real symmetric matrix A there is a real orthogonal matrix P such that $PAP^T = PAP^{-1}$ is diagonal.*

In other words, we have shown that any real symmetric matrix is *similar* to a diagonal matrix. Comparing with Theorem 4, we see that the λ_i in the canonical form (36) are just the characteristic roots of A.

In the plane the canonical forms are simply $\lambda_1 x^2 + \lambda_2 y^2$; they include the usual standard equations for an ellipse ($\lambda_1 \geq \lambda_2 > 0$) or hyperbola ($\lambda_1 > 0 > \lambda_2$); the coefficients determine the lengths of the axes. In three-space a similar remark applies to the three coefficients λ_1, λ_2, λ_3. If all are positive, the locus $Q = 1$ is an ellipsoid; if one is negative, a hyperboloid of one sheet; if two are negative, a hyperboloid of two sheets; if all three are negative, no locus. (Note again the role of the signature and of the rank.)

Corollary 3.   *Every nonsingular real matrix A can be expressed as a product $A = SR$, where S is a symmetric positive definite matrix and R is orthogonal.*

Proof.   We already know (Theorem 20) that AA^T is symmetric and positive definite. By the present theorem, there is an orthogonal matrix P with $P^{-1}AA^TP$ diagonal and positive definite. The diagonal entries are thus positive; by extracting their square roots we obtain a positive definite diagonal matrix T with $T^2 = P^{-1}AA^TP$ and hence a positive definite symmetric matrix $S = PTP^{-1}$ with $S^2 = AA^T$. The corollary will be proved if we show that $R = S^{-1}A$ is orthogonal, for then $A = SR$, as desired. But $RR^T = S^{-1}AA^T(S^{-1})^T = S^{-1}S^2(S^{-1})^T = S(S^{-1})^T = SS^{-1} = I$, since $(S^{-1})^T = S^{-1}$ for symmetric S.

EXERCISES

1. Consider the real quadratic form $ax^2 + 2bxy + cy^2$.
   (a) Show that $a + c$ and $b^2 - ac$ are invariant under orthogonal transformations.
   (b) If $\cot 2\alpha = (a - c)/2b$, show that the form is diagonalized by the orthogonal substitution $x = x' \cos \alpha - y' \sin \alpha$, $y = x' \sin \alpha + y' \cos \alpha$.

2. Prove that every real skew-symmetric matrix A has the form $A = P^{-1}BP$, where P is orthogonal and B^2 diagonal.

3. Reduce the following quadratic forms to diagonal forms by orthogonal transformations, following the method given:

   (a) $5x^2 - 6xy + 5y^2$,   (b) $2x^2 + 4\sqrt{3}xy - 2y^2$.

4. To the quadratic form $9x_1{}^2 - 9x_2{}^2 + 18x_3{}^2$ apply the orthogonal transformation:

$$3x_1 = 2y_1 - y_2 + 2y_3, \qquad 3x_2 = -y_1 + 2y_2 + 2y_3, \qquad 3x_3 = 2y_1 + 2y_2 - y_3.$$

For the resulting form Q in y_1, y_2, and y_3 show directly that the vector $(2/3, 2/3, -1/3)$ yields the maximum value 18 for Q when $y_1^2 + y_2^2 + y_3^2 = 1$. Check by the calculus.

5. (a) Show that the coordinates x_0, y_0 of the vector which makes the quadratic form $ax^2 + 2bxy + cy^2$ a maximum, subject to $x^2 + y^2 = 1$, satisfy $y_0/x_0 = [(c - a) \pm \sqrt{(a - c)^2 + 4b^2}]/2b$, if $b \neq 0$.

     (b) Show that the two choices of sign in this formula give orthogonal vectors.

6. Show that there is no orthogonal matrix with rational entries which reduces xy to diagonal form.

7. A Lorentz transformation is defined to be a linear transformation leaving $x_1^2 + x_2^2 + x_3^2 - x_4^2$ invariant. Show that a matrix P defines a Lorentz transformation if and only if $P^{-1} = SP^TS = SP^TS^{-1}$, where S is the special diagonal matrix with diagonal entries, 1, 1, 1, -1.

8. (a) If $A = SR$, with S symmetric and R orthogonal, prove that $S^2 = AA^T$.

     (★b) Show that there is only one positive definite symmetric matrix S which satisfies $S^2 = AA^T$. (*Hint:* Any characteristic vector for S^2 must be one for S.)

11. Quadrics under the Affine and Euclidean Groups

Consider next an arbitrary *nonhomogeneous* quadratic function of a vector ξ with coordinates $x_1, \cdots, x_n$,

$$(37) \quad f(\xi) = \sum_i \sum_j x_i a_{ij} x_j + \sum_k b_k x_k + c \quad (i, j, k = 1, \cdots, n).$$

This may be written $f(\xi) = XAX^T + BX^T + c$, where $A = \| a_{ij} \|$ is a symmetric matrix and $B = (b_1, \cdots, b_n)$ a row matrix. In the simple case of a function $f = ax^2 + bx + c$ of one variable, observe that a translation $x = y + k$ leaves invariant the quadratic coefficient a, for

$$(38) \qquad \begin{aligned} f &= a(y + k)^2 + b(y + k) + c \\ &= ay^2 + (2ak + b)y + ak^2 + bk + c. \end{aligned}$$

A similar computation works for n variables; a translation $X \to Y = X - K$ (K a row matrix) gives

$$\begin{aligned} f(\xi) &= (Y + K)A(Y + K)^T + B(Y + K)^T + c \\ &= YAY^T + KAY^T + YAK^T + KAK^T + BY^T + BK^T + c. \end{aligned}$$

The product YAK^T (row matrix $\times$ matrix $\times$ column matrix) is a scalar, hence equals its transpose $KA^TY^T = KAY^T$; all told,

$$(39) \qquad f(\xi) = YAY^T + (2KA + B)Y^T + KAK^T + BK^T + c,$$

an exact analogue of the formula (38). This proves the

Lemma. *A translation leaves unaltered the matrix A of the homogeneous quadratic part of a quadratic function $f(\xi)$.*

On the other hand, a homogeneous linear transformation $X = YP$ changes $f(\xi)$ to $Y(PAP^T)Y^T + (BP^T)Y^T + c$; in this quadratic function the new matrix of quadratic terms is PAP^T, just as in the case of transformation of a homogeneous form alone.

Now to reduce the real function $f(\xi)$ by a rigid motion with equations $X = YP + K$, P orthogonal! By the remarks above, the orthogonal transformation by P alone may be used to simplify the matrix A of the quadratic terms, exactly as for a homogeneous quadratic form. As in §10, one finds (with new coefficients b_i')

$$f(\xi) = \lambda_1 z_1^2 + \cdots + \lambda_n z_n^2 + b_1' z_1 + \cdots + b_n' z_n + c.$$

The b_j' associated with non-zero λ_j can now be eliminated by the simple device of "completing the square," using a translation $y_j = z_j + b_j'/2\lambda_j$. Now, permuting the variables so that the non-zero λ's come first, we get

$$f(\xi) = \lambda_1 y_1^2 + \cdots + \lambda_r y_r^2 + b_{r+1}' z_{r+1} + \cdots + b_n' z_n + c'.$$

If the linear part of this function is not just the constant c', it may be changed by a suitable translation and orthogonal transformation, as in Theorem 13, to the form dy_{r+1}. This transformation need not affect the first r variables. The result is one of the forms

$$(40) \qquad f(\xi) = \lambda_1 y_1^2 + \cdots + \lambda_r y_r^2 + dy_{r+1},$$
$$(41) \qquad f(\xi) = \lambda_1 y_1^2 + \cdots + \lambda_r y_r^2 + c',$$

where $\lambda_1 \geqq \lambda_2 \geqq \cdots \geqq \lambda_r$, no $\lambda_i = 0$, $d > 0$.

Theorem 22. *Under the Euclidean group of all rigid motions, any real quadratic form (37) is equivalent to one of the forms (40) or (41).*

These reduced forms are actually canonical under the Euclidean group, but the proof is much more difficult. In outline, it goes as follows.

The λ_i are (see §10) the *characteristic roots* of the matrix A of (37); the uniqueness of these (including multiplicity) will be proved in Chap. X, §4. In particular, the number r of squares in (40) or (41) is an invariant; note that r is also the rank of A, unaltered under $A \to PAP^T$. The invariants d and c' are most simply characterized intuitively using the calculus. Consider the locus where the vector

$$\operatorname{grad} f = \left(\frac{\partial f}{\partial y_1}, \cdots, \frac{\partial f}{\partial y_n} \right)$$

is the zero vector. In (41) it is the subspace $y_1 = \cdots = y_r = 0$, and c' is the constant value of $f(\xi)$ on this (invariant) locus. In (40), the locus is empty since $\partial f/\partial y_{r+1} = d \neq 0$; but d can be characterized as the minimum of $|\operatorname{grad} f|$; this minimum can also be proved invariant under the Euclidean group.

For affine transformations $X = YP + K$, with P nonsingular, a similar treatment applies. In reducing the quadratic part to diagonal form, the coefficients now can all be made ± 1, as in §9. The linear part is then treated as in §6.

Theorem 23. *By an affine transformation (or, by an affine change of coordinates) any real quadratic function in n variables may be reduced to one of the forms*

$$(42) \quad y_1^2 + \cdots + y_p^2 - y_{p+1}^2 - \cdots - y_r^2 + y_{r+1} \qquad (r < n),$$
$$(43) \quad y_1^2 + \cdots + y_p^2 - y_{p+1}^2 - \cdots - y_r^2 + c \qquad (r \leqq n).$$

Since the quadratic terms are unaffected by translation, the rank r and the number p of positive terms must be invariants by the law of inertia (Theorem 17).

From a geometrical point of view, each quadratic function $f(\xi) = XAX^T + BX^T + c$ defines a *figure* or *locus*, which consists of all those vectors ξ which satisfy the equation $f(\xi) = 0$. In two-dimensional space, the figure found from such a quadratic equation is simply an ordinary conic section; in three-space, it is a quadric surface, and in general it may be called a *hyperquadric* (or, a quadric hypersurface). An affine transformation $Y = XP + K$ applied to the equation of this surface amounts simply to applying the same transformation to the points of the figure, and the new figure is said to be *equivalent* to the old one under the given affine transformation.

Clearly, the results found above for the classification of quadratic functions under equivalence will yield a similar classification of the corresponding figures. Observe first, however, that an equation $f(\xi) = 0$ and a scalar multiple $cf(\xi) = 0$ of the same equation give identical loci. This may be used to simplify the canonical forms such as $y_1^2 - y_2^2 + c = 0$ found above. When $c \neq 0$, this equation gives the same locus as does $(c^{-1})y_1^2 - (c^{-1})y_2^2 + 1 = 0$; when $c > 0$, this may be reduced by an affine transformation $y_1 = \sqrt{c}z_1$, $y_2 = \sqrt{c}z_2$ to the form $z_1^2 - z_2^2 + 1 = 0$, while for $c < 0$ the transformation $y_i = \sqrt{-c}z_i$ gives a similar result $z_2^2 - z_1^2 + 1 = 0$. In general, this device can always be applied to change the constant c which appears in (43) to 1 or 0. Therefore, in an n-dimensional vector space over the field of real numbers, any hyperquadric is equivalent under the affine group to a locus given by an equation of one of the following forms:

$$(44) \qquad y_1^2 + \cdots + y_p^2 - y_{p+1}^2 - \cdots - y_r^2 + y_{r+1} = 0,$$
$$(45) \qquad y_1^2 + \cdots + y_p^2 - y_{p+1}^2 - \cdots - y_r^2 + 1 = 0,$$
$$(46) \qquad y_1^2 + \cdots + y_p^2 - y_{p+1}^2 - \cdots - y_r^2 = 0,$$

where $0 \leqq p \leqq r \leqq n$, with $r < n$ in the case of (44).

For example, in the plane the possible types of loci with $r > 0$ are

$r = 2$		$r = 1$	
$x_2 + y^2 + 1 = 0$	no locus	$x^2 + y = 0$	parabola
$x^2 - y^2 + 1 = 0$	hyperbola	$-x^2 + y = 0$	parabola
$-x^2 - y^2 + 1 = 0$	circle	$x^2 + 1 = 0$	no locus
$x^2 + y^2 = 0$	one point	$-x^2 + 1 = 0$	two parallel
$x^2 - y^2 = 0$	two intersecting		lines
	lines	$x^2 = 0$	one line.
$-x^2 - y^2 = 0$	one point.		

Observe in particular that the *different* canonical functions $x^2 + y^2 + 1$ and $x^2 + 1$ give the *same* locus (namely, the figure consisting of no points at all). So do the canonical functions $x^2 + y^2$ and $-x^2 - y^2$.

EXERCISES

1. Classify under the Euclidean group the forms
   (a) $4xz + 4y^2 + 8y + 8$,
   (b) $9x^2 - 4xy + 6y^2 + 3z^2 + 2\sqrt{5}x + 4\sqrt{5}y + 12z + 16$.
2. Classify under the affine group the forms
   (a) $x^2 + 4y^2 + 9z^2 + 4xy + 6xz + 12yz + 8x + 16y + 24z + 15$,
   (b) $x^2 - 6xy + 10y^2 + 2xz - 20z^2 - 10yz - 40z - 17$,
   (c) $x^2 + 4z^2 + 4xz + 4x + 4z - 6y + 6$,
   (d) $-2x^2 - 3y^2 - 7z^2 + 2xy - 8yz - 6xz - 4x - 6y - 14z - 6$.
3. In a quadratic function $XAX^T + BX^T + c$ with a nonsingular matrix A, prove that the linear terms may be removed by a translation.
4. Compute the effect of an arbitrary affine transformation on a quadratic function $XAX^T + BX^T + c$.
5. Generalize the affine classification of quadratic functions given in Theorem 23 to functions with coefficients in any field in which $1 + 1 \neq 0$.
6. (a) List the possible affine types of quadric surfaces in three-space.
   (b) Give a brief geometric description of each type.
7. Classify (i) ellipses, (ii) parabolas, and (iii) hyperbolas under the extended similarity group (§4, end). Find complete sets of numerical invariants in each case.
★8. Classify quadric hypersurfaces in n-dimensional Euclidean space under the group of rigid motions (use Theorem 22).
9. Find a hexagon of minimum area inscribed in the ellipse $x^2 + 3y^2 = 3$.

X. Determinants and Canonical Forms

1. Definition and Elementary Properties of Determinants

Each square matrix A has a determinant; though the determinant can be used in the elementary study of the rank of a matrix and in the solution of simultaneous linear equations, its most essential application in matrix theory is to the definition of the characteristic polynomial of a matrix. In this chapter we shall define determinants, examine their geometric properties, and show the relation of the characteristic polynomial to characteristic roots. These concepts will then be applied to the study of canonical forms for matrices under similarity.

The formulas for the solution of simultaneous linear equations lead naturally to determinants. Two linear equations $a_1x + b_1y = k_1$, $a_2x + b_2y = k_2$ have the unique solution

$$x = (k_1b_2 - k_2b_1)/(a_1b_2 - a_2b_1), \qquad y = (a_1k_2 - a_2k_1)/(a_1b_2 - a_2b_1),$$

provided $a_1b_2 - a_2b_1 \neq 0$. The polynomials which appear here in numerator and denominator are known as *determinants*,

$$(1) \qquad \begin{vmatrix} a_1 & b_1 \\ a_2 & b_2 \end{vmatrix} = a_1b_2 - a_2b_1, \qquad \begin{vmatrix} k_1 & b_1 \\ k_2 & b_2 \end{vmatrix} = k_1b_2 - k_2b_1.$$

Similarly, one may compute the simultaneous solutions of three linear equations $\sum a_{ij}x_j = k_i$. The denominator of each solution x_j turns out to be

$$(2) \qquad \begin{vmatrix} a_{11} & a_{12} & a_{13} \\ a_{21} & a_{22} & a_{23} \\ a_{31} & a_{32} & a_{33} \end{vmatrix} = \begin{aligned} & a_{11}a_{22}a_{33} + a_{12}a_{23}a_{31} + a_{13}a_{21}a_{32} \\ & - a_{11}a_{23}a_{32} - a_{12}a_{21}a_{33} - a_{13}a_{22}a_{31}. \end{aligned}$$

On the right are six products. Each involves one factor a_{1i} from the first row, one from the second row, and one from the third. Each column is also represented in every product, so that a term of (2) has the form $a_{1-}a_{2-}a_{3-}$, with the blanks filled by some permutation of the column indices 1, 2, 3. Of the six possible permutations, the three even permutations I, (123), (132) appear in products with a prefix $+$, while the odd permutations are associated with a minus sign. Experience has shown that the solutions of n equations in n unknowns are expressed by analogous formulas.

Definition. *The determinant* $|A|$ *of an* $n \times n$ *matrix* $A = \|a_{ij}\|$ *is the following polynomial in the entries*† $a_{ij} = a(i, j)$:

$$
(3) \qquad \det(A) = |A| = \sum_{\phi} \operatorname{sgn} \phi \left[\prod_{i=1}^{n} a_{i, i\phi} \right]
$$
$$
= \sum_{\phi} (\operatorname{sgn} \phi) a(1, 1\phi) a(2, 2\phi) \cdots a(n, n\phi).
$$

Summation is over the $n!$ different permutations ϕ of the integers $1, \cdots, n$. The factor $\operatorname{sgn} \phi$ prefixing each product $\Pi a_{i, i\phi}$ is $+1$ or -1, according as ϕ is an even or an odd permutation.

Thus, the determinant $|A| = \|a_{ij}\|$ is a sum of $n!$ terms $\pm a_{1-} a_{2-} \cdots a_{n-}$, where the blanks are filled in by a variable permutation ϕ of the digits $1, \cdots, n$. Writing a_{ij} as $a(i, j)$, and letting $i\phi$ be the image of i under ϕ, the general term can be written $\pm a(1, 1\phi) a(2, 2\phi) \cdots a(n, n\phi)$, where the sign $\pm$ is called $\operatorname{sgn} \phi$ (for *signum* ϕ). Each term has exactly one factor from each row, and exactly one factor from each column.

Each row appears once and only once in each term of $|A|$, which means that $|A|$ is a linear homogeneous function of the entries $a_{i1}, \cdots, a_{in}$ in the ith row of A. Collecting the coefficients of each such a_{ij}, we get an expression

$$
(4) \qquad\qquad |A| = A_{i1} a_{i1} + A_{i2} a_{i2} + \cdots + A_{in} a_{in},
$$

where the coefficient A_{ij} of a_{ij} is called the *cofactor* of a_{ij}; it is a polynomial in the entries of the remaining rows of A. This cofactor can also be described as the partial derivative $A_{ij} = \partial |A| / \partial a_{ij}$. Since each term of $|A|$ involves each row and each column only once, the cofactor A_{ij} can involve neither the ith row nor the jth column. It contains only entries from the "minor" or submatrix M_{ij}, which is the matrix obtained from A by crossing out the ith row and the jth column.

Rows and columns enter symmetrically in $|A|$:

Theorem 1. *If* A^T *is the transpose of* A, $|A^T| = |A|$.

Proof. The entry $a_{ij}{}^T = a_{ji}$ of A^T is found by inverting subscripts. A sample term of $|A|$ with $j = i\phi$ and $i = j\phi^{-1}$ is

$$
(\operatorname{sgn} \phi) \prod_i a(i, i\phi) = (\operatorname{sgn} \phi) \prod_j a(j\phi^{-1}, j) = (\operatorname{sgn} \phi) \prod_j a^T(j, j\phi^{-1}).
$$

This result is a sample term of $|A^T|$, for every permutation is the inverse ϕ^{-1} of some permutation ϕ. Even the signs $(\operatorname{sgn} \phi) = (\operatorname{sgn} \phi^{-1})$ agree, for ϕ is even (i.e., in the alternating group) if and only if its inverse ϕ^{-1} is also even (Chap. VI, §10). Hence $|A| = |A^T|$, Q.E.D.

What is the effect of elementary row operations on a determinant?

† The entries are elements of a field F or, more generally, of a commutative ring.

Rule 1.   To multiply the ith row of A by a scalar $c \neq 0$, multiply the determinant $| A |$ by c. For, in the linear homogeneous expression (4), an extra factor c in each term $a_{i1}, \cdots, a_{in}$ from the ith row simply gives an extra factor c in $| A |$.

Rule 2.   To permute two rows of A, change the sign of $| A |$. By symmetry (Theorem 1) we may prove instead that the interchange of two columns changes the sign. This interchange is represented by an odd permutation ϕ_0 of the column indices; thus it replaces A by $B = \| b_{ij} \|$ where $b(i, j) = a(i, j\phi_0)$. Then,

$$| B | = \sum_{\phi} (\text{sgn } \phi) \prod_i b(i, i\phi) = \sum_{\phi} (\text{sgn } \phi) \prod_i a(i, i\phi\phi_0).$$

Since the permutations form a group, the products $\phi\phi_0$ (with ϕ_0 fixed) include all permutations, so that $| B |$ above has all the terms of $| A |$. Only the signs of the terms are changed, for ϕ_0 is odd, so $\phi\phi_0$ is even when ϕ is odd, and vice versa. ($\text{sgn } \phi\phi_0 = - \text{sgn } \phi$.) This gives the rule.

Lemma 1.   *If A has two rows alike, $| A | = 0$.*

Proof.   By Theorem 1, it suffices to prove that $| A | = 0$ if A has two like columns. Let ψ be the transposition which interchanges the two like columns. Then the summands $(\text{sgn } \phi)\Pi a(i, i\phi)$ in (3) occur in pairs $\{\phi, \psi\phi\}$, consisting of the cosets of the subgroup generated by ψ. Since ψ is odd, $\text{sgn } \phi = - \text{sgn } \psi\phi$; since the columns are alike, $\Pi a(i, i\phi) = \Pi a(i, i\psi\phi)$. Hence the paired summands are equal in magnitude and opposite in sign, and their sum is zero, Q.E.D.

For the consideration of adjoints (§2), it is convenient to express this lemma by an equation. In A, replace row i by row k. Then two rows become alike, and the determinant is zero. But this determinant may be found by replacing row i by row k in the linear homogeneous expression (4), so that

(5) $0 = A_{i1}a_{k1} + A_{i2}a_{k2} + \cdots + A_{in}a_{kn}$ $(i \neq k)$.

Rule 3.   The addition of a constant c times row k to row i leaves $| A |$ unchanged. This operation replaces each a_{ij} by $a_{ij} + ca_{kj}$; by the linear homogeneous expression (4), the new determinant is

$$\sum_j A_{ij}(a_{ij} + ca_{kj}) = \sum_j A_{ij}a_{ij} + c \sum_j A_{ij}a_{kj} = | A | + 0,$$

by (4) and (5). The determinant is indeed unchanged.

These rules may be summarized in terms of elementary matrices. Any elementary row operation carries the identity I into an elementary matrix E, and A into its product EA. The determinant $| I | = 1$ is thereby changed to $|E| = c$, (-1), or 1 (Rule 1, 2, or 3), while $|A|$ goes to $|EA| = c|A|$, $(-1)|A|$, or $|A|$ as the case may be. This proves $|EA| = |E||A|$; by symmetry (Theorem 1) the same applies to post-factors E. This establishes

Theorem 2.   *If E is an elementary matrix,*

$$|EA| = |E||A| = |AE|.$$

Another rule is that for explicitly getting the cofactors from the sub-matrices M_{ij} discussed above.

RULE 4. $A_{ij} = (-1)^{i+j}|M_{ij}|$; in words, each cofactor A_{ij} is found from the determinant of the corresponding submatrix by prefixing the sign $(-1)^{i+j}$. This is the sign to be found in the (i, j) position on a $\pm$ checkerboard which starts with a plus in the upper left-hand corner. First, consider the proof of this rule for $i = j = 1$. The definition (3) shows at once that the terms involving a_{11} are exactly the terms belonging to permutations ϕ with $1\phi = 1$. An even (odd) permutation of this type is actually an even (odd) permutation of the remaining digits $2, \cdots, n$, so the terms with a_{11} removed are exactly the terms in the expansion of $|M_{11}|$. Any other cofactor A_{ij} may now be reduced to this special case by moving the a_{ij} term to the upper left position by means of $i - 1$ successive interchanges of adjacent rows and $j - 1$ interchanges of adjacent columns. These operations do not alter $|M_{ij}|$ because the relative position of the rows and columns in M_{ij} is unaffected, but they do change the sign of $|A|$, and hence the sign of the cofactor of a_{ij}, $i + j - 1 - 1$ times. This reduction proves the rule.

An especially useful case is that in which all the first row is zero except for the first term. The expansion (4) then need involve only the first cofactor $|M_{11}| = A_{11}$, so

$$(6) \qquad \begin{vmatrix} c & O \\ K & B \end{vmatrix} = c|B|,$$

where O is $1 \times (n - 1)$, K is $(n - 1) \times 1$, and B is $(n - 1) \times (n - 1)$. By this rule and induction, one obtains the following result.

Lemma 2.   *The determinant of a triangular matrix is the product of its diagonal entries.*

The preceding rules provide a system for computing a determinant $|A|$. Reduce A by elementary operations to a triangular form T, and record t, the number of interchanges of rows (or columns) used, and $c_1, \cdots, c_s$, the various scalars used to multiply rows (or columns) of A. By Theorem 2, $|A| = (-1)^t (c_1 \cdots c_s)^{-1}|T|$. The computation is completed by setting $|T| = t_{11} \cdots t_{nn}$, using Lemma 2.

EXERCISES

1. Prove Lemma 2 directly from the definition of a determinant.
2. Compute the determinants of the matrices of Ex. 2, Chap. VII, §6.
3. (a) If $A = \begin{pmatrix} 1 & -1 & 0 \\ -1 & 0 & 1 \\ 2 & 1 & 1 \end{pmatrix}$, compute $|A|$ both by the minors of the first row and by the minors of the first column, and compare the results.
   (b) Compute $|A|$ on the assumption that the entries of A are integers modulo 2.
4. Write out the positive terms in the expansion of a general 4×4 determinant.
5. If n is odd and $1 + 1 \neq 0$, show that an $n \times n$ skew-symmetric matrix A has determinant 0.
6. (a) Deduce the following expansion of the "Vandermonde" determinant

$$\begin{vmatrix} 1 & x_1 & x_1^2 \\ 1 & x_2 & x_2^2 \\ 1 & x_3 & x_3^2 \end{vmatrix} = (x_2 - x_1)(x_3 - x_1)(x_3 - x_2).$$

   (b) Generalize the result to the 4×4 case.
   (c) Generalize to the $n \times n$ case, by proving that if $a_{ij} = x_i^{j-1}$, then $|A| = \prod_{i>j} (x_i - x_j)$.
7. Show that, for any 4×4 skew-symmetric matrix A,

$$|A| = (a_{12}a_{34} - a_{13}a_{24} + a_{14}a_{23})^2.$$

8. (a) Show that the determinant of any permutation matrix is ± 1.
   (b) Show that the determinant of a monomial matrix is the product of the non-zero entries, times ± 1.
9. A real $n \times n$ matrix is called *diagonally dominant* if $\sum_{j \neq i} |a_{ij}| < a_{ii}$ for $i = 1, \cdots, n$. Show that if A is diagonally dominant, then $|A| > 0$.
10. In the plane show that the line joining the point (a_1, a_2) to the point (b_1, b_2) has the equation

$$\begin{vmatrix} x_1 & x_2 & 1 \\ a_1 & a_2 & 1 \\ b_1 & b_2 & 1 \end{vmatrix} = 0.$$

★11. (a) If each entry a_{ij} in a matrix A is a function of x, show that

$$\frac{d|A|}{dx} = \sum_{j,k=1}^{n} \frac{da_{jk}}{dx} A_{jk}.$$

   (b) Use this to verify that $A_{ij} = \frac{\partial |A|}{\partial a_{ij}}$.

★12. If A and C are square matrices, prove that $\begin{vmatrix} A & B \\ 0 & C \end{vmatrix} = |A||C|$.

★13. If Ω is the $n \times n$ matrix $\| \omega^{ij} \|$, where ω is a primitive complex n-th root of unity, show that $|\Omega| = n^{n/2}$, provided $n \equiv 1 \pmod{4}$.

2. Products of Determinants

Under elementary row and column operations any square matrix A is equivalent to a diagonal matrix D (Theorem 18, Chap. VIII), so A can be obtained from D by pre- and postmultiplication by elementary matrices E_i and $E^{(i)}$, as in Theorem 13 of Chap. VIII,

$$(7) \qquad A = E_s \cdots E_1 D E^{(1)} \cdots E^{(t)}.$$

The rules $|EA| = |E| \cdot |A|$ and $|AE| = |A| \cdot |E|$ of Theorem 2 show that in the determinant of the product (7) the factors $|E|$ may be taken out one at a time, to give

$$(8) \qquad |A| = |E_s| \cdots |E_1| |D| |E^{(1)}| \cdots |E^{(t)}|.$$

Since each $|E_i| \neq 0$, the whole determinant $|A| \neq 0$ if and only if $|D| \neq 0$. The canonical form D has exactly r entries 1 along the diagonal, where r is the rank of A, while the determinant $|D|$ is the product of its n diagonal entries. Hence $|D| \neq 0$ if and only if $r = n$; that is, if and only if A is nonsingular. Therefore (8) proves

Theorem 3.   *A square matrix A is nonsingular if and only if $|A| \neq 0$.*

A nonsingular matrix A is a product $A = E_t \cdots E_1$ of elementary matrices. If $B = E_s^* \cdots E_1^*$ is a second such matrix, the product AB has a determinant which may be computed, as in (8), as

$$\begin{aligned} |AB| &= |E_t \cdots E_1 E_s^* \cdots E_1^*| \\ &= |E_t| \cdots |E_1| \cdot |E_s^*| \cdots |E_1^*| = |A| \cdot |B|. \end{aligned}$$

Theorem 4.   *The determinant of a matrix product is the product of the determinants: $|AB| = |A| \cdot |B|$.*

The computation above proves this rule only when A and B are both nonsingular. But if A (or B) is singular, so is AB, and both sides of $|AB| = |A| \cdot |B|$ are zero, Q.E.D.

The inverse of a matrix A with a determinant $|A| \neq 0$ exists and may be found explicitly by using cofactors of A. The original equations (4) and (5) involving the cofactors may be written as

$$(9) \quad a_{k1}A_{i1} + \cdots + a_{kn}A_{in} = \delta_{ki}|A|, \text{ where } \delta_{ki} = \begin{cases} 1 \text{ if } i = k, \\ 0 \text{ if } i \neq k. \end{cases}$$

This number δ_{ki} is exactly the (k, i) entry of the identity matrix $I = \| \delta_{ki} \|$. The equation (9) is much like a matrix product; if the subscripts of the cofactors A_{ij} are interchanged, the left side of (9) gives the (k, i) entry of the product of $A = \| a_{kj} \|$ by the transposed matrix of cofactors. On the right of (9) is the (k, i) entry of the identity multiplied by a scalar $|A|$, so

$$(10) \qquad A \| A_{ij} \|^T = |A| I.$$

The matrix $\| A_{ij} \|^T$ which appears in this equation is the *transposed* matrix of the cofactors of elements of A, and is known as the *adjoint* of A. In case $| A | = 1$, the equation (10) states that the adjoint is the inverse of A; in general, if $| A | \neq 0$, (10) proves

Theorem 5.   *If $| A | \neq 0$, the inverse is $A^{-1} = | A |^{-1} \| A_{ij} \|^T$.*

Cramer's rule for solving n linear equations in n unknowns is a consequence of this formula for the inverse. A given system of equations has the form

$$\sum_j a_{ij}x_j = b_i,$$

where i and j range from 1 to n. In matrix notation the equation is $AX^T = B^T$, where B^T stands for the transposed or column matrix $(b_1, \cdots, b_n)^T$. If $| A | \neq 0$, the equation $AX^T = B^T$ premultiplied by A^{-1} gives the unique matrix solution $X^T = A^{-1}B^T$. This solution may be expanded if we observe that the (i, j) entry in the inverse A^{-1} is just $A_{ji}/| A |$. This proves

Theorem 6 (Cramer's Rule).   *If n linear equations*

$$\sum_j a_{ij}x_j = b_i$$

in n unknowns have a nonsingular matrix $A = \| a_{ij} \|$ of coefficients, there is a unique solution

$$(11) \qquad x_j = (A_{1j}b_1 + \cdots + A_{nj}b_n)/| A |, \qquad j = 1, \cdots, n,$$

where A_{ij} is the cofactor of a_{ij} in the coefficient matrix A.

The numerator of this formula may itself be written as a determinant, for it is the expansion by cofactors of the jth column of a determinant obtained from A by replacing the jth column by the column of constants b_j. Observe, however, that large sets of simultaneous equations may usually be solved more efficiently by reducing the matrix (or augmented matrix) to a row-equivalent "echelon" form, as in Chap. VII, §7.

Cramer's rule evidently applies to any field—and so in particular to all equations discussed in Chap. II, §3. (Cf. Ex. 9 below.) It is especially convenient for solving simultaneous linear equations in 2 and 3 unknowns.

Appendix.   Determinants and Rank.   A *submatrix* (or "minor") of a rectangular matrix A is any matrix obtained from A by crossing out certain rows and certain columns of A (this is to include the case when *no* rows or *no* columns are omitted). A "determinant rank" d for any rectangular matrix $A \neq O$ may be defined as the number of rows in the biggest square minor of A with a nonvanishing determinant; in other words, d has the properties: (i) A has at least one $d \times d$ minor M, with $| M | \neq 0$; (ii) if $h > d$, every $h \times h$ square minor N of A has $| N | = 0$. It can be shown that *the rank of any matrix equals its determinant rank.*

EXERCISES

1. Write out the adjoint of a 2×2 matrix $A = \begin{pmatrix} a & b \\ c & d \end{pmatrix}$ and the product of A by its adjoint.

2. (a) Compute the adjoint of the matrix of Ex. 2a, Chap. VII, §6, and verify in this case the rule for the product of a matrix by its adjoint.

   (b) Do the same for the matrix of Ex. 2b, Chap. VII, §6.

3. By the adjoint method, find the inverses of the 4×4 elementary matrices H_{24}, $I + 2E_{33}$, and $I + dE_{21}$ of Chap. VIII (50).

4. Find the inverses of Ex. 5, Chap. VIII, §8, by the adjoint method.

5. If A is nonsingular, prove that $|A^{-1}| = |A|^{-1}$.

6. Prove that the product of a singular matrix by its adjoint is the zero matrix.

7. Prove that the adjoint of any orthogonal matrix is its transpose.

8. Write out Cramer's Rule for 3 equations in 3 unknowns.

9. Solve the simultaneous congruences of Ex. 1, §3, Chap. II, by Cramer's Rule.

10. (a) Show that the pair of homogeneous linear equations

$$a_1 x + b_1 y + c_1 z = 0, \qquad a_2 x + b_2 y + c_2 z = 0$$

has a simultaneous solution

$$x = \begin{vmatrix} b_1 & c_1 \\ b_2 & c_2 \end{vmatrix}, \qquad y = \begin{vmatrix} c_1 & a_1 \\ c_2 & a_2 \end{vmatrix}, \qquad z = \begin{vmatrix} a_1 & b_1 \\ a_2 & b_2 \end{vmatrix}.$$

   (b) When is this solution a basis for the whole set of solutions?

   (c) Derive similar formulas for three equations in 4 unknowns.

11. Prove that the determinant of an orthogonal matrix is ± 1.

12. Show that the determinant of the adjoint of a matrix A is $|A|^{n-1}$.

13. Prove that the adjoint of the adjoint of A is $|A|^{n-2}A$.

14. Show directly from the definition of determinant rank that an elementary row operation does not alter the determinant rank.

★15. (a) If A and B are 3×3 matrices, show that the determinant of any 2×2 submatrix of AB is the sum of a number of terms, each of which is a product of the determinant of a 2×2 submatrix of A by that of a 2×2 submatrix of B.

   (b) Generalize this result and use it to prove that rank $(AB) \leq$ rank A.

★16. If an $n \times n$ matrix A has rank r, prove that the rank s of the adjoint of A is determined as follows: If $r = n$, then $s = n$; if $r = n - 1$, then $s = 1$; if $r < n - 1$, then $s = 0$.

★17. Prove that the rank of any matrix equals its determinant rank.

★3. Determinants as Volumes

Determinants of real $n \times n$ matrices can be interpreted geometrically as volumes in n-dimensional Euclidean space. The connection is suggested by the formula for the area of a parallelogram.

Each real 2×2 matrix A with rows α_1 and α_2 may be represented as a parallelogram with vertices at

$$0, \ \alpha_1, \ \alpha_2, \ \alpha_1 + \alpha_2;$$

and conversely, each such parallelogram determines a matrix (cf. Figure 1). The area of the parallelogram is

$$(12) \qquad \text{base} \times \text{altitude} = | \, \alpha_1 \, | \cdot | \, \alpha_2 \, | \cdot | \sin C \, |,$$

where C denotes the angle between the given vectors α_1 and α_2. By the cosine formula (41) of Chap. VII, the *square* of the area is

$$(\alpha_1, \, \alpha_1)(\alpha_2, \, \alpha_2)(1 - \cos^2 C) = (\alpha_1, \, \alpha_1)(\alpha_2, \, \alpha_2) - (\alpha_1, \, \alpha_2)(\alpha_2, \, \alpha_1).$$

The result looks very much like the determinant of a 2×2 matrix; it is in fact the determinant of $\| \, (\alpha_i, \, \alpha_j) \, \| = A A^T$.

A similar formula holds for parallelograms in Euclidean space of any dimension—and can even be extended to m-dimensional analogues of parallelograms in n-dimensional Euclidean space. These analogues are called *parallelepipeds*.

Figure 1

To establish the generalization, let A be any $m \times n$ matrix, with rows $\alpha_1, \ \cdots, \ \alpha_m$. These rows represent vectors issuing from the origin in n-dimensional Euclidean space E_n. The parallelepiped Π in E_n spanned by the m vectors α_i consists of all vectors of the form

$$t_1 \alpha_1 + \cdots + t_m \alpha_m, \qquad (0 \leq t_i \leq 1, \qquad i = 1, \ \cdots, \ m).$$

(Picture this in case $m = n = 3$; you will get something affinely equivalent to a cube!) This construction establishes a correspondence between real $m \times n$ matrices and m-dimensional parallelepipeds in n-dimensional space; the α_i are called *edges* of the parallelepiped Π.

The m-dimensional *volume* (including as special cases length if $m = 1$ and area if $m = 2$) $V(\Pi)$ of this figure can be defined by induction on m. Let the parallelepiped with the edges $\alpha_2, \ \cdots, \ \alpha_m$ be called the *base* of Π. The *altitude* is the component of α_1 orthogonal to $\alpha_2, \ \cdots, \ \alpha_m$; it is to be found from the remaining edge α_1 by writing α_1 as the sum of a component γ in the space S_{m-1} spanned by $\alpha_2, \ \cdots, \ \alpha_m$ and a component β orthogonal to S_{m-1} (see Figure 1; this is always possible by Chap. VII, §11).

$$(13) \qquad \alpha_1 = \beta + \gamma, \qquad \beta \perp S_{m-1}, \qquad \gamma \text{ in } S_{m-1}.$$

The volume of Π is defined as the *product* of the $(m - 1)$-dimensional volume of the *base* by the length $| \, \beta \, |$ of the *altitude*.

Theorem 7. *The square of the volume of the parallelepiped with edges* $\alpha_1, \cdots, \alpha_m$ *is the determinant* $|AA^T|$, *where A is the matrix with the coordinates of α_i in the ith row.*†

(*Note.* Since a permutation of the rows of A replaces A by PA, where P is an $m \times m$ permutation matrix with $|P| = |P^T| = \pm 1$, and

$$|(PA)(PA)^T| = |P| \cdot |AA^T| \cdot |P^T| = |AA^T|,$$

the "volume" of Π is independent of which $m + 1$ vectors are said to span its "base.")

Proof. Since A is an $m \times n$ matrix, the product AA^T is an $m \times m$ square matrix. We now argue by induction on m. If $m = 1$, the matrix A is a row, and the "inner product" $AA^T = (\alpha_1, \alpha_1)$ is the square of the length, as desired. Suppose that the theorem is true for matrices of $m - 1$ rows, and consider the case of m rows. As in (13), the first row A_1 may be written $A_1 = B_1 + C_1$, where the "altitude" B_1 is orthogonal to each of the rows $A_2, \cdots, A_m$ ($B_1 A_i{}^T = 0$), while $C = c_2 A_2 + \cdots + c_m A_m$ is a linear combination of them. Subtract successively c_i times the ith row from the first row of A. This changes A into a new matrix A^* with first row B_1; furthermore, the elementary row operations involved each premultiply A by an elementary matrix of determinant 1, hence $A^* = PA$, where $|P| = 1$, and $|A^* A^{*T}| = |PAA^TP^T| = |P| |AA^T| |P^T| = |AA^T|$. But if D is the block composed of the $m - 1$ rows $A_2, \cdots, A_m$ of A^*, then

$$A^* A^{*T} = \begin{pmatrix} B_1 \\ D \end{pmatrix} (B_1{}^T D^T) = \begin{pmatrix} B_1 B_1{}^T & B_1 D^T \\ D B_1{}^T & DD' \end{pmatrix} = \begin{pmatrix} B_1 B_1{}^T & 0 \\ 0 & DD' \end{pmatrix}$$

where $B_1 D^T = O$ because $B_1 A_i{}^T = 0$ for each row A_i of D. By (6), the determinant is

$$|AA^T| = |A^* A^{*T}| = (B_1 B_1{}^T) \cdot |DD^T|.$$

Here D is the matrix whose rows $A_2, \cdots, A_m$ span the base of Π, so $|DD^T|$ is the square of the volume of the base, by induction on m. Furthermore, the scalar $B_1 B_1{}^T$ is the square of the length of the altitude, so we have the desired base $\times$ altitude formula for AA^T. Q.E.D.

In the special case when the number of rows is n, evidently $|AA^T| = |A| \cdot |A^T| = |A|^2$, and we have proved‡

---

† Throughout §3, the coordinates of a vector are taken relative to a fixed normal orthogonal basis.
‡ The line of argument in this proof was originally suggested to us by Professor J. S. Frame.

Theorem 8. *Let A be any real $n \times n$ matrix with rows $\alpha_1, \cdots, \alpha_n$. The determinant of A is (except possibly for sign) the volume of the parallelepiped in E_n having the vectors $\alpha_1, \cdots, \alpha_n$ as edges.*

The absolute value of a determinant is unaltered by any permutations of the rows, so this theorem shows also that our definition of the volume of a parallelepiped is independent of the arrangement of the edges in a sequence.

Theorem 9. *A linear transformation $Y = XP$ of an n-dimensional Euclidean vector space multiplies the volumes of all n-dimensional parallelepipeds by the factor $\pm \mid P \mid$.*

Proof. Consider a parallelepiped which has n edges with respective coordinates $A_1, \cdots, A_n$. The row vectors $A_1, \cdots, A_n$ are transformed into $A_1P, \cdots, A_nP$: the matrix with these new rows is simply the matrix product AP, where A has the rows $A_1, \cdots, A_n$. The new signed volume is then $\mid AP \mid = \mid A \mid \mid P \mid$, where $\mid A \mid$ is the old volume.

From this it follows that the transformation $Y = XP$ preserves signed volumes if and only if its matrix satisfies $\mid P \mid = +1$. The set of all matrices (or, of all transformations) with this property is known as the *unimodular group*. Sometimes this group is enlarged to include all P with $\mid P \mid = \pm 1$ (that is, all transformations which preserve the absolute magnitude of volumes).

The volume of any region f in n-dimensional Euclidean space may be defined loosely as follows: circumscribe f by a finite set of parallelepipeds $\Pi_1, \cdots, \Pi_s$ of given shape and orientation, take the sum $\sum V(\Pi_i)$, and define the volume of f to be the greatest lower bound (Chap. IV) of all these sums for different such sets of parallelepipeds. (This is commonly done in the integral calculus, the parallelepipeds being cubes with sides parallel to the coordinate axes.)

By Theorem 9, a linear transformation with matrix P changes the volume of any parallelepiped in the ratio $1 : \mid P \mid$; hence it changes the volume of f in the same ratio. Since translations leave volumes unaltered, we obtain the following result.

Corollary. *An affine transformation $Y = XP + K$ alters all volumes by the factor $\mid P \mid$ (or rather, its absolute value).*

EXERCISES

1. (a) Compute the area of the parallelogram with vertices $(0, 0)$, $(3, 0)$, $(1, 4)$, and $(4, 4)$ in the plane.
   (b) Do the same for the parallelepiped in space with the adjacent vertices $(0, 2, 0)$, $(2, 0, 0)$, $(1, 1, 5)$, and $(0, 0, 0)$.
2. Show that the medians of any triangle divide it into six parts of equal

area. (*Hint:* Reduce to the case of an equilateral triangle, by an affine transformation.)

3. Prove that the diagonals of any parallelogram divide it into four parts of equal area.

4. (a) If P is the intersection of the diagonals of a parallelogram, prove that any line through P bisects the area of the parallelogram.
   (b) Extend this result to 3 dimensions.

5. Describe 3 planes which divide a tetrahedron into 6 parts of equal volume.

6. In the case of a 3×3 determinant, interpret geometrically the elementary operations used in the proof of Theorem 7.

7. (a) If m vectors $\alpha_1, \cdots, \alpha_m$ in E_n are linearly dependent, prove that the parallelepiped which they span has m-dimensional volume zero.
   (b) State and prove the converse of this result.

8. In the group of orthogonal matrices, show that the matrices with $|A| = +1$ (the "proper" orthogonal matrices) form a normal subgroup of index 2.

9. (a) Show that the correspondence $A \to |A|$ maps the full linear group homomorphically onto the multiplicative group of non-zero scalars.
   (b) Infer that the unimodular group is a normal subgroup of the full linear group.
   (c) Is the extended unimodular group (all P with $|P| = \pm 1$) a normal subgroup of the full linear group?

10. (a) Prove that, if A is any matrix with rows α_i, then AA^T is the matrix of inner products $\| (\alpha_i, \alpha_j) \|$.
    (b) Using (a), prove that, if the α_i are orthogonal, then

$$| AA^T | = (| \alpha_1 | \cdots | \alpha_m |)^2.$$

11. (a) If A is a real $m \times n$ matrix, use the proof of Theorem 7 to show that $| AA^T | \geq 0$. Show that the case $m = 2$ of this result is the Schwarz inequality of Chap. VII, Theorem 17.
    (b) Show that the area of a triangle with vertices $(0, 0, 0)$, (x_1, y_1, z_1), and (x_2, y_2, z_2) is $(1/2) | AA^T |^{1/2}$, where $A = \begin{pmatrix} x_1 & y_1 & z_1 \\ x_2 & y_2 & z_2 \end{pmatrix}$.
    ($\star$c) The volume of the tetrahedron with three unit edges along the x-, y-, and z-axes is $1/6$. Prove the volume of a tetrahedron with vertices $\alpha_1, \alpha_2, \alpha_3, \alpha_4$ is $(1/6) | BB^T |^{1/2}$, where B is the $3 \times n$ matrix with rows $(\alpha_2 - \alpha_1)$, $(\alpha_3 - \alpha_1)$, $(\alpha_4 - \alpha_1)$.
    ($\star$d) Generalize to "tetrahedra" of higher dimensions.

$\star$12. Let $-K \leq a_{ij} \leq K$ for $i, j = 1, \cdots, n$.
    (a) Show that if $\alpha_i = (a_{i1}, \cdots, a_{in})$, then $| \alpha_i | \leq K \sqrt{n}$.
    (b) Infer $|A| \leq |\alpha_1| \cdot |\alpha_2| \cdots |\alpha_n| \leq K^n n^{n/2}$ (Hadamard's determinant theorem).

4. The Characteristic Polynomial

We have already seen (Chap. IX, Theorem 5) that λ is a characteristic root of the $n \times n$ matrix A if and only if the matrix $A - \lambda I$ is singular. By Theorem 3, this is the case if and only if $| A - \lambda I | = 0$, which proves the following lemma.

Lemma. *The characteristic roots of a matrix A are the scalars λ such that $|A - \lambda I| = 0$.*

This lemma provides a straightforward means for reducing a matrix to diagonal form, when such a reduction is possible.

EXAMPLE. Let A be the real symmetric matrix

$$A = \begin{pmatrix} 1 & 3 & 0 \\ 3 & -2 & -1 \\ 0 & -1 & 1 \end{pmatrix}.$$

Then, expanding $|A - \lambda I|$ by minors of the first row,

$$|A - \lambda I| = \begin{vmatrix} 1 - \lambda & 3 & 0 \\ 3 & -2 - \lambda & -1 \\ 0 & -1 & 1 - \lambda \end{vmatrix} = -\lambda^3 + 13\lambda - 12.$$

Factoring, we have $|A - \lambda I| = -(\lambda - 1)(\lambda + 4)(\lambda - 3)$, so that the characteristic roots of A are 1, 3, -4. (In general, to find the characteristic roots of a 3×3 matrix, one must solve a cubic equation, as in Chap. IV, §4, or Chap. V, §5.) For each characteristic root there is a characteristic vector of the transformation T_A.

Since

$$(x, y, z)T_A = (x + 3y, 3x - 2y - z, -y + z),$$

a vector $\xi = (x, y, z)$ is characteristic, with characteristic root $\lambda = 1$, if and only if $x + 3y = x$, $3x - 2y - z = y$, $-y + z = z$; i.e., if and only if $y = 0$ and $z = 3x$, giving $\xi = (x, 0, 3x)$. Similarly, it is characteristic for $\lambda = 3$ if and only if $x + 3y = 3x$, $3x - 2y - z = 3y$, $-y + z = 3z$; this is the case only for scalar multiples of $(3, 2, -1)$. The characteristic vectors for $\lambda = -4$ are likewise the scalar multiples of $(-3, 5, 1)$. The three characteristic vectors

$$(1, 0, 3), \qquad (3, 2, -1), \qquad (-3, 5, 1)$$

are mutually orthogonal, hence linearly independent. The matrix P with these vectors as rows is nonsingular. Relative to the new basis formed by these three vectors, the transformation T_A is nonsingular with matrix PAP^{-1} (cf. Chap. IX, Theorems 3′ and 4). We may also normalize this basis, to obtain the normal orthogonal basis of characteristic vectors

$$\alpha_1 = \frac{1}{\sqrt{10}}(1, 0, 3), \quad \alpha_2 = \frac{1}{\sqrt{14}}(3, 2, -1), \quad \alpha_3 = \frac{1}{\sqrt{35}}(-3, 5, 1).$$

The matrix Q with these rows is orthogonal, and $QAQ^{-1} = QAQ^T$ is the diagonal matrix with diagonal entries 1, 3, -4.

The 3×3 symmetric matrix A displayed above is the matrix of the quadratic form $x^2 + 6xy - 2y^2 - 2yz + z^2$. The preceding analysis shows that this quadratic form, relative to the normal orthogonal basis α_1, α_2, α_3, takes on the diagonal form $x^2 + 3y^2 - 4z^2$.

In general, let A be any $n \times n$ matrix. Since a determinant is a polynomial, linear in the entries of each row, the determinant $|A - \lambda I|$ is a polynomial of degree n in the indeterminate λ, of the form

$$(14) \qquad |A - \lambda I| = (-1)^n \lambda^n + b_{n-1} \lambda^{n-1} + \cdots + b_1 \lambda + b_0.$$

We shall define the *characteristic polynomial* of A as the polynomial $c_A(\lambda) = |A - \lambda I|$, and the *characteristic equation* of A as the equation $|A - \lambda I| = 0$. We can now restate the lemma above as follows:

Theorem 10.   *The characteristic roots of a matrix A are the roots of the characteristic equation of A.*

Since a complex polynomial has at least one root, we infer the following

Corollary.   *Over the complex field, a linear transformation has at least one (non-zero) characteristic vector.*

Theorem 11.   *Similar matrices have the same characteristic polynomial.*

Proof.   Let the matrices be A and $B = P^{-1}AP$. Since $|P^{-1}| = |P|^{-1}$ and $|P|$ are scalars, they commute, and so the rule for multiplying determinants gives

$$|P^{-1}AP - \lambda I| = |P^{-1}AP - \lambda P^{-1}IP| = |P^{-1}(A - \lambda I)P|$$
$$= |P^{-1}| \cdot |A - \lambda I| \cdot |P| = |A - \lambda I|.$$

It is a corollary that the successive coefficients $b_0 = |A|$, b_1, $\cdots$,

$$b_{n-2} = (-1)^n \sum_{i<j} (a_{ii}a_{jj} - a_{ij}a_{ji}), \quad b_{n-1} = (-1)^n (a_{11} + \cdots + a_{nn})$$

of $|A - \lambda I|$ are *invariants* of the matrix A, under the group $A \to P^{-1}AP$. Suitable polynomials in the b_i give other useful invariants. One such invariant is

$$\sum_{i,j=1}^{n} a_{ij}a_{ji} = \sum_{i=1}^{n} a_{ii}^2 + 2\sum_{i<j} a_{ij}a_{ji} = b_{n-1}^2 + (-1)^{n-1}2b_{n-2}.$$

In the case of symmetric matrices, this invariant is simply $\sum a_{ij}^2$.

Theorem 12.   *The characteristic polynomial of a triangular matrix T with diagonal entries d_1, $\cdots$, d_n is*

$$|T - \lambda I| = (d_1 - \lambda)(d_2 - \lambda) \cdots (d_n - \lambda).$$

The proof follows from Lemma 2 of §1, since $T - \lambda I$ is itself a triangular matrix. It is a corollary that the set of diagonal entries (with multiplicity) consists of the *roots* (with multiplicity) of the characteristic polynomial. Hence the set of diagonal entries and the number of occurrences of each diagonal entry are the same for any two similar diagonal matrices. This can be stated as follows:

Corollary. *Two diagonal matrices are similar if and only if they differ only in the order of their diagonal terms.*

The properties of similarity throw a new light on the orthogonal transformation of a real quadratic form (Chap. IX, §10). If a quadratic form XAX^T with matrix A has been reduced by an orthogonal transformation $Z = XP$ to a diagonal form $\lambda_1 z_1^2 + \cdots + \lambda_n z_n^2$, the diagonal matrix D of this new form is $D = PAP^T$. Since P is orthogonal, $P^T = P^{-1}$ and $D = PAP^{-1}$; hence the new matrix D and the original matrix A are similar. The characteristic roots $\lambda_1, \cdots, \lambda_n$ of D are therefore the characteristic roots of the given matrix A. This gives the following sharpened form of Theorem 21 of Chap. IX.

Theorem 13. *Any real quadratic form XAX^T may be reduced by an orthogonal transformation to a diagonal form* $\lambda_1 z_1^2 + \cdots + \lambda_n z_n^2$, *in which the coefficients λ_i are the roots of the characteristic equation* $|A - \lambda I| = (\lambda_1 - \lambda) \cdots (\lambda_n - \lambda)$ *of A.*

But the characteristic equation, and hence its roots, is uniquely determined by A. This proves the essential uniqueness of the diagonal form—and gives a direct way to compute the coefficients. Knowing the coefficients, one can also compute the principal axes as the associated characteristic vectors in the way indicated above.

Since we know that any real symmetric matrix is orthogonally equivalent to a real diagonal matrix, we get the

Corollary. *All characteristic roots of a real symmetric matrix are real.*

Remark. If A is symmetric, then characteristic vectors X_1 and X_2 having distinct characteristic values $\lambda_1 \neq \lambda_2$ are necessarily orthogonal. For the bilinear expression $X_1 A X_2^T$ may be computed in two ways as

$$(X_1 A)X_2^T = \lambda_1(X_1 X_2^T), \qquad X_1(A X_2^T) = X_1(X_2 A)^T = \lambda_2(X_1 X_2^T).$$

Since $\lambda_1 \neq \lambda_2$, $X_1 X_2^T$ must be zero, and X_1 is therefore orthogonal to X_2.

Hence if the $n \times n$ symmetric matrix A has n distinct characteristic roots $\lambda_1, \cdots, \lambda_n$, any n associated characteristic vectors $X_1, \cdots, X_n$ will be orthogonal, and the unit vectors $X_1/|X_1|, \cdots, X_n/|X_n|$ will form the rows of an orthogonal matrix P such that $PAP^T = PAP^{-1}$ will be diagonal.

EXERCISES

1. Let D be a diagonal matrix with diagonal entries 3, 1, and -1, while P is a triangular matrix with rows $(1, 2, -3)$, $(0, -1, 4)$, $(0, 0, 1)$. Compute the characteristic equation of $P^{-1}DP$ and compare with that of D.

2. Compute the characteristic roots and the characteristic vectors of the matrices:

(a) $\begin{pmatrix} -1 & 2 & 2 \\ 2 & 2 & 2 \\ -3 & -6 & -6 \end{pmatrix}$;   (b) $\begin{pmatrix} 3 & 2 & 2 \\ 1 & 4 & 1 \\ -2 & -4 & -1 \end{pmatrix}$;   (c) $\begin{pmatrix} 4 & 9 & 0 \\ 0 & -2 & 8 \\ 0 & 0 & 7 \end{pmatrix}$.

3. Find the lengths of the principal axes of the quadric $xy + yz + zx + x + y + z = 1$.

4. Write down a diagonal quadratic form equivalent under orthogonal transformation to the forms given below. (*Hint:* In (a), show that all integral characteristic roots are multiples of 9.)
   (a) $-2x^2 - 11y^2 - 5z^2 + 4xy + 16yz + 20xz$,
   (b) $3x^2 - y^2 - 3z^2 - t^2 - 4xz - 10yt$.

5. Exhibit an orthogonal transformation which reduces each form of Ex. 4 to its diagonal equivalent.

6. Find a necessary and sufficient condition that the characteristic roots of a 2×2 matrix be equal.

7. Find all 2×2 matrices with characteristic roots $+1$ and -1.

★8. Show that, if A and B are square matrices, the characteristic polynomial of the matrix $\begin{pmatrix} A & 0 \\ C & B \end{pmatrix}$ is the product of those for A and B.

9. Prove that the transposed matrices A and A^T have the same characteristic equation, and that so do AB and BA for nonsingular A.

10. (a) Prove that, in (14), $b_{n-1} = \pm(a_{11} + \cdots + a_{nn})$. (The invariant $a_{11} + \cdots + a_{nn}$ is called the *trace* of A.)
    (b) Prove that $b_{n-2} = (-1)^n \sum (a_{ii}a_{jj} - a_{ij}a_{ji})$.

11. Prove the formula $\sum a_{ij}^2 = b_{n-1}^2 + (-1)^{n-1}2b_{n-2}$ for symmetric $n \times n$ matrices.

12. Prove directly from the definition that all characteristic roots of a real symmetric A are real. (*Hint:* For X characteristic, show $XAX^{*T} = \lambda XX^{*T} = \lambda^* XX^{T*}$, where X^* denotes the complex conjugate of X.)

13. (a) Prove that all characteristic roots of a hermitian matrix are real.
    (b) Prove that the characteristic vectors span the space of all vectors.

★14. Show that every unitary matrix U has a characteristic vector ξ with $\xi U = d\xi$, where $|d| = 1$.

★15. If Q and R are two orthogonal matrices which both reduce the same symmetric matrix A to diagonal forms $Q^T A Q$ and $R^T A R$, and if A is nonsingular and has distinct characteristic roots, prove that $R = QP$, where P is a monomial matrix with entries ± 1 or 0.

★16. Prove the principal axis theorem for a real symmetric matrix A by the following analysis of the linear transformation $X \to XA$.
    (a) The matrix A has a characteristic vector α_1 of length 1.
    (b) If α_1 is chosen as the first vector in a new normal orthogonal basis, the new matrix for the given transformation has zeros in the first column and the first row, except for the first entry.
    (c) The argument is continued by induction.

★17. Prove that the volume of the ellipsoid $\sum a_{ij}x_i x_j \leq 1$ is $(4\pi/3) \cdot |A|^{-1/2}$, where $A = \| a_{ij} \|$. (*Hint:* Transform to principal axes, and use Theorem 9.)

5. The Minimal Polynomial

The construction of canonical forms for a matrix under similarity depends upon the study of the polynomial equations satisfied by the matrix or by the corresponding transformation. Specifically, let V be an n-dimensional vector space over a field F, and $T: V \to V$ a linear transformation of V. The various powers T^m of T are then also linear transformations of V. Since transformations can also be added or multiplied by scalars, we can consider for each polynomial form $f(x) = a_0 + a_1x + \cdots + a_kx^k$ with coefficients a_i in F the corresponding polynomial

$$(15) \qquad f(T) = a_0I + a_1T + \cdots + a_kT^k$$

in T. It represents a linear transformation $f(T): V \to V$, and, in particular, the constant polynomial $f(x) = 1$ yields the identity transformation $I: V \to V$. Since powers of T are permutable ($T^mT^q = T^qT^m = T^{m+q}$), the polynomials $f(T)$ are added and multiplied like the polynomials $f(x)$.

Similarly, each $n \times n$ matrix A with entries in F yields polynomials

$$(16) \qquad f(A) = a_0I + a_1A + \cdots + a_kA^k$$

in A; they are again $n \times n$ matrices with entries in F. Since there are exactly n^2 linearly independent $n \times n$ matrices over F, the $n^2 + 1$ matrices $I, A, \cdots, A^{n^2}$ are certainly linearly dependent, and the dependence relation provides a non-zero polynomial $f(x)$ of degree at most n^2 with $f(A) = O$. Because of the isomorphism $A \to T_A$ between $n \times n$ matrices and linear transformations of V_n, there will also exist for each linear transformation T of an n-dimensional vector space V a non-zero polynomial $f(x)$ with $f(T) = O$.

Theorem 14. *For each linear transformation T of a finite-dimensional vector space V over F, the polynomials $f(x)$ over F such that $f(T) = O$ are the multiples of a unique monic polynomial $m(x)$.*

Proof. Consider the set M of all polynomials $f(x)$ over F such that $f(T) = O$. We have just seen that M contains a non-zero polynomial. Moreover, M is closed under addition, subtraction, and multiplication by any polynomial $g(x)$: it is an *ideal* of the ring $F[x]$. Hence, by Theorem 11 of Chap. III, M consists of the multiples of the monic polynomial $m(x)$ of least degree with $m(T) = O$.

We call $m(x)$ the *minimal polynomial* of T. It is the monic polynomial characterized by the properties

$$(17) \qquad m(T) = O; \qquad f(T) = O \text{ implies } m(x) \mid f(x),$$

where the symbol $m(x) \mid f(x)$ means that $m(x)$ divides $f(x)$ in the polynomial ring $F[x]$, as in Chap. III. The *minimal polynomial* of an $n \times n$ matrix A is described similarly; it is identical with the minimal polynomial of the corresponding transformation T_A of $V_n(F)$. Since similar matrices are different representations of the same linear transformations, we have

Corollary. *Similar matrices over a field F have the same minimal polynomial over F.*

As an illustration, consider a *nilpotent* transformation (or matrix); that is, a linear transformation T with $T^m = O$ for some m. Since T then satisfies $T^m = O$, its minimal polynomial is x^h for some integer h; indeed, h is the least positive integer with $T^h = O$. As a special case, suppose that T acts on an h-dimensional space. Since $T^{h-1} \neq O$, there is a vector α with $\alpha T^{h-1} \neq O$. We assert then that the h vectors $\alpha, \alpha T, \alpha T^2, \cdots, \alpha T^{h-1}$ are linearly independent. If not, there would be a linear dependence relation $O = a_0\alpha + a_1\alpha T + \cdots + a_{h-1}\alpha T^{h-1}$ with coefficients a_i not all zero. If a_j is the first non-zero coefficient, we apply T^{h-j-1} to the equation to get $O = OT^{h-j-1} = a_j\alpha T^j T^{h-j-1} = a_j\alpha T^{h-1}$; but α was chosen so that $\alpha T^{h-1} \neq O$; hence $a_j = 0$, a contradiction.

When these independent vectors $\alpha, \alpha T, \cdots, \alpha T^{h-1}$ are chosen as a basis, T carries each vector of the basis into the next and the last vector to zero, and hence is represented by the $h \times h$ matrix

$$\begin{pmatrix} 0 & 1 & 0 & \cdots & 0 \\ 0 & 0 & 1 & \cdots & 0 \\ & \cdot & \cdot & & \cdot \\ & \cdot & \cdot & & \cdot \\ & \cdot & \cdot & & \cdot \\ 0 & 0 & 0 & \cdots & 1 \\ 0 & 0 & 0 & \cdots & 0 \end{pmatrix},$$

in which the only non-zero entries are 1's along the diagonal just above the principal diagonal. This matrix, which is clearly nilpotent, is known as the "companion matrix" of the polynomial x^n.

More generally, to each monic polynomial

$$g(x) = c_0 + c_1 x + \cdots + c_{n-1}x^{n-1} + x^n$$

of degree n we can construct an $n \times n$ matrix with minimal polynomial $g(x)$. This matrix, called the *companion matrix* of $g(x)$ is, for $n = 4$,

$$(18) \qquad C_g = \begin{pmatrix} 0 & 1 & 0 & 0 \\ 0 & 0 & 1 & 0 \\ 0 & 0 & 0 & 1 \\ -c_0 & -c_1 & -c_2 & -c_3 \end{pmatrix};$$

for any n, C_g has entries zero except for entries 1 in the diagonal just above the main diagonal, and entries $-c_0, \cdots, -c_{n-1}$ in the last row.

Theorem 15. *For each monic polynomial $g(x)$, the companion matrix C_g has minimal polynomial $g(x)$ and characteristic polynomial $(-1)^n g(\lambda)$.*

Proof. Let T be the linear transformation of V_n represented by the companion matrix C_g of (18). Since the rows of the matrix are the coordinates of the transforms of the unit vectors $\varepsilon_1, \cdots, \varepsilon_n$ of V_n, we have

$$\varepsilon_1 T = \varepsilon_2, \cdots, \qquad \varepsilon_{n-1} T = \varepsilon_n, \qquad \varepsilon_n T = -c_0 \varepsilon_1 - \cdots - c_{n-1} \varepsilon_n.$$

In other words, the vectors $\varepsilon_1, \varepsilon_1 T, \cdots, \varepsilon_1 T^{n-1}$ are a basis of V_n so, that any vector ξ can be written uniquely as

$$(19) \qquad \xi = a_0 \varepsilon_1 + a_1 \varepsilon_1 T + \cdots + a_{n-1} \varepsilon_1 T^{n-1} = \varepsilon_1 f(T),$$

where $f(x) = a_0 + a_1 x + \cdots + a_{n-1} x^{n-1}$ is a polynomial of degree at most $n - 1$. Furthermore, $\varepsilon_1 T^n = -c_0 \varepsilon_1 - \cdots - c_{n-1} \varepsilon_1 T^{n-1}$, so that $\varepsilon_1 g(T) = O$. Therefore, for any vector ξ,

$$\xi g(T) = \varepsilon_1 f(T) g(T) = \varepsilon_1 g(T) f(T) = O,$$

which asserts that T satisfies the monic polynomial equation $g(T) = O$. For any $f(x) \neq 0$ of smaller degree, $\varepsilon_1 f(T) = \xi \neq O$ by (19), hence $f(T) \neq O$. Thus $g(x)$ is indeed the minimal polynomial of C_g.

The characteristic polynomial of C_g is found by expanding the determinant $|C_g - \lambda I|$ by minors of the last row. Since the minor of $-c_k$ is triangular with k diagonal entries $-\lambda$ and the others 1, $|C_g - \lambda I|$ is exactly $(-1)^n g(\lambda)$; the sign $(-1)^n$ occurs because the characteristic polynomial of any $n \times n$ matrix has $(-1)^n \lambda^n$ as its leading term.

EXERCISES

1. (a) Show that any 2×2 matrix which satisfies $X^2 = O$ is similar to $\begin{pmatrix} 0 & 1 \\ 0 & 0 \end{pmatrix}$ or is $\begin{pmatrix} 0 & 0 \\ 0 & 0 \end{pmatrix}$.

   (b) Prove a corresponding result for 3×3 matrices.

2. Show that every real 2×2 matrix whose determinant is negative is similar to a diagonal matrix. Interpret geometrically.

3. (a) For any nonsingular $n \times n$ matrix P, prove that the correspondence $A \to PAP^{-1}$ is an automorphism of the algebra of all $n \times n$ matrices A.

   (b) Deduce from (a) a direct proof that similar matrices have the same minimal polynomial.

4. Show that the characteristic polynomial of any diagonal matrix is a multiple of its minimal polynomial.

★5. (a) Show that every real 2×2 orthogonal matrix, whose determinant is negative, is a rigid reflection. (*Hint:* See Ex. 2 or Chap. IX, §4.)

   (b) Show that every 2×2 orthogonal matrix, whose determinant is positive, is a rigid rotation.

★6. (a) Show that any real 3×3 matrix A has a real characteristic vector.

   (b) Show that any orthogonal 3×3 matrix is similar, under an orthogonal change of basis, to a matrix of the form $\begin{pmatrix} \pm 1 & 0 \\ 0 & B \end{pmatrix}$, where B is an orthogonal 2×2 matrix.

(c) Using Ex. 5, show that if A is an orthogonal 3×3 matrix and $|A| > 0$, then A has a characteristic root $+1$ and is a rigid rotation. (This is Euler's Theorem.)

★7. (a) Show that the characteristic roots of the matrix C displayed to the right are ± 1, $\pm i$, the complex fourth roots of unity.

$$\begin{pmatrix} 0 & 1 & 0 & 0 \\ 0 & 0 & 1 & 0 \\ 0 & 0 & 0 & 1 \\ 1 & 0 & 0 & 0 \end{pmatrix}$$

   (b) What are the complex characteristic vectors of C?

   (c) To what complex diagonal matrix is C similar?

★8. Show that if λ is a characteristic root of A, and $q(\lambda)$ is any polynomial, then $q(\lambda)$ is a characteristic root of $q(A)$.

★9. An $n \times n$ matrix A is called *cyclic* if $a_{i,j} = a_{i+1,j+1}$ for all i, j—subscripts being all taken modulo n. Show that the characteristic roots $\lambda_1, \cdots, \lambda_n$ of any cyclic matrix are

$$\lambda_p = a_{11} + a_{12}\omega^p + \cdots + a_{1n}\omega^{(n-1)p},$$

where ω is a primitive nth root of unity. (*Hint:* Use Exs. 7–8.)

6. Cayley-Hamilton Theorem

We shall now show that every square matrix A satisfies its characteristic equation—i.e., that the minimal polynomial of A divides the characteristic polynomial of A.

This is easily proved using the concept of a matric polynomial or λ-*matrix*. By this is meant a matrix like $A - \lambda I$ whose entries are polynomials in a symbol λ. Collecting terms involving like powers of λ, one can write any non-zero λ-matrix $B(\lambda)$ in the form

$$B(\lambda) = B_0 + \lambda B_1 + \cdots + \lambda^r B_r,$$

where the B_r are matrices of constants and $B_r \neq O$. (Equality means equality in every coefficient of λ in each entry.)

Lemma.   *If* $C = B(\lambda)(A - \lambda I)$ *is a matrix of constants, then* $C = O$.

Proof.   Expanding $B(\lambda)(A - \lambda I)$, we get

$$-\lambda^{r+1}B_r + \sum_{k=1}^{r} \lambda^k(B_k A - B_{k-1}) + B_0 A,$$

where $B_r \neq O$ unless $B(\lambda) = O$. The conclusion is now obvious.

Theorem 16 (Cayley-Hamilton).   *Every square matrix satisfies its characteristic equation.*

This means that if each power λ^i in the characteristic polynomial $f(\lambda) = |A - \lambda I|$ of (14) is replaced by the same power A^i of the matrix (*and if* λ^0 is replaced by $A^0 = I$), the result is zero;

(20) $b_0 I + b_1 A + \cdots + b_{n-1}A^{n-1} + (-1)^n A^n = O.$

Proof. In the matrix $A - \lambda I$ the entries are linear polynomials in λ, so that its non-zero minors are determinants which are also polynomials in λ, of degree $n - 1$ or less. Each entry in the adjoint C of $A - \lambda I$ is such a minor, so that this adjoint may be written as a sum of n matrices, each involving terms in a fixed power $\lambda^0, \lambda^1, \cdots, \lambda^{n-1}$ of λ. In other words, the adjoint $C = C(\lambda)$ is a λ-matrix $C = C(\lambda) = \sum \lambda^i C_i$. According to (10), the product of $A - \lambda I$ by its adjoint is

$$(21) \qquad C(\lambda)(A - \lambda I) = |A - \lambda I| \cdot I = f(\lambda) \cdot I,$$

where $f(\lambda)$ is the characteristic polynomial.

Now observe that the familiar factorization $(i \geq 1)$

$$A^i - \lambda^i I = (A^{i-1} + \lambda A^{i-2} + \cdots + \lambda^{i-1} I)(A - \lambda I)$$

will give, in terms of the coefficients b_i of the characteristic polynomial (14),

$$f(A) - f(\lambda) \cdot I = \sum_{i=0}^{n} b_i A^i - \sum_{i=0}^{n} b_i \lambda^i I = \sum_{i=1}^{n} b_i (A^i - \lambda^i I)$$

$$= \sum_{i=1}^{n} b_i (A^{i-1} + \lambda A^{i-2} + \cdots + \lambda^{i-1} I)(A - \lambda I),$$

where $f(A)$ is obtained from the characteristic polynomial $f(\lambda)$ by substituting A for λ. That is,

$$(22) \qquad f(A) - f(\lambda) \cdot I = -G(\lambda)(A - \lambda I),$$

where $G(\lambda)$ is a new λ-matrix. If we add (22) to (21), we get

$$[C(\lambda) - G(\lambda)](A - \lambda I) = f(A),$$

where $f(A)$ is a matrix of constants. By the lemma, this implies $f(A) = O$.

EXERCISES

1. Prove by direct substitution that every 2×2 matrix satisfies its characteristic equation.

2. Show that if A is nonsingular, and has the characteristic polynomial (14), then the adjoint of A is given by

$$-[b_1 I + b_2 A + \cdots + b_{n-1} A^{n-2} + (-1)^n A^{n-1}].$$

3. In the notation of Ex. 2, show that the characteristic polynomial of A^{-1} is

$$(-1)^n \left[\lambda^n + \frac{b_1}{|A|} \lambda^{n-1} + \cdots + \frac{(-1)^n}{|A|} \right].$$

4. (a) Prove the Cayley-Hamilton theorem for strictly triangular matrices, by direct computation.
   (★b) Same problem for triangular matrices.

5. (a) Show by explicit computation that the 4×4 companion matrix C_g of (18) satisfies its characteristic equation.
   (b) The same, for the companion matrix of a polynomial of degree n.

XI. Boolean Algebras and Lattices

1. Basic Definition

We will now analyze more closely, from the standpoint of modern algebra, the fundamental notions of "set" (or class) and "subset," briefly introduced in Chap. I, §11. Suppose that I is any set, while $X, Y, Z, \cdots$ denote subsets of I. Thus I might be a square, and X, Y, Z three overlapping congruent disks located in I, as in the "Venn diagram" of Figure 1.

Figure 1

One writes $X \subset Y$ (or $Y \supset X$) whenever X is a subset of Y—i.e., whenever every element of X is in Y. This relation is also expressed by saying that X is "contained" or "included" in Y.

The relation of inclusion is reflexive: trivially, any set X is a subset of itself. It is also transitive: if every element of X is in Y and every element of Y is in Z, then clearly every element of X is in Z. But the inclusion relation is *not* symmetric. On the contrary, if $X \subset Y$ and $Y \subset X$, then X and Y must contain exactly the same elements, so that $X = Y$.

In summary, the inclusion relation for sets shares with the inequality relation of arithmetic the following properties:

Reflexive: For all X, $X \subset X$;
Antisymmetric: If $X \subset Y$ and $Y \subset X$, then $X = Y$.
Transitive: If $X \subset Y$ and $Y \subset Z$, then $X \subset Z$.

It is however *not* true that, given two sets X and Y, either $X \subset Y$ or $Y \subset X$.

There are, therefore, four possible ways in which two sets X and Y can be related by inclusion. It may be that $X \subset Y$ and $Y \subset X$, in which case, by antisymmetry, $X = Y$. We can have $X \subset Y$ but not $Y \subset X$, in which case we say that X is *properly contained* in Y, and we write $X < Y$ or $Y > X$. We can have $Y \subset X$ but not $X \subset Y$, in which case X *properly contains* Y. And finally, we can have neither $X \subset Y$ nor $Y \subset X$, in which case X and Y are said to be *incomparable*. It is principally the existence of incomparable sets which distinguishes the inclusion relation from the inequality relation between real numbers.

The subsets of a given set I are not only related by inclusion; they can also be combined by two binary operations of "union" and "intersection," analogous to ordinary "plus" and "times." The extent and importance of this analogy were first clearly recognized by the British mathematician George Boole (1815–64), who founded the algebraic theory of sets little more than a century ago.

We define the *intersection* of X and Y (written $X \cap Y$) as the set of all elements in both X and Y; and we define the *union* of X and Y (in symbols, $X \cup Y$) as the set of all elements in either X or Y, or both. The symbols $\cap$ and $\cup$ are called "cap" and "cup," respectively.

Finally, we write X' (read, "the complement of X") to signify the set of all elements not in X. For example, I' is the empty set $\varnothing$, which contains no elements at all! This is because we are considering only *subsets* of I.

The operations of the algebra of classes can be illustrated graphically by means of the Venn diagram of Figure 1. In this diagram, X, Y, and Z are the interiors of the three overlapping disks. Combinations of these regions in the square I can be depicted by shading appropriate areas: thus, Y' is the exterior of Y, and $X \cap (Y' \cup Z)$ is the area shaded in Figure 1.

EXERCISES

1. The Venn diagrams for X, Y, and Z cut the square into eight nonoverlapping areas. Label each such area by an algebraic combination of X, Y, and Z which represents exactly that area.

2. On a Venn diagram shade each of the following areas:

$$(X' \cap Y) \cup (X \cap Z'), \qquad (X \cup Y)' \cap Z, \qquad (X \cup Y') \cup Z'.$$

3. By shading each of the appropriate areas on a Venn diagram, determine which of the following equations are valid:

(a) $(X' \cup Y)' = X \cap Y'$; 　　　　(b) $X' \cup Y' = (X \cup Y)'$;
(c) $(X \cup Y) \cap Z = (X \cup Z) \cap Y$; 　(d) $X \cup (Y \cap Z)' = (X \cup Y') \cap Z'$.

2. Laws: Analogy with Arithmetic

The analogy between the algebra of sets and ordinary arithmetic will now be described in some detail, and used to define Boolean algebra. The analogy between $\cap$, $\cup$ and ordinary $\cdot$, $+$ is in part described by the following laws, whose truth is obvious:

Idempotent: 　$X \cap X = X$ 　　and 　　$X \cup X = X$;
Commutative: 　$X \cap Y = Y \cap X$ 　　and 　　$X \cup Y = Y \cup X$;

Associative: $X \cap (Y \cap Z) = (X \cap Y) \cap Z$ and
$\qquad\qquad X \cup (Y \cup Z) = (X \cup Y) \cup Z;$

Distributive: $X \cap (Y \cup Z) = (X \cap Y) \cup (X \cap Z)$ and
$\qquad\qquad X \cup (Y \cap Z) = (X \cup Y) \cap (X \cup Z).$

Clearly, all of these except for the idempotent laws and the second distributive law correspond to familiar properties of $+$ and $\cdot$, as postulated in Chap. I.

Intersection and union are related to each other and to inclusion by a fundamental principle of

Consistency: The three conditions $X \subset Y$, $X \cap Y = X$, and $X \cup Y = Y$ are mutually equivalent.

Further, the void (empty) set being denoted by $\varnothing$, we have the following special properties of $\varnothing$ and I,

Universal Bounds: $\varnothing \subset X \subset I$ for all X;
Intersection: $\varnothing \cap X = \varnothing$ and $I \cap X = X$;
Union: $\varnothing \cup X = X$ and $I \cup X = I$.

The first three intersection and union properties are analogous to properties of 0 and 1 in ordinary arithmetic.

Finally, complementation is related to intersection and union by three new laws,

Complementarity: $X \cap X' = \varnothing$ and $X \cup X' = I$;
Dualization: $(X \cap Y)' = X' \cup Y'$ and $(X \cup Y)' = X' \cap Y'$;
Involution: $(X')' = X.$

The first and third laws correspond to laws of ordinary arithmetic, if X' is interpreted as $1 - X$, and $XX = X$ is assumed.

The truth of the above laws can be established in various ways. First, one can test them in particular examples, thus verifying them by "induction." Appropriate examples are furnished by the Venn diagrams. If X and Y are the respective interiors of the left- and right-hand circles in Figure 2, then the area X' is shaded by horizontal lines and Y' by vertical lines. The cross-hatched area is then just the intersection $X' \cap Y'$; the figure shows at once that this area is the complement of the sum $X \cup Y$, as asserted by the second dualization law. Such an argument is convincing to our common sense, but it is not permissible technically, since only deductive proofs are allowed in mathematical reasoning.

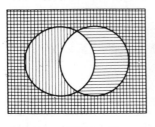

Figure 2

Secondly, we can consider separately each of the possible cases for an element of I: first, an element b in X and in Y; second, an element in X but not in Y; and so on. For example, an element of the first type is in $X \cap Y$, hence not in $(X \cap Y)'$ and not in $X' \cup Y'$, while an element of the second type is in $(X \cap Y)'$ and in Y', hence in $X' \cup Y'$. By looking at the other two cases also, one sees that $(X \cap Y)'$ and $X' \cup Y'$ have the same elements, as in the first dualization law. Note that for two classes X and Y, all four possible cases for an element are represented by points in the four areas of the Venn diagram; while for three classes there are eight cases and eight areas (Figure 1).

Thirdly, we can use the verbal definitions of the operations cup and cap to reformulate the laws. Consider the distributive law. Here

"b in $X \cap (Y \cup Z)$" means "b is both in X and in Y or Z,"
"b in $(X \cap Y) \cup (X \cap Z)$" means
$\qquad\qquad\qquad$ "b is either in both X and Y or in both X and Z."

A little reflection convinces one that these two statements are equivalent, according to the ordinary usage of the connectives "and" and "either $\cdots$ or." This verification of the distributive law may indicate how the laws of the algebra of classes are paraphrases of the properties of the words "and," "or," and "not." If one assumes these properties as basic, as one normally does in mathematical reasoning, one can then prove from them all the above laws for classes.

EXERCISES

1. Use Venn diagrams to verify the distributive laws.
2. Use the method of subdivision into cases to verify the associative and commutative laws and the consistency principle.
3. Reformulate the laws of complementarity, dualization, and involution in terms of "and," "or," and "not," as in the third method described above.
4. (a) In treating an algebraic expression in four sets by considering all possible cases for an element, how many cases occur?
   (⋆b) Draw a diagram for four sets which shows every one of these possible cases as a region.
   (c) Show that no such diagram can be made, in which the four given sets are discs.
5. Show that the intersection and union properties of $\varnothing$ and I may be derived from the universal bounds property and the consistency principle.
6. Of the six implications obtained by replacing "equivalent" by "if" and "only if" in the Consistency postulate, show that four hold for real numbers x, y if $0 \leqq x, y \leqq 1$.
7. In Ex. 6, which of the intersection and union properties of $\varnothing$, I fails if $\varnothing$ is replaced by the number 0, and I by 1? Which of the properties of complements fails if X' is replaced by $1 - x$ and Y' by $1 - y$?
8. Prove that, for arbitrary subsets X, Y of I, $X \subset Y$ if and only if $X' \cup Y = I$.

3. Boolean Algebra

We will not concern ourselves further with deriving the preceding algebraic laws from the fundamental principles of logic. Instead, we will simply assume the most basic of these laws as *postulates*, as was done in Chap. I for the laws of arithmetic, and then deduce from these postulates as many interesting consequences as possible. Accordingly, we now lay down our basic definition, using a slightly different notation to emphasize the fact that the postulates assumed may apply to other things than sets.

Definition. *A* Boolean algebra *is a set B of elements a, b, c, $\cdots$ with the following properties:*

(i) *B has two binary operations, $\wedge$ (wedge) and $\vee$ (vee), which satisfy the idempotent laws $a \wedge a = a \vee a = a$, the commutative laws*
$$a \wedge b = b \wedge a, \qquad a \vee b = b \vee a,$$
and the associative laws
$$a \wedge (b \wedge c) = (a \wedge b) \wedge c, \qquad a \vee (b \vee c) = (a \vee b) \vee c.$$

(ii) *These operations satisfy the absorption laws:*
$$a \wedge (a \vee b) = a \vee (a \wedge b) = a,$$

(iii) *These operations are mutually distributive:*
$$a \wedge (b \vee c) = (a \wedge b) \vee (a \wedge c), \qquad a \vee (b \wedge c) = (a \vee b) \wedge (a \vee c),$$

(iv) *B contains universal bounds O, I which satisfy*
$$O \wedge a = O, \qquad O \vee a = a, \qquad I \wedge a = a, \qquad I \vee a = I,$$

(v) *B has a unary operation $a \rightarrow a'$ of* complementation, *which obeys the laws*
$$a \wedge a' = O, \qquad a \vee a' = I.$$

It is understood that the preceding laws are assumed to hold for all $a, b, c \in B$.

Using this definition, the conclusions of §§1–2 can be summarized in the following statement.

Theorem 1. *Under intersection, union, and complement, the subsets of any set I form a Boolean algebra.*

To illustrate more selectively the significance of the preceding postulates, we now describe examples in which some of them hold, but not all.

EXAMPLE 1.   Let L have as "elements" the subspaces of the n-dimensional Euclidean vector space of Chap. VII, §10. Define $S \wedge T = S \cap T$ as the intersection of S and T, $S \vee T = S + T$ as their linear sum, O as the null vector O, I as the whole space, and S' as the orthogonal complement $S^\perp$ of the subspace S.

Then postulates (i), (ii), (iv) and (v) are satisfied, although the distributive laws (iii) are not. (Let S, T, U be the subspaces of the plane spanned by $(1, 0)$, $(0, 1)$, $(1, 1)$, respectively, for example.)

EXAMPLE 2. Let L have as "elements" the normal subgroups M, N, $\cdots$ of a finite group G. Let $M \wedge N = M \cap N$ be the intersection of M and N, while $M \vee N = MN$ is the set of all products xy $(x \in M, y \in N)$. Then $M \wedge N$ and $M \vee N$ are normal subgroups of G. If O denotes the group identity 1, and I is G itself, then postulates (i), (ii), and (iv) are satisfied, although in general (iii) and (v) are not.

Since the systems constructed in Examples 1–2 satisfy postulates (i)–(ii) they are lattices in the following sense.

Definition. *A lattice is a set L of elements, with two binary operations* $\wedge$ and $\vee$ which are idempotent, commutative, and associative, and which satisfy the absorption law (ii). If in addition the distributive laws (iii) hold, then L is called a* distributive lattice.

For example, if the void set $\varnothing$ is included, then the set of all polygonal plane areas is a distributive lattice under intersection and union. Again, the set of positive integers is a distributive lattice, with $m \wedge n$ the greatest common divisor of m and n, and $m \vee n$ their least common multiple.

The various laws postulated above have many interesting algebraic consequences, of which we will now derive a few of the simplest.

The effect of the associative and commutative laws has already been studied in Chap. I, §5. The associative law means essentially that we can form multiple intersections or unions without using parentheses; the commutative law, that we can permute terms in any way we like in an expression involving only vees or only wedges.

In conjunction with the above laws, the effect of the idempotent laws is clearly to permit elimination of repeated occurrences of the same term—all but one of the occurrences of a given term can be deleted. In summary, we have

Lemma 1. *Let f and g be two expressions formed from the letters $a_1, \cdots,$ a_n using only vees $\vee$ and using all these letters (possibly with some repetitions). Then the idempotent, commutative, and associative laws imply that $f = g$. The same holds for expressions involving only wedges $\wedge$.*

If N is the *set* of subscripts $i = 1, \cdots, n$, we can without ambiguity write

$$\bigvee_N a_i \text{ or } \bigvee_{i=1}^n a_i, \quad \text{and} \quad \bigwedge_N a_i \text{ or } \bigwedge_{i=1}^n a_i$$

to denote the join and meet of all the a_i, respectively. These notations are analogous to the Σ, Π notations of algebra.

Again, just as in Chap. I, §5, starting from the commutative, associa-

---

* The wedge operation $\wedge$ is also called *meet*, and the vee operation $\vee$ called *join*; we will use these names interchangeably below.

tive, and distributive laws we can derive generalized distributive laws such that

$$x \wedge (y_1 \vee \cdots \vee y_n) = (x \wedge y_1) \vee \cdots \vee (x \wedge y_n),$$
$$x \vee (y_1 \wedge \cdots \wedge y_n) = (x \vee y_1) \wedge \cdots \wedge (x \vee y_n),$$
$$(x_1 \vee \cdots \vee x_m) \wedge (y_1 \vee \cdots \vee y_n)$$
$$= (x_1 \wedge y_1) \vee (x_1 \wedge y_2) \vee \cdots \vee (x_m \wedge y_n).$$

EXERCISES

1. Use induction to prove in detail that

(a) $x \wedge \bigvee\limits_{i=1}^{n} y_i = \bigvee\limits_{i=1}^{n} (x \wedge y_i)$, in any distributive lattice,

(b) $\left(\bigvee\limits_{i=1}^{n} x_i\right)' = \bigwedge\limits_{i=1}^{n} x'_i$ in any Boolean algebra.

★2. Prove in detail by induction that, in any distributive lattice,

$$\left(\bigvee_{i=1}^{m} x_i\right) \wedge \left(\bigvee_{j=1}^{n} y_j\right) = \bigvee_{k=1}^{mn} (x_i \wedge y_j),$$

where $k = (i - 1)n + j$.

3. Prove in detail that Example 1 defines a lattice which is not distributive if $n > 1$.

4. Prove that Example 2 defines a lattice, which is distributive if G is cyclic.

5. Prove that the lattice of all subgroups of the four-group is not distributive.

4. Deduction of Other Basic Laws

We now show that the postulates for Boolean algebra listed above imply the other basic formulas of the algebra of classes which were discussed in §§1–2. For instance, they imply the *uniqueness* of O and I, which we did not postulate.

Lemma 2. *In any Boolean algebra, each of the identities $a \wedge x = a$ and $a \vee x = x$ (for all x) implies that $a = O$; dually, each of the identities $a \vee x = a$ and $a \wedge x = x$ implies that $a = I$.*

Proof. If $a \wedge x = a$ for all x, then in particular $a \wedge O = a$; but $a \wedge O = O$ by (iii); hence $a = O$. Likewise, if $a \vee x = x$ for all x, then $a \vee O = O$; but $a \vee O = a$ by (iii); hence again $a = O$. The proof of the unicity of I is similar.

Lemma 3. *For elements a, b of any lattice $a \wedge b = a$ holds if and only if $a \vee b = b$.*

Proof. If $a \vee b = b$, then by the absorption law (ii) $a \wedge b = a \wedge (a \vee b) = a$. Conversely, if $a \wedge b = a$, then by the same law $a \vee b =$

$(a \wedge b) \vee b$. Hence, by the commutative laws, $a \vee b = b \vee (b \wedge a) = b$, where the last step uses (ii) again.

Corollary. *In the definition of a Boolean algebra, conditions* (iv) *can be replaced by either of the following postulates:*

(iv') *For all* x, $x \wedge O = O$ *and* $x \vee I = I$
(iv'') *For all* x, $O \vee x = x$ *and* $I \wedge x = x$.

The definition of a Boolean algebra given above did not mention the inclusion relation, even though this is the most fundamental concept of all. We shall now define this relation and deduce its basic properties from the postulates stated above. The proof restates the Law of Consistency, of which a part was already proved as Lemma 2 above.

Definition. *Define* $a \leq b$ *to mean that* $a \wedge b = a$ — *or equivalently* (*Lemma 2*), *that* $a \vee b = b$.

Lemma 4. *The relation* $a \leq b$ *is reflexive, antisymmetric, and transitive, in any lattice.*

Proof. Since $a \wedge a = a$, $a \leq a$ for all a, proving the reflexive law. Again, $a \leq b$ and $b \leq a$ imply

$$a = a \wedge b = b \wedge a = b,$$

which proves the antisymmetric law. Finally, $a \leq b$ and $b \leq c$ imply $a = a \wedge b = a \wedge (b \wedge c) = (a \wedge b) \wedge c = a \wedge c$, whence $a \leq c$. This proves the transitive law, Q.E.D.

The power of the absorption laws was exhibited above in the proof of Lemmas 2–3 above. Actually, the absorption, commutative, and associative laws imply the idempotent laws: the latter are redundant in the definition of a lattice. For, one absorption law is $x = x \wedge (x \vee z)$ for all x, z. Setting $z = x \wedge y$, we infer $x = x \wedge (x \vee (x \wedge y))$ for all x, y. Applying the dual absorption law $x \vee (x \wedge y) = x$, we conclude $x = x \wedge x$ (one idempotent law). The proof that $x = x \vee x$ is similar, interchanging $\wedge$ and $\vee$.

Lemma 5. *In any distributive lattice,* $a \vee x = a \vee y$ *and* $a \wedge x = a \wedge y$ *together imply* $x = y$.

Proof. By substitution of equals for equals, and the absorption and distributive laws,

$$\begin{aligned}
x = x \wedge (x \vee a) &= x \wedge (y \vee a) \\
&= (x \wedge y) \vee (x \wedge a) = (y \wedge x) \vee (y \wedge a) \\
&= y \wedge (x \vee a) = y \wedge (y \vee a) = y.
\end{aligned}$$

Now recall that the operation $a \to a'$ of complementation satisfies

$$a \wedge a' = O   \quad \text{and} \quad   a \vee a' = I.$$

But any element x with $a \wedge x = O$ and $a \vee x = I$ must, by Lemma 5, satisfy $x = a'$. In other words, the complement a' is *uniquely* determined by the complementation laws (v) in the definition of a Boolean algebra. We now show that the remaining properties of set-complements also hold in any Boolean algebra.

Lemma 6. *In any Boolean algebra, we have*

$$(1) \quad (x')' = x, \qquad (x \wedge y)' = x' \vee y', \qquad \text{and} \qquad (x \vee y)' = x' \wedge y'.$$

Proof. The statement that x' is a complement of x implies by the commutative law that x is a complement of x', since $x' \wedge x = x \wedge x' = 0$ and $x' \vee x = x \vee x' = I$. But we have just seen that complements are unique; hence x is *the* unique complement of x', and $(x')' = x$. Again, by the distributive laws,

$$
\begin{aligned}
(x \wedge y) \wedge (x' \vee y') &= (x \wedge y \wedge x') \vee (x \wedge y \wedge y') \\
&= ((x \wedge x') \wedge y) \vee (x \wedge O) \\
&= (O \wedge y) \vee O = O \vee O = O \\
(x \wedge y) \vee (x' \vee y') &= (x \vee x' \vee y') \wedge (y \vee x' \vee y') \\
&= (I \vee y') \wedge (y \vee y' \vee x') \\
&= I \wedge (I \vee x') = I.
\end{aligned}
$$

This shows that $x' \vee y'$ is *a* complement of $x \wedge y$. Hence, again by the uniqueness of complements, $x' \vee y' = (x \wedge y)'$ is *the* complement of $x \wedge y$. The identity $(x \vee y)' = x' \wedge y'$ can be proved similarly.

Corollary. *To find the complement of an expression built up from primed and unprimed letters by iterated vees and wedges (but not using primed parentheses), interchange $\vee$ and $\wedge$ throughout, prime each unprimed letter and unprime each primed letter.*

Thus, the complement of $(x' \wedge y) \vee (z \wedge w')$ is, by this rule, $(x \vee y') \wedge (z' \vee w)$.

Proof. If the number n of letters in the given expression f (counting repetitions) is 1, then the lemma is true, since $(x)' = x'$ and $(x')' = x$. Otherwise, since no parentheses are primed, we can write the expression as $f = a \wedge b$ or $f = a \vee b$—giving, respectively, $f' = a' \vee b'$ or $f' = a' \wedge b'$. But the expressions a and b contain fewer letters than does f; hence by induction on n we can assume the lemma to be true for them. Substituting in the expressions $f' = a' \vee b'$ or $f' = a' \wedge b'$, we get the desired formula for the complement.

EXERCISES

1. Prove that the idempotent law $x \vee x = x$ follows from the commutative, associative, and absorption laws.

Exercises 2–10 refer to Boolean algebras

2. Prove in detail that $(x \lor y)' = x' \land y'$.
3. Simplify the following Boolean expressions:
   (a) $(x' \land y')'$,   (b) $(a \lor b) \lor (c \lor a) \lor (b \lor c)$,
   (c) $(x \land y) \lor (z \land x) \lor (x' \lor y')'$.
4. Prove that $(x \land y) \lor (x \land y') \lor (x' \land y) \lor (x' \land y') = I$.
   Interpret in terms of the 2-circle analog of Venn's diagram.
5. Prove that $x = y$ if and only if $(x \land y') \lor (x' \land y) = O$.
6. Prove Poretzky's law: For given x and t, $x = O$ if and only if

$$t = (x \land t') \lor (x' \land t)$$

7. Prove that (a) $y \leqq x'$ if and only if $x \land y = O$;
             (b) $y \geqq x'$ if and only if $x \lor y = I$.
8. Find complements of the following expressions:
   (a) $x \lor y \lor z'$,   (b) $(x \lor y' \lor z') \land (x \lor (y \lor z'))$,
   (c) $x \lor (y \land (z \lor w'))$,   (d) $(x' \lor y)' \land (x \lor y')$.
9. Apply the argument of the corollary to Lemma 5 to the expression $(x' \land y \land z') \lor (x \land y')$, justifying each step.
10. Prove that $(x \lor y) \land (x' \lor z) = (x' \land y) \lor (x \land z)$.
11. Prove that $(x \land y) \lor (y \land z) \lor (z \land y) = (x \lor y) \land (y \lor z) \land (z \lor x)$ in any distributive lattice.
12. An element a of a lattice L with universal bounds O, I is said to be *complemented* when, for some $x \in L$, $a \land x = O$ and $a \lor x = I$. Show that, if a and b are complemented elements of a distributive lattice, the same is true of $a \land b$ and $a \lor b$.

5. Canonical Forms of Boolean Polynomials

Various expressions built up from the $\land$, $\lor$, and $'$ operations have been studied in the preceding section. Such expressions are called "Boolean polynomials" (or "Boolean functions"); the analogy with ordinary polynomials (Chap. III) is obvious.

We now define a *subalgebra* of a Boolean algebra B as a nonvoid subset S of B which contains, with any two elements x and y, also $x \land y$, $x \lor y$, and x' (and hence $O = x \land x'$ and I). Given an arbitrary nonvoid subset X of B, the set of all values $p(x_1, \cdots, x_n)$ of elements $x_i \in X$ is clearly the smallest subalgebra of B which contains X. As in the case of groups, this subalgebra is said to be *generated* by X. For example, the subalgebra generated by any one element x consists of the four elements x, x', O, I.

This is a special instance of the following surprising fact: *the number of different Boolean polynomials in n variables* $x_1, \cdots, x_n$ *is finite*. This we now show, illustrating the argument by the polynomial

$$f(x, y, z) = [x \lor z \lor (y \lor z)']' \lor (y \land x).$$

First, if any prime occurs outside any parenthesis in the polynomial, it may be moved inside by an application of the dualization law, as in

Lemma 5 of §4. When all the primes have been moved all the way inside, the polynomial becomes an expression involving only vees and wedges acting on primed and unprimed letters. Thus, in our example:

$$f = [x' \wedge z' \wedge (y \vee z)] \vee (y \wedge x).$$

Secondly, if any $\wedge$ stands outside a parenthesis which contains a $\vee$, then the $\wedge$ can be moved inside by applying the distributive law, as in $c \wedge (a \vee b) = (c \wedge a) \vee (c \wedge b)$. There results a polynomial in which all meets $\wedge$ are formed before any join $\vee$; that is, the expression is a join of terms $T_1, \cdots, T_k$ in which each T_k is a meet of primed and unprimed letters. In the example above,

$$f = (x' \wedge z' \wedge y) \vee (x' \wedge z' \wedge z) \vee (y \wedge x).$$

Thirdly, certain expressions can be shortened or omitted. If a letter "c" appears twice in one term, one occurrence can be omitted since $c \wedge c = c$. If c appears both primed and unprimed, then the whole term is O since $c \wedge a \wedge c' = O$ for all a; hence it can be omitted since $O \vee b = b$ for all b. Thus, above

$$f = (x' \wedge z' \wedge y) \vee (y \wedge x).$$

Finally, the letters appearing in each term can be rearranged so as to appear in their natural order, thus

$$f = (x' \wedge y \wedge z') \vee (x \wedge y).$$

This expresses the polynomial as a join of terms in which each letter c appears *at most* once, as c or c'. If c does not occur in T, we can write

$$T = T \wedge I = T \wedge (c \vee c') = (T \wedge c) \vee (T \wedge c'),$$

replacing T by two terms in which c occurs *exactly* once. Thus, in our example

$$f = (x' \wedge y \wedge z') \vee (x \wedge y \wedge z) \vee (x \wedge y \wedge z').$$

This is called the *disjunctive canonical form* for f.

By eliminating repeated terms ($T \vee T = T$), this process reduces any Boolean polynomial $f(x, y, z)$ either to O or some join of the terms

(2) $\quad$
$$x \wedge y \wedge z, \quad x' \wedge y \wedge z, \quad x \wedge y' \wedge z, \quad x \wedge y \wedge z',$$
$$x \wedge y' \wedge z', \quad x' \wedge y \wedge z', \quad x' \wedge y' \wedge z, \quad x' \wedge y' \wedge z'.$$

It is no accident that these eight polynomials represent the eight regions into which the three circles of Figure 1 divide the square. This means geometrically that any Boolean combination of the three circles X, Y, and Z will be the union of some selection of the eight regions of the diagram.

The ultimate terms, such as those listed in (2), will be called minimal Boolean polynomials. In other words, a *minimal* polynomial

$M(x_1, \cdots, x_n)$ in n variables $x_1, \cdots, x_n$ is a meet $\bigwedge\limits_{i=1}^{n} a_i$ of n elements in which each ith element a_i is either x_i or x_i'. There are 2^n minimal polynomials,

$$(x_1 \wedge x_2 \wedge \cdots \wedge x_n),$$
$$(x_1' \wedge x_2 \wedge \cdots \wedge x_n), \cdots, (x_1' \wedge x_2' \wedge \cdots \wedge x_n').$$

Theorem 2. *There is one and only one way to write a given Boolean polynomial as O or as a join of minimal polynomials.*

(Since O may be regarded as the join of the void set of minimal polynomials, the exception mentioned is only apparent.)

The assertion of the theorem that there is at least one such representation was proved by the reduction process described above. To prove that there is at most one representation—in other words, that joins of distinct sets of minimal polynomials represent distinct Boolean functions—we construct a simple example.

Let $I = V_n(\mathbf{Z}_2)$ be the n-dimensional vector space over the field $\mathbf{Z}_2$ whose elements are 0 and 1. Let $S_i \subset I$ consist of those vectors $\gamma = (c_1, \cdots, c_n)$ whose ith component $c_i = 1$; S_i' will consist of those with $c_i = 0$. Hence the set representing a *minimal* polynomial $M(S_1, \cdots, S_n)$ consists of a single vector $\alpha(M) = (a_1, \cdots, a_n)$, whose ith entry is 0 or 1 according as S_i is primed or unprimed in M. Different minimal polynomials $M = M_\alpha$ are clearly represented by different vectors; the joins of different sets of M_α therefore represent different subsets of I. This proves the following result.

Corollary. *There are just 2^{2^n} different Boolean functions of n variables.*

We can now replace haphazard manipulation of Boolean polynomials by a systematic procedure. The truth or falsity of any purported equation $E_1 = E_2$ in Boolean algebra can be settled definitely, simply by reducing each side to disjunctive canonical form.

EXERCISES

1. Reduce each of the following expressions to canonical form:
   (a) $(x \vee y) \wedge (z' \wedge y)'$, (b) $(x \vee y) \wedge (y \vee z) \wedge (x \vee z)$.
2. Test each of the following proposed equalities by reducing both sides to (disjunctive) canonical form:
   (a) $[x \wedge (y \vee z)']' = (x \wedge y)' \vee (x \wedge z)$,
   (b) $x = (x' \vee y')' \vee [z \vee (x \vee y)']$.
3. Show that every Boolean polynomial has another canonical form which is a "meet" of certain "prime" polynomials. Describe these prime polynomials carefully, and show that they are complements of minimal polynomials. How is the result analogous to the theorem that every ordinary poly-

nomial over a field has a unique representation as a product of irreducible polynomials?

4. Use the canonical form of Ex. 3 to test the equality of Ex. 2a.

5. Prove that the canonical form of $f(x, y)$ is

$$f(x, y) = [f(I, I) \wedge x \wedge y] \vee [f(I, O) \wedge x \wedge y'] \vee [f(O, I) \wedge x' \wedge y] \\ \vee [f(O, O) \wedge x' \wedge y'].$$

6. Prove that the meet of any two distinct minimal polynomials is O.

7. Expand $I = (x_1 \vee x_1') \wedge \cdots \wedge (x_n \vee x_n')$ by the generalized distributive law to show that I is the join of the set of all minimal Boolean polynomials.

8. Prove from Ex. 7 and $x_i = x_i \wedge I$ that each x_i is the join of all those minimal polynomials with ith term x_i.

9. (a) Let $\bigvee_A M_\alpha$ denote the join of all minimal polynomials in the set A. Prove that

$$\left(\bigvee_A M_\alpha \right) \vee \left(\bigvee_B M_\beta \right) = \bigvee_{A \cup B} M_\gamma, \qquad \left(\bigvee_A M_\alpha \right) \wedge \left(\bigvee_B M_\beta \right) = \bigvee_{A \cap B} M_\gamma.$$

   (b) Show that the preceding formulas are valid also if we define the join $\bigvee_\phi M_\alpha$ of the void set of minimal polynomials to be O.

★10. Using Ex. 7 and Ex. 9, prove $\left(\bigvee_A M_\alpha \right)' = \bigvee_{A'} M_\alpha$. (*Hint:* Use Lemma 5 of §4.)

★11. Using only Exercises 8, 9, 10, give an independent proof that every Boolean polynomial can be written as a join of minimal polynomials.

6. Partial Orderings

Little use has been made above of the reflexive, antisymmetric, and transitive laws of inclusion. Yet these are the most fundamental laws of all; thus they apply to many systems which are not Boolean algebras.

For example, they clearly hold the system of all subsets of a set which are distinguished by any special property (writing either $\subset$ or $\leqq$). Thus, they hold for the subgroups (or the normal subgroups!) of any group, the subfields of any field, the subspaces of any linear space, and so on— even though these do not form Boolean algebras. They also hold for the less-than-or-equal-to relation $x \leqq y$ between real numbers, for the divisibility relation $x \mid y$ between positive integers, and so on.

These examples suggest the abstract concept of a "partial ordering." By this is meant any reflexive, antisymmetric, and transitive relation.

Definition.   *A partially ordered set is a set P with a binary relation $\leqq$, which is reflexive, antisymmetric, and transitive.*

For any relation $a \leqq b$ (read, b includes a) of this type, we may define $a < b$ to mean that $a \leqq b$ but $a \neq b$, while b may be said to *cover* a if $a < b$, and if $a < x < b$ is possible for no x.

Partially ordered sets with a finite number of elements can be conveniently represented by diagrams. Each element of the system is represented by a small circle so placed that the circle for a is above that for b if $a > b$. One then draws a descending line from a to b in case a covers b. One can reconstruct the relation $a \geqq b$ from the diagram, for $a > b$ if and only if it is possible to climb from b to a along ascending line segments in the diagram.

For example, in Figure 3, the first diagram represents the system of all subgroups of the four-group; the second, the Boolean algebra of all subsets of a set of three points; the third, the numbers 1, 2, 4, 8 under the divisibility relation. The others have been constructed at random, and show how one can construct abstract partially ordered sets simply by drawing diagrams. In Chap. VI, §7, is a diagram for the partially ordered set of all the subgroups of the groups of the square.

Figure 3

It is clear that in any partially ordered set, the relation $\geqq$ is also reflexive, antisymmetric, and transitive (simply read the postulates from right to left, to see this). Therefore any statement which can be proved from the postulates defining partially ordered sets by using the relation $a \leqq b$ could be established by exactly the same train of reasoning, if everywhere $a \leqq b$ were replaced by the converse relation $a \geqq b$, and vice versa. This is the

Duality Principle. *Any theorem which is true in every partially ordered set remains true if the symbols $\leqq$ and $\geqq$ are interchanged throughout the statement of the theorem.*

It is to be emphasized that this principle is not a theorem about partially ordered sets in the usual sense, but is a theorem about theorems. As such, it belongs to the domain of "metamathematics."

EXERCISES

1. Show in detail how the second diagram of Figure 3 does represent the algebra of all subsets of a set I of three points.
2. Draw a diagram for each of the following partially ordered sets:
   (a) The Boolean algebra of all subsets of a set of four points,

(b) The system of all subgroups of a cyclic group of order 12,

(c) The system of all subgroups of the quaternion group,

(d) The numbers 1, 2, 3, 4, 6, 8, 12, 24 under divisibility,

(e) The system of all subgroups of a cyclic group of order 54,

(f) The system of all subrings of the ring $\mathbf{Z}_{40}$ of integers modulo 40.

3. Discuss the interrelation of the partially ordered sets of parts (d), (e), (f) of Ex. 2.

4. Which of the following sets are partially ordered sets?

(a) All subfields of the field $\mathbf{R}$ of real numbers, under the inclusion relation;

(b) All pairs of numbers (a, b) if $(a, b) \leq (a', b')$ means that $a \leq a'$ and $b \leq b'$;

(c) All pairs of real numbers, if $(a, b) \leq (a', b')$ means that either $a < a'$ or $a = a'$ and $b \leq b'$;

(d) All pairs of real numbers, if $(a, b) \leq (a', b')$ means that $a + b \leq a'$ and $b \leq b'$;

(e) All subdomains of a given integral domain, under the inclusion relation;

(f) All polynomials in $F[x]$, if $f(x) \leq g(x)$ means that $f(x)$ divides $g(x)$.

5. Consider a system of elements with a relation $a < b$ which is transitive and irreflexive ($a < a$ is never true). If $a \leq b$ is defined to mean that either $a < b$ or $a = b$, prove that one gets a partially ordered set.

6. Draw a diagram of the lattice of all subgroups of the group of symmetries of a regular hexagon.

7. (a) Show that, in Example 1 of §3, the lattice L is defined by the relation of set-inclusion between subspaces.

(b) Make and prove a similar statement about Example 2 of §3.

(c) If $m \mid n$ is used to define a partial ordering of the positive integers, what do $\wedge$ and $\vee$ signify?

7. Lattices

The consistency principle shows how to define inclusion in terms of join or meet; we shall now show that, conversely, one can define join and meet in terms of inclusion. Namely, $x \vee y$ is the least thing which contains both x and y, while $x \wedge y$ is the greatest thing contained in both x and y. This observation is due to C. S. Peirce; we shall state it more precisely as follows.

By a "lower bound" to a set X of elements of a partially ordered set P is meant an element a satisfying $a \leq x$ for all $x \in X$. By a "greatest lower bound" (g.l.b.) is meant as in Chap. IV a lower bound including every other lower bound: a lower bound c such that $c \geq a$ for any other lower bound a. Clearly, g.l.b.'s are unique if they exist—for if a and b are both g.l.b.'s of the same set X, then $a \geq b$ and $b \geq a$, whence $a = b$.

Dually, we can define "upper bounds" and "least upper bounds" (l.u.b.), and prove the uniqueness of the latter when they exist. We are here applying our metamathematical Duality Principle! Hence it is legitimate to speak of *the* g.l.b. and *the* l.u.b. of a set of elements, whenever these bounds exist.

Lemma 1. *In any lattice, the meet $x \wedge y$ and the join $x \vee y$ are the g.l.b. and l.u.b., respectively, of the set consisting of the two elements x and y.*

Proof. Since $x \wedge x \wedge y = x \wedge y$ and $y \wedge x \wedge y = x \wedge y$, the consistency principle shows that $x \wedge y$ is a lower bound of x and y. It is a greatest lower bound, since $z \leq x$ and $z \leq y$ imply $z = x \wedge z = x \wedge (y \wedge z)$, and so $z \leq x \wedge y$, again by the consistency principle. The proof is completed by duality.

This shows that any lattice is a partially ordered set having the "lattice property" that any two elements have a g.l.b. and a l.u.b. We will now show that this property completely characterizes lattices.

Theorem 3. *Let L be any partially ordered set in which any two elements x, y have a g.l.b. $x \wedge y$ and a l.u.b. $x \vee y$. Then L is a lattice under the operations $\wedge$, $\vee$, in which $a \leq b$ if and only if $a \wedge b = a$ (or, equivalently, $a \vee b = b$).*

Proof. It suffices to prove the idempotent, commutative, associative, and absorption laws, together with the consistency principle. Moreover by the Duality Principle, it suffices to prove each of the first three laws for g.l.b. The commutative law is obvious from the symmetry of the definition; the associative law, since both $x \wedge (y \wedge z)$ and $(x \wedge y) \wedge z$ are g.l.b.'s of the three elements x, y, and z. The idempotent law is trivial, by substitution in the definition. For the consistency principle, assume first that $x \leq y$; then any z with $z \leq x$ and $z \leq y$ satisfies $z \leq x$, while $x \leq x$ and $x \leq y$, so that x satisfies the definition of the g.l.b. $x \wedge y$. Conversely, if $x = x \wedge y$, then x is a lower bound of y, so that $x \leq y$; this proves the consistency principle. The absorption law now follows by a proof similar to that of Lemma 3 in §4.

The distributive laws were not mentioned above, because they do not hold in all lattices. For example, they do not hold if x, y, z are chosen to be the three subgroups of order 2 in the four group. (Figure 3, first diagram.)

Theorem 4. *In any lattice, the semidistributive laws*

$$x \wedge (y \vee z) \geq (x \wedge y) \vee (x \wedge z), \qquad x \vee (y \wedge z) \leq (x \vee y) \wedge (x \vee z)$$

hold. Moreover, either distributive law implies its dual.

Proof. The labor of proof is cut in half by the Duality Principle. As regards the first semidistributive law, note that both terms on the left have both terms on the right for lower bounds; hence the g.l.b. of x and $y \vee z$ is an upper bound both to $x \wedge y$ and to $x \wedge z$, and hence to their l.u.b. $(x \wedge y) \vee (x \wedge z)$. Finally, assuming the first distributive law of §3, (iii), we get by expansion

$$(x \vee y) \wedge (x \vee z) = ((x \vee y) \wedge x) \vee ((x \vee y) \wedge z)$$
$$= x \vee (x \wedge z) \vee (y \wedge z) = x \vee (y \wedge z),$$

which is the other distributive law of §3, (iii). The proof is completed by the Duality Principle.

It is a corollary of the preceding theorems that, to prove that the algebra of classes is a Boolean algebra, we need only know that (i) set-inclusion is reflexive, antisymmetric, and transitive; (ii) the union of two sets is the least set which contains both, and dually for the intersection; (iii) $S \cap (T \cup U) = (S \cap T) \cup (S \cap U)$ identically; (iv) each set S has a "complement" S' satisfying $S \cap S' = 0$, $S \cup S' = I$. This also proves

Theorem 5. *A Boolean algebra is a distributive lattice which contains elements O and I with $O \leq a \leq I$ for all a, and in which each a has a complement a' satisfying $a \wedge a' = O$, $a \vee a' = I$.*

EXERCISES

1. Which of the diagrams of Figure 3 represent lattices?
2. Draw two new diagrams for partially ordered sets which are not lattices.
3. Which of the examples of Ex. 4, §6, represent lattices?
4. Show that if $b \leq c$ in a lattice L, then $a \wedge b \leq a \wedge c$ and $a \vee b \leq a \vee c$ for all $a \in L$.
5. State and prove a Duality Principle for Boolean algebras.
6. Illustrate the Duality Principle by writing out the detailed proof of the second half of Lemma 1 from the proof given for the first half.
7. Show that a lattice having only a finite number of elements has elements O and I satisfying $O \leq x \leq I$ for all elements x.
★8. Show that a finite partially ordered set with O and I is a lattice whenever between any elements a_1, a_2, b_1, b_2 with $a_i \geq b_j$ $(i, j = 1, 2)$ there is an element c such that $a_i \geq c \geq b_j$ for all i and j.
9. A *chain* is a simply ordered set (i.e., a partially ordered set in which any x and y have either $x \geq y$ or $y \geq x$).
   (a) Prove that every chain is a distributive lattice.
   (b) Prove that a lattice is a chain if and only if all of its subsets are sublattices.
★10. A lattice is called *modular* if and only if $x \geq z$ always implies $x \wedge (y \vee z) = (x \wedge y) \vee z$.
   (a) Prove that every distributive lattice is modular.
   (b) Construct a diagram for a lattice of five elements which is not modular.
   (c) Prove that each of the following is a modular lattice: (i) all subspaces of a vector space; (ii) all subgroups of an Abelian group; (iii) all normal subgroups of any group.
   (d) Show that in a modular lattice, $x \leq z$ always implies $x \vee (y \wedge z) = (x \vee y) \wedge z$. Hence infer that the Duality Principle holds for modular lattices.
★11. In any Boolean algebra the symmetric difference of two elements x and y is defined by $x + y = (x \wedge y') \vee (x' \wedge y)$.
   (a) What does this mean if x and y are classes? Draw a figure.
   (b) Show that $x + y$ is associative, commutative, and has a zero element.
   (c) With the symmetric difference as a sum and the meet as a product, show that every Boolean algebra is a commutative ring.

List of Special Symbols

A	Matrix
A^T	Transposed matrix
A^*	Complex conjugate of matrix
$A_n(F)$	Affine group over F
B	Boolean algebra
$\mathbf{C}$	Complex field
D	Integral domain
$D[x]$	Polynomial forms in x, coefficients in D
$D(x)$	Rational forms in x, coefficients in D
$D\langle x \rangle$	Polynomial functions in x, coefficients in D
$\mathbf{E}_n$	Euclidean n-space
E_{ij}	Special matrix, (i, j)-entry 1, others 0
e, 1	Group identity
F	Field
$F[x]$	Polynomial forms in x, coefficients in F
$F(x)$	Rational forms in x, coefficients in F
G	Group,
g.l.b.	Greatest lower bound
i	$\sqrt{-1}$
I	Identity matrix or transformation; greatest element of lattice
J	Ideal in ring (also H, L)
K	Field
$L_n(F)$	Full linear group over F
l.u.b.	Least upper bound
O	Zero vector; least element of lattice
$O_n(F)$	Orthogonal group
p, q	Positive prime number
$Q(D)$	Field of quotients of domain D
$\mathbf{Q}$	Rational field
R	Ring
$\mathbf{R}$	Real field
S	Set; subgroup; subspace

S'	Set-complement
$S^\perp$	Orthogonal complement (of subspace)
T	Linear transformation
T_A	Transformation given by matrix A
V, W	Vector spaces
$V_n(F)$	Space of n-tuples over F
X	Vector or row matrix
$\mathbf{Z}$	Domain or group of integers
$\mathbf{Z}_n$	Integers mod n
α, β	Vectors
(α, β)	Inner product of vectors
δ_{ij}	Kronecker delta
$\in$	Is a member of
ε_i	Unit vector
ϕ, ψ	Transformations
Π	Product
$\sum$	Summation
ξ, η	Vectors
$\varnothing$	Void set (distinguish from ϕ for function)
$\cap, \cup$	Intersection, union (of sets)
$\wedge, \vee$	Meet, join (in Boolean algebra, lattice)
$\subset$	Is a subset of
$<$	Less than; properly included in
$\leqq$	Inequality
$\perp$	Orthogonal to
$\oplus$	Direct sum
$\rightarrow$	Transformation
$*$	Conjugate complex number
$\sim$	Associate
$\equiv$	Congruent
$|A|$	Determinant of A
$|a|$	Absolute value of a
$\|a_{ij}\|$	Matrix
$a|b$	a divides b
(a, b)	Greatest common divisor (g.c.d.)
$[a, b]$	Least common multiple (l.c.m.)

Index